ↄ⸰ GREENPORT HARBOR ⸱c

LONG ISLAND, NEW YORK

Photo: Gil Amiaga

An authentic, working deep water port
surrounded by seaside farms & vineyards...

Official 2004 TALL SHIPS CHALLENGE® Atlantic Coast Port

Tall Ships 2000® Cruise Port

Americas' Sail Host-1995 & 1998

Visit Mitchell Park & Marina.
Deep water dockage, vintage carousel, amphitheater
and boardwalk—all in the heart of the village!
Easy walk to stores, galleries, beach,
hospital & Historic District.

Special arrangements made for visiting tall ships.

Services available include hauling, shipbuilding,
welding, engine repair & hardware.

For more information contact:
Major David Nyce, Village of Greenport
236 Third Street, Greenport, New York 11944
631-477-0248 • FAX 631-477-1877
or hail the harbormaster on VHF channel 9

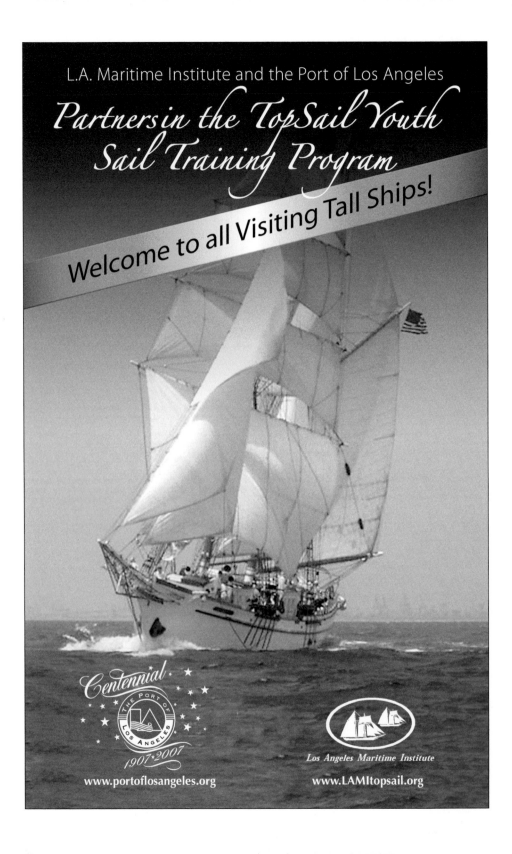

L.A. Maritime Institute and the Port of Los Angeles

Partners in the TopSail Youth Sail Training Program

Welcome to all Visiting Tall Ships!

Centennial
THE PORT OF LOS ANGELES
1907★2007

www.portoflosangeles.org

Los Angeles Maritime Institute

www.LAMItopsail.org

The mission of the American Sail Training Association is to encourage character building through sail training, promote sail training to the North American public, and support education under sail.

Dedicated in Memory of
Captain David W. Hiott IV
1958 - 2006

Table of Contents

The mission of the American Sail Training Association is to encourage character building through sail training, promote sail training to the American public, and support education under sail.

Published by

American Sail Training Association (ASTA)
PO Box 1459, 240 Thames Street
Newport, RI 02840 USA
Phone: (401) 846-1775
Fax: (401) 849-5400
E-mail: asta@sailtraining.org
Web site: http://tallships.sailtraining.org

Acknowledgments

Many of the photographs in this edition of Sail Tall Ships! have been generously donated by:

Thad Koza
Tall Ships Photography
24 Mary St.
Newport, RI 02840 USA
Phone: (401) 846-5274
thadkoza@yahoo.com
www.tallshipsinternational.net

MAX
Bywater Lodge-Pierside
Lymington, Hants, ENGLAND
SO41 5SB UK
Phone: + 44 (0) 1590 672047
max@tallshipstock.com

Matthew Maples
8N246 Cheviot Drive
Bartlett, IL 60103
Phone: 630-707-0632
mfmaples@gmail.com

Onne van der Wal
Onne van der Wal, Inc.
One Bannister's Wharf
Newport, RI 02840
Phone: 401-849-5556
www.vanderwal.com
info@vanderwal.com

Registered Trademarks

The following registered trademarks and service marks are owned by the American Sail Training Association:

Tall Ships®
Tall Ships are Coming!®
TALL SHIPS CHALLENGE®

Sail Tall Ships! A Directory of Sail Training and Adventure at Sea, 17th edition

Directory Team

Compiled and edited by Lori A. Aguiar, ASTA Director of Operations
Design by Artinium Inc., www.artinium.com
Consulting by Pucino Print Consultants, 631 Fletcher Road, North Kingstown, RI 02852
Printed in Canada by Dollco Printing, www.dollco.com
ISBN 978-0-9799878-0-9   Cover photo: US Brig NIAGARA, Photo by John Baker

Foreword

By Mike Rauworth

These ships exist to give you a chance to face real-world, right-now challenges — the kind that give you pride that no one can take away from you. Other people may not always understand why, but your shipmates will, and you will — that's what matters most. The sea is real as real can get — and taking on the challenge of the sea makes people feel alive and energized. Nothing else like it. This world of these ships draws some of the best people you'll ever meet — people who don't want their life pre-digested for them, people who have no use for excuses, double-talk, or spin-doctoring, people who will help show you how great it is to live a different way. The sea does not care if the dog ate your homework, or if the check is in the mail. At sea you'll find out how great it is to do things that really matter, to have people really rely on you, and to create bonds with people you can rely on when the going gets tough.

We borrow windships from the past — some people would call them an anachronism. But they're a window to the future, too. Sail power is the ultimate clean, cost-free, power for propulsion. No carbon footprint — use it all you want, because you can't exhaust it, you won't pollute, and you won't add to our dependence on oil. The wind will still blow tomorrow. Isn't this where we should be going?

Many of the world's seagoing nations maintain sail training ships to train professional seafarers for their navies and merchant ship fleets — mostly diesel-powered ships. And more sail training ships are being added to the world's fleet each year — by governments and non-profit organizations. These ships don't exist to train people for careers on windships, because most ships today aren't. Instead, they exist because the fellowship of the sea understands the special value of working a windship at sea — no matter what one's future will turn out to be.

These pages are your portal to the fellowship of the sea. Your experience will enrich you in ways that will surprise you. Sign up for the experience of getting real.

Michael Rauworth

4

A Brief History of the American Sail Training Association

In the summer of 1972 Barclay Warburton III, of Newport, Rhode Island, his two sons, and several friends, sailed his brigantine *Black Pearl* across the Atlantic to participate in a tall ships race from Cowes on the south coast of England to Malmo in Sweden, organized by what was then known as The Sail Training Association. He was so inspired by the enthusiasm and spirit he saw in that international gathering of tall ships and young people that he set out to create a similar organization in order to bring the same kind of spirit to the United States, and through his efforts the American Sail Training Association was founded the following year. ASTA soon became the first national association to formally affiliate with what eventually became known as the International Sail Training Association.

The Tall Ships Races in which the *Black Pearl* took part had first been held in 1956, when a London solicitor, Bernard Morgan, had the idea of bringing what he imagined to be the last of the world's great square-riggers together for a race as a sort of last hurrah—a farewell salute—for the Great Age of Sail. A committee was formed, and with the support and assistance of the Portuguese Ambassador in London, a race was organized from Torbay, on England's Cornish coast, to Lisbon. Five square-rigged schoolships entered the race: Denmark's *Danmark*, Norway's *Christian Radich* and *Sorlandet*, Belgium's *Mercator*, and Portugal's first *Sagres*. The event proved to be anything but a funeral procession, however, and it has since grown into an annual series that would astonish its original organizers. Today, hundreds of tall ships from around the world come together annually for friendly competition in international and regional Tall Ships Races organized by Sail Training International in Europe and national affiliates such as ASTA. These races, along with waterfront festivals in designated start and finish ports, bring together the ships and young people of most European countries, Russia and the former Soviet states, the Americas, and the Pacific Rim. The key elements uniting these events are an emphasis on youth—from the beginning, tall ship racing rules have required that not less than half those onboard participating vessels be between 15 and 25 years of age—and a formula for rating participating vessels which allows vessels ranging in size from the largest square-riggers down to yachts of 30 or more feet in length.

> "This is the Great Purpose of sail training - that the greatest handiwork of man, the sailing ship, shall be borne across the greatest handiwork of God, the sea, to bring together our young people in friendship"
>
> **Barclay Warburton III**

The American Sail Training Association's efforts in its first decade were primarily focused on organizing tall ships races on the European model, but from the mid-1980s to the mid-1990s it worked on a multitude of activities broadly aimed at promoting sail training and supporting education under sail in North America. Thus at the beginning of the 21st century, the American Sail Training Association has evolved into an organizer of tall ships races, a strong industry association for the growing numbers of vessels involved in providing opportunities for people of all ages to take part in deep water sailing experiences and a public charity which makes sail training more available and affordable for young people.

With an organizational membership of over 250 vessels, the American Sail Training Association serves as a forum for information exchange, professional development, and program standards. Through such initiatives as the Council of Educational Ship Owners, which worked successfully for the passage of the Sailing School Vessels Act of 1982 and the Sailing School Vessels Council, founded the following year, ASTA has continued to work with the US Coast Guard and other agencies to create and maintain a friendly regulatory climate for the development of sail training.

Safety at sea has been an enduring emphasis, and in conjunction with the Australian bicentennial gathering of tall ships in Sydney in 1988, a group of ASTA members organized the first international discussion on safety standards and practices, and equipment for sail training programs. Since 1992, ASTA has organized a biennial Safety Forum, which regularly draws professional sail trainers from around the world. Also in the 1980s, ASTA developed the concept of the Sail Training Rally; a competition among crews both at sea and ashore, which provides trainees with an opportunity to demonstrate their seamanship skills in a friendly but competitive format. During shore side events, the general public can observe the sort of team-work and maritime skills that are learned on board sail training vessels at sea.

Over the years, the American Sail Training Association has undertaken many other projects to meet the needs of a rapidly growing sail training community. These include a variety of publications including SAIL TALL SHIPS! *A Directory of Sail Training and Adventure at Sea*, an Annual Conference on Sail Training which attracts international interest and participation, a Billet Bank to assist vessels in finding qualified crewmembers, and vice versa, a growing program of scholarships and grants to support trainees, vessels, and professional crew, and a constantly expanding website. In 2001, building on the spectacular success of Tall Ships 2000®, ASTA launched its most ambitious project to date—the TALL SHIPS CHALLENGE® Series, an annual series of tall ships races and maritime port festivals that informs the general public about tall ships, our maritime heritage and the incredible power of sail training to change lives.

The mission of the American Sail Training Association is to encourage character building through sail training, promote sail training to the North American public, and support education under sail.

 Sail training, like reading, is not a subject in and of itself. It is a means to an end. A medium. An environment. We at ASTA often say that sail training is not learning to sail, it is learning from sailing. From the ship, from the sea and perhaps most importantly, from yourself.

What is Sail Training?

By Pamela Dewell

In the United States and Canada, there are many sail training vessels which serve as laboratories and classrooms at sea. College and high school students regularly embark on semester-long voyages of offshore discovery while younger children explore local waters on grade school field trips. Water, sediment and biological sampling provide students with tangible lessons in the marine environment as they themselves physically encounter the effect of wind and wave. Formal study aboard a ship is frequently referred to as sea education.

Historic vessels, or their reproductions, function as interpretive museum exhibits, conducting voyages of outreach to the public. Most North Americans can trace their ancestors' arrival by ship. The last sailing vessel to regularly carry immigrants to America still plies New England waters, now a sailing school vessel, extending her venerable history of more than one hundred years service -- from fishing the Grand Banks to Arctic exploration to African packet. There are reproductions and restorations of ships representative of each of America's naval conflicts. We may board important sailing ships of the American Revolution, the War of 1812, the Civil War and some which played their part in the World Wars. We may experience life at sea aboard Grand Banks fishing schooners, mackerel seiners, oyster boats and whalers. Cargo ships. Pilot boats. Merchant vessels. Immigrant ships. Those pressed into the slave trade. There is not a chapter of our history which does not have a waterborne link. The smell of pine tar and manila, the sounds of a working ship, the view of a whale-spotted horizon from the top of the rig, the motion of a rolling deck -- history is a compelling study of this physical context.

Other North American ships sail ambassadorial missions for the public they serve, issuing invitations of hospitality and promoting opportunities for economic development. Others sail to save the environment. Or to promote international relations through citizen diplomacy, as did a Soviet-American crew sailing past the final sputters of the Cold War. These vessels draw our attention and focus us on their missions because sailing ships are powerful icons, symbolizing strength, beauty and harmony wherever they go. Those who sail know the ocean to be that which connects us to foreign lands -- not a boundary which separates us.

9

Several American sail training ships serve as treatment centers for adjudicated youth while others provide exclusive corporate team building exercise or offshore adventure travel -- from coastal cruising with gourmet cooking to blue water voyaging. While the clientele could not be more different, these ships are all in the business of enrichment. As diverse an agenda as this may seem at first glance, these ships all provide sail training. The common denominator is that each uses the wind and sea to teach us something else. Sail training, like reading, is not a subject

The US Brig *Niagara* was built in 1988 as a reconstruction of the warship aboard which Oliver Hazard Perry won the Battle of Lake Erie in 1813 during the War of 1812. Her mission is to interpret War of 1812 history, promote the Commonwealth of Pennsylvania and the Erie Region, and preserve the skills of square-rig seafaring. People ages 16 and up may sail onboard as sailing school students for a six-hour daysail (an introduction to square-rig seafaring and the history of Niagara). For the more adventurous and physically fit, the Square-Rig Seamanship Training Program offers 22 trainees the opportunity to live onboard, learn the ropes, scrub the decks, climb aloft, handle sails, and for 3 weeks taste the sailor's life.

in and of itself. It is a means to an end. A medium. An environment. We at ASTA often say that sail training is not learning to sail, it is learning from sailing. From the ship, from the sea and perhaps most importantly, from yourself.

A ship at sea has been described as a microcosm of the planet. Resources are finite, waste must be managed responsibly and success depends on one's ability to work as a team. One quickly learns that many hands lighten a load. In a similar way, so do good shipmates -- those who are focused, considerate, and good humored. There is no place on earth which better illuminates leadership qualities, nor marks the path so clearly toward achieving them. The rewards of a smoothly run ship are immediate, obvious and sweetly satisfying. As sailors have said for centuries, take care of your ship and she'll take care of you.

There is no better feeling in the world than coming off an early morning watch having watched the sun rise and helped to scrub everything down for the start of a new day. As you leave the ship in the hands of the next watch you realize how happy you are to see them -- and even happier to leave them to it - as you go below for the sort of breakfast you'd never eat ashore and a grateful climb into a narrow berth assuming any angle of heel. Adjusting to sleeping when you can is strangely easy, and you find yourself sleeping easily in your bunk no matter what the time of day or the weather (well, with the occasional notable exception!). You find yourself frequently aware of living completely in the moment, and you take great pride in accomplishing tasks and seeking new challenges for yourself.

Aboard a sail training vessel, as in life, our small piece is a critical part of the whole. The quality of work, and the spirit in which we do it, has a profound effect on the well-being of everyone else aboard. Leadership, paradoxically, is arrived at by learning to take direction. Becoming a team player. Pulling your share of the load. Being absolutely responsible. Dependable. And, learning to depend on the responsibility of others. For no matter what the particular mission of a ship might be, it is essential that she be safely navigated and handsomely attended.

This is true of the larger world, but in the larger world, the quality of our actions are not so immediately apparent. In our day to day lives, most of us do not have at hand accessible evidence of collisions we've safely avoided, environmental conditions we gained advantage from, or courses accurately steered no matter the conditions. Our actions seem at times to be in a vacuum and feedback is often clouded by other issues. It often takes years to measure the efficacy of our navigation and our ability to "hand, reef and steer" our lives. Nor do we often have the simple yet somehow completely thrilling affirmation of perfectly set sails in a stiff breeze and a ship "with a bone in her teeth." On a sail training vessel, it's right there. Right now.

For some, sail training offers first time successes. For others, it is a much needed refresher course in life when we find ourselves, for instance, knocking hats off passerby's or staring too long at funeral processions -- which Herman Melville describes as "high time to get to sea" in Moby Dick. For all, sail training offers an absolutely unique experience.

So no, we don't just teach sailing. ASTA member vessels and programs foster opportunities for intensive personal development -- intensive life experience in order to advance leadership development, an utter reverence for nature, a sense of time and place, an appreciation for history, and teamwork ability. Sail training really teaches the qualities of stewardship, resourcefulness, pride, humility, bravery, strength and grace. And we learn to sail, too.

TALL SHIPS CHALLENGE®

The **TALL SHIPS CHALLENGE®** Race Series is a series of sailing races, cruises, crew rallies and maritime festivals organized by the American Sail Training Association in conjunction with United States and Canadian ports on the Pacific and Atlantic Coasts of North America and in the Great Lakes.

TALL SHIPS CHALLENGE.

Are you ready...

Traditionally-rigged sailing vessels from Canada, the United States and other countries are crewed by young people (either civilians or cadets) ages 13 - 25 who are engaged in sail training programs under the supervision of captains and professional crewmembers.

The TALL SHIPS CHALLENGE® Race Series began in 2001 on the Great Lakes. Thirty vessels from six countries, and 1000 sail trainees and cadets participated in the races, sail training rallies and port festivals in seven United States and Canadian ports. Detroit and Windsor celebrated their 300th Anniversary; additional ports were Kingston and Port Colborne, Ontario; Cleveland, Ohio; and Bay City and Muskegon, Michigan.

The 2002 series was sailed on the Pacific Coast of North America: Sixty vessels from seven countries participated in the series which included port festivals in Richmond, British Columbia; Seattle, Washington; San Francisco and Los Angeles, California. Races were sailed from the mouth of the Strait of Juan de Fuca to San Francisco and then on to Los Angeles. More than 1200 sail trainees enjoyed the experience.

The 2003 series was again on the Great Lakes: Twenty-seven vessels from India, the Netherlands, the British Virgin Islands, the United States and Canada participated. Port festivals were held in Cleveland and Toledo, Ohio as part of the Ohio Bicentennial; Chicago, Illinois; Muskegon and Bay City, Michigan; and Sarnia, Ontario. Four races were held between ports and more than 1000 trainees enjoyed the races and cruises aboard vessels in the fleet. Millions of spectators came to the city waterfronts to see the vessels and talk with their crew/trainees to learn about life under sail and the opportunities to sail on ASTA member vessels.

The 2004 TALL SHIPS CHALLENGE® Race Series brought vessels together from ten different countries: Belgium, Brazil, Canada, the Cook Islands, Mexico, Poland, Romania, the United Kingdom, the United States, and Uruguay. Across 2,300 nautical miles these traditional sailing vessels tested their crews in friendly competition. The sailors aboard proudly displayed their ships to fascinated crowds in a dozen ports between race segments. Under blistering Florida sunshine and through impenetrable Nova Scotia fog, the ships' crews led their trainees in every aspect of running the vessels. Hand in hand with learning the ropes, the ships promoted team effort, responsibility, and personal development.

The 2005 TALL SHIPS CHALLENGE Race Series returned to the Pacific Coast. Seven United States and Canadian ports and nearly sixty traditionally-rigged sailing vessels from Canada, the United States, Mexico, New Zealand, Russia and other countries took part. Ports included Victoria, Vancouver and Port Alberni, British Columbia; Tacoma, Washington; Channel Islands Harbor, Oxnard; Los Angeles and San Diego, California.

The maritime festivals in each host port give visitors a chance to board the vessels and meet the crew and trainees and learn about the many varied opportunities to sail and travel on ASTA member vessels.

Racing is one of the most important components of the series. Historically, when two or more sailing vessels are found to be heading in the same direction, an impromptu race almost always ensues. The crews pay closer attention to the other ships and to the trim of their own sails in hopes of outdoing their counterparts.

But how can you compare the racing of a 60-foot sailboat with a 240-foot sailing ship carrying 10 times as much sail area? A special rating system developed in the European tall ships races is used to assign vessels of any size a relative performance factor. This gives all vessels an equal chance of winning if they are sailed well. Before the series starts, six pages of hull, rigging and sail measurements for each vessel are submitted to Sail Training International headquarters in England. They compute Time Correction Factors (TCFs) for each vessel using a program that has been fine-tuned over many years of competition. After each race, the ASTA race team multiplies the time it takes for a vessel to complete the course – its elapsed time – by its TCF in the race to determine the corrected time; corrected times are then compared to determine final standings.

Safety at sea is critical and each participating sailing vessel has been inspected and certified for its intended use either by a national maritime authority (the Coast Guard in the US) or by an internationally-endorsed society. At the beginning of the season, the safety equipment on each vessel is double-checked by the ASTA race team and any discrepancies are remedied prior to the first race.

While underway, racers use VHF or SSB radio to keep in contact once or twice daily with the race communications officer on the escort vessel and often with the ASTA race office by satellite-assisted email.

When the series starts, it is likely that not every trainee berth will have been spoken for and interested youth are encouraged to sail in a race or cruise between host ports. ASTA has a scholarship program for eligible youth. More information is available at www.sailtraining.org. Berths are also available for adults on a number of the participating vessels.

Since the first TALL SHIPS CHALLENGE® Race Series in 2001, ASTA and the host cities have strived to bring the experience of sail training to the North American public. As part of its continuing mission to encourage character building through sail training, both trainees and visitors have an opportunity to learn about life at sea aboard a tall ship. Whether it is learning to sail for the first time or learning about local maritime history, the TALL SHIPS CHALLENGE® Race Series brings to the public the opportunity to see and touch history. In this way, we can further our mission of education under sail through the unique experience that the TALL SHIPS CHALLENGE® Race Series offers to youth of all ages.

Pacific Coast  2008

Tall Ships® Victoria
Victoria, British Columbia
June 25 - 29, 2008
www.tallshipsvictoria.ca

Tall Ships® Tacoma
Tacoma, Washington
July 3 - 7, 2008
www.tallshipstacoma.com

Port Alberni Tall Ships® Festival
Port Alberni, British Columbia
July 10 - 12, 2008
www.portalbernitallships.ca

Festival of Sail San Francisco
San Francisco, California
July 23 - 28, 2008
www.festivalofsail.org

Atlantic Coast 2007

Tarangini

Prince William

Gorch Fock II

Gloria

The 2007 TALL SHIPS CHALLENGE® Race Series visited the Atlantic Coast ports of Charleston, South Carolina; Norfolk, Virginia; Newport, Rhode Island and Halifax, Nova Scotia. Participating vessels came from India, Indonesia, the Netherlands, England, Germany, Colombia, Brazil, Uruguay, France, Canada and the US. The ships were gorgeous, the crews were enthusiastic and the public showed their support by the thousands.

The first port of call was the charming and historic city of Charleston, SC. The ships were introduced to true southern hospitality as the organizers and volunteers showed the visiting crews why the state motto is "Smiling Faces, Beautiful Places". . Charleston was also the start of the first race of the TALL SHIPS CHALLENGE® Race Series, easily won by the Indian Naval ship, *Tarangini*.

A fleet of over 25 international vessels then arrived in the naval port of Norfolk, VA. The Parade of Sail into port was an awesome experience, both for those on board the ships and the lucky spectators. The weather was perfect and the ships were in all their glory.

The fleet then cruised-in-company up the East Coast to Newport, RI, the homeport of the American Sail Training Association. Throughout the day, we could look out our windows and see masts sail by, at which point the office would empty as we headed down to the docks to greet the newest arrival. Newport is a sailor's city and the crews were welcomed with open arms.

The second race of the series started after the Parade of Sail out of Newport. It was quite the upset with the British vessel *Prince William* beating the US vessel *Pride of Baltimore II* by a mere ten seconds and the German naval vessel *Gorch Fock II* by 45 seconds. The third and final race took place several days later from Portsmouth, NH to Halifax, NS. The ships had mustered, the starting line was set up and the cameras poised, but there was no wind. With five minutes to the gun, the sun broke through the clouds and a gust of wind picked up enough for everyone to sail across the start line, with the Dutch naval vessel *Urania* winning line honors. Despite some harrowing weather in the midst of the race, *Spirit of Bermuda* won with *Urania* coming in a close second.

The final port of the race series was Halifax, ASTA Port of the Year in 2004. The fleet sailed into port through fog as thick as pea soup, but by the time the festival started the damp weather had burned off and the days were warm and sunny. The public flocked to the ships and they were not disappointed. The final awards ceremony took place in Halifax with *Urania* announced as the overall winner of the TALL SHIPS CHALLENGE® Race Series VECTRIX trophy.

Great Lakes 2006
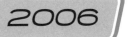

For the third time, the TALL SHIPS CHALLENGE ® Race Series sailed into the Great Lakes the summer of 2006. Although it was a shorter race series with only four ports, the crowds were enthusiastic and the ships ready to compete. The fleet started in Cleveland, Ohio with a rainy parade into port. Luckily, the weather broke just as the ships were mustering out in the lake, making for a dramatic entrance. The first race a few days later was from Cleveland to Pelee Island, Ontario, about 37 nautical miles away. As the ships prepared at the starting line, a sudden shift in the wind caused some scrambling as the ships tacked desperately to find a bit of wind to get them over the starting line. *Pride of Baltimore II* won with *Windy II* coming in at second place.

Pride of Baltimore II

The vessels sailed into three-time host port, Bay City, MI, and again were treated like long lost family. Port of the Year in 2001, Bay City lived up to expectations both in generosity and public support by providing the crews with free haircuts, laundry and meals. From Bay City, the vessels cruised in company for five days up and over Lake Michigan through the Mackinac Straights and down to Green Bay, Wisconsin.

Windy II

The people of Green Bay love their tall ships almost as much as they love their football. Even though the temperatures reached the triple digits, the crowds remained captivated by the majestic vessels lining the river and turned out by the thousands. The start of Race Two from Green Bay to the Sturgeon Bay Canal (approx. 40nm), did not go as smoothly as desired with a malfunctioning bridge wreaking a bit of havoc early in the morning, causing many of the racing vessels to be delayed by an hour. Also, because of light winds there were no finishers. Standings were instead calculated based on the ships position when they "retired" from racing and turned on their engines. Despite a rocky start and the fickle winds, the unstoppable *Pride of Baltimore II* came in first with the *Appledore IV* in second place. The ships then sailed together to the fourth and final port of Chicago, IL.

Picton Castle

Deep dish pizza and tall ships came together in the Windy City of Chicago, Port of the Year in 2003. Over a million people toured the vessels during the week long event. Throngs of people visited the ships on Navy Pier and Riverwalk along the Chicago River.

By the end of the summer, there was a true sense of comradeship between the vessels, evident in the commingled groups of sailors walking through the port cities. These events and competitions are an exceptional way to bring sail training to the public and introduce youth of all ages to the excitement and adventure that awaits them on a tall ship.

Appledore IV

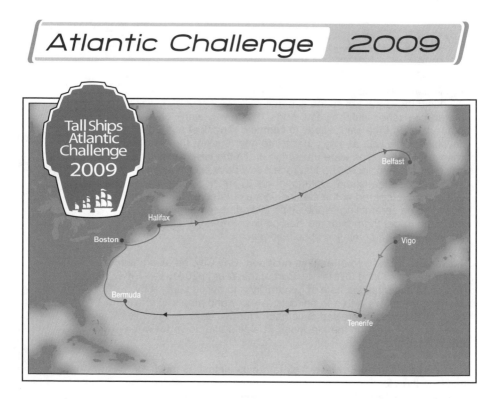

Atlantic Challenge 2009

The Tall Ships Atlantic Challenge 2009 will start in Vigo, Spain from where the fleet will race to Tenerife in the Canary Islands, en route to Bermuda. The fleet will then race to a port on the east coast of the USA for a series of races and cruises-in-company north to Halifax, Canada. From there the fleet will race back across the North Atlantic to Belfast, Northern Ireland. Ports in the USA are currently being finalized for this phase of the event.

Vigo, Spain
April 30 - May 3, 2009

Tenerife, Canary Islands
May 14 - May 17, 2009

Bermuda
June 12 - June 15, 2009

Boston, MA, USA
July 8 - 13, 2009

Halifax, Canada
July 16 - July 19, 2009

Belfast, UK
August 13 - August 16, 2009

Sail Training International

ASTA

Photo by Onne van der Wal

What did *you* do on your summer vacation?

From the Logs of the ASTA 2006 and 2007 Summer Interns

Each summer during the TALL SHIPS CHALLENGE® Race Series, the American Sail Training Association offers a team of young people the opportunity to serve as interns with the ASTA Race Team. Throughout the course of the summer series, the interns assist the race director, work in the race office, man the ASTA information booths, interact with the participating vessels and their crews and trainees, the port organizers and volunteers, and represent ASTA to the hundreds of thousands of people who come out to see the tall ships. Not to mention, sailing! Long days and hard work are a part of the job – but so are enduring friendships and memories that will last a lifetime. Since the first TALL SHIPS CHALLENGE® Series in the summer of 2001, young people from as far away as Japan and the United Kingdom, as well as Canada and the United States have had the chance to experience the CHALLENGE from this unique perspective.

Great Lakes 2006: Mary Schneider

My name is Mary Schneider, and I have just finished my senior year of college where I received a Bachelor of Science degree in the field in Marine Transportation. I hope to soon obtain a position onboard a vessel sailing as a Third Mate and putting all of my training to good use. I can not wait to visit the exciting ports the ASTA team will be visiting in the next few months. I am most excited to have the opportunity to sail aboard one of the tall ships during the race series.

You Bet I'm Going Back To Sea!

After three days at sea, Meredith and I are back on land. Our stories are still fresh in our minds, and our sea legs have not yet begun to wear off. We began our adventure on Sunday, July 17, arriving at the US Brig *Niagara* just before its departure from the docks in Cleveland.

It was all hands throughout the morning as the Captain and the Mates prepared for the race to begin. At the 20 minute preparatory gun, you could feel the excitement of the crew as they manned their stations to prepare to cross the line and get underway with the race. Just as the race was about to begin and the starting gun fired, there was a sudden shift in the winds, causing the ship to lose its ability to sail on the proper course across the line. This natural occurrence caused the vessel to miss the start of the race and lose approximately 20 minutes of race time, a disappointment to everyone onboard.

Once the race had begun, a "life as normal" resumed onboard with the vessels race position at the forefront of everyone's minds. Meredith and I were split into our watch "divisions" and we embarked on the task of learning the ships layout and rigging. As the race continued I received my aloft training from Eric my division "AB" (Able Bodied Seaman). I would be lying if I told you I was not nervous about climbing the shrouds, but Eric led me through it making it all the way to the top. At the top, I was able to take in the true grandeur of the ship. The sun was shining across the sea, crewmembers below were tidying up lines and the sails were flying. As I sat there, I tried to take as much of it in as I could, hoping it would create an imprint on my mind. I traveled back down the shrouds just in time to haul lines for a tack.

As the day progressed, the trainees, volunteers, and crew helped me find my way about, told me which lines needed hauling and easing and showed me some of their extraordinary seamanship skills. By the time 1200 came the thought of lunch seemed heavenly. As my division was called to the mess the spicy smells of chili filled the air. Sitting down for our meal was the first real opportunity I had to converse with my shipmates. One particularly interesting set of diners at my table were Emily and MaryAnn, a mother and daughter hailing from Texas. As lunch progressed, I learned that MaryAnn had been on the *Niagara* the previous summer sailing for a full seven weeks, and enjoyed the experience so much that she rejoined the ship this summer and brought her daughter Emily along.

Another intriguing group I encountered on my first day were the professor and student trio of Jeremy, Larry and Nadine, earning credits for their Master's degrees in Nautical Archeology from Eastern Carolina University. Jeremy and Nadine are able to participate in ship life writing journals and being observed in their daily activates by Larry, their professor, who is in his ninth year running this program on the *Niagara*. After lunch we were able to take a much needed break. I organized my sea bag and took a quick nap on the berth deck. After my short nap it was time to begin watch. On watch I rotated positions with my shipmates, from lookout - reporting ships and lights onshore to helmsman - using the tiller to the steer the ship and trying as best as I could to keep it on its proper course. Just ahead I was able to see *Pride of Baltimore II* ahead of us in the race (no doubt only due to our delay in the start). It was on my watch, at approximately 2100 when we reached Point Pelee the end of our 35 mile race course, and as far as we could tell, we finished second to the *Pride*. After watch, I made my way down to the berth deck and Frank, an OS (Ordinary Seaman), showed me the proper way to string up my hammock. After brushing my teeth and washing my face I weaved my way through the hammocks lifting one leg up to climb in just as the Chief Mate poked his head down below to call all hands. I threw on my raingear and headed up and into a fierce rainstorm. The noise from the 35 knot winds whipping through the rigging was incredible, and the deck was hectic with deckhands running about laying out anchor lines in preparation to drop the hook and weather out the storm. After dropping the hook the crew remained on deck to assist the Captain and the Chief Mate in any way possible. After everything was secured, I headed back down to my rack, and prepared to rest up for my next watch which was only hours away. With such an eventful first day, I could not wait to see what the next day held in store for me.

- *Mary Schneider*
2006 ASTA Summer Intern

Great Lakes 2006: Alexandra Hagerty

My name is Alexandra Hagerty. Influenced by having spent part of my high school career in Lausanne, Switzerland (French area), I have been very busy over the past few years studying international relations and comparative languages at Earlham College. Last year I studied economics/politics in India and Sri Lanka during my first semester and in Spain during my second semester. I have a love of adventures such as bungee jumping, camping, horseback riding, skiing, and ice climbing. In general, I love challenges and I look forward to this summer as something that will surely be memorable!

An Evening Reception on a Spanish Tall Ship

Over these past weeks, I have been learning and meeting many wonderful people from the tall ship community. When I first decided to take this internship, I had an idea of what I was getting into, but not completely; now I have a better understanding of the purpose of it, and where it can take me in the future regarding my career path. Working with the other interns, Mary and Meredith, has already opened my mind to the types of sailing opportunities available. Before coming into this internship, I found myself in NYC working exhausting hours, running around without knowing whether all these part time jobs/internships were honestly worth my time or even my interest. At this point in time, I can say that this internship was definitely worth doing. The people I work with in the office have been teaching me so much from computing, marketing, publicizing, how to engage people in the world of sail-training and make connections with people on an international level. I have spent time meeting captains, first mates, and other members of the tall ship community.

At the Mass. Sail-Ocean's Classrooms reception in Boston two days ago, I found myself talking with students who recently participated in sail training programs, as well as teachers with marine science backgrounds who shared interesting stories. Touring the three large sailing vessels visiting the Boston Seaport harbor was also lovely as a live music band played waltzes on the other side of the port near the

24

Bluenose II. That evening as the speeches starting to come to an end, the raw bar was getting a little empty (I'm an oyster lover, that was probably my fault) and the cannoli's and coffees were diminishing, we ASTA interns decided to go over to the *Bluenose II* to say our farewells to the Canadian crew from Halifax. Little did we realize that an hour later we would have made connections with two regular-dressed gentlemen who would invite us on their spectacular ship, the *Juan Sebastian de Elcano* of Spain, since they worked as engineers aboard her! It was wonderful! Our photographer Thad Koza and the Canadian crew joined us on this invite that would lead to yet another one the following day. It was exciting, and enjoyable as a group from three different countries shared stories about our own sailing experiences and sail training. I thoroughly enjoyed the evening and thought to myself; what a wonderful chance to meet so many great people in one night who all have one common interest…sailing tall ships!

The next evening we were invited to join the Spanish crew and captain at their reception. What an event it was! We reconnected with the same Spanish engineers dressed now in their cleanest white officer suits, and were introduced to a host of people, some from the Spanish consulate, first mates, and finally Captain Salvador. I got his attention by saluting him in Castilian Spanish on behalf of ASTA, stating our hope of continuing international camaraderie between our countries. He was so delighted that we were able to speak to him in his native tongue that he quickly grabbed our hands and brought us to his adorned private captains' cabin. Speaking to us of his love of STI (Sail Training International) and explaining the history of the *Juan Sebastian de Elcano* from 1976 to the present. We presented him with several gifts including an ASTA flag that he said he would fly over Lisbon - what a night! Live music playing in the background, tasting the finest cheese and ham of Spain, good conversation …it was one of the most unforgettable evenings of my life! I look forward to more events that foster the importance of sail training and the bonds that are made between people of all places!

- *Alexandra Hagerty*
2006 ASTA Intern

Great Lakes 2006 - Meredith McKinnon

My name is Meredith McKinnon and I am from Ottawa Ontario, Canada. I just completed my first year of University at the Memorial University of Newfoundland in St. John's. I sailed aboard STV Fair Jeanne for the 2003 Tall Ships Challenge Race Series from Kingston, Ontario to Chicago, Illinois as an officer in training. My two favorite things in the world are sailing and traveling, and so I am very excited to be a summer intern with ASTA and I am looking forward to the challenges and experiences it will bring!

[July 24th...It Begins...Again!]

Alexandra and I got to sail from Bay City to Green Bay on the U.S. Brig *Niagara*. We left the dock at 9am on Monday the 24th. Alexandra was in Starboard Watch, and I was in Port Watch with fourth mate Robert Blood, or just "Blood" when you need his attention, as the mate of my division. We were on watch from 12-4 pm and set EVERYTHING...it was a little piece of sailing heaven, but my favorite part of that day came during night watch. My division was on from 2-4, also known as the twilight zone, and Captain Heerssen was on deck and gave us all a little lesson on celestial navigation, so now I will never be lost because I know exactly where that north star is...just don't test me on it!

July 25th...the longest day I can remember
I woke up at 7 for a hearty breakfast created by our very own "gastronomic artistes" Josh and Nate. We started setting sail at 8am and did not stop until we were cruising along 8 knots. What a workout hoisting yards and halyards can be...forget the gym, sail training will whip anybody into shape! Later in the afternoon we all mustered for class which consisted of the Captain throwing everybody back to 1812 and the Battle of Lake Erie. Of course this day couldn't have been complete without a visit from a VIB (very important bird) who decided to drop by the *Niagara* in the middle of Lake Huron and sup on bugs and water from Chief Mate Jamie T.

July 26th...a little rendez-vous
Last night we anchored just outside of Mackinac, in plain sight of the Mackinac Bridge which is the dividing link between Lake Huron and Lake Michigan. Sharing our anchorage was the *Picton Castle*, and Captain Dan Moreland invited some of the *Niagara* crew over for an evening of music and shipmates...the best part was being able to take pictures of the *Niagara*.

July 27th...I survived major galley!
As I was sitting eating lunch after standing watch from 8-12 pm I was getting very excited about the possibility of taking a 'nap' as I would be off watch for the next four hours when Josh walks by and informs me that I would be taking over major galley... so sleep was put on hold! Major galley went smoothly and I was able to be on deck when we crossed under the Mackinac bridge, holding our breath as our t'gallant masts "just' swept underneath the bridge cables. Of course, the best way to finish off a day of hard work on board is with a guitar (or two), a sunset, and some of the best shipmates I've ever had.

Keep this in your hearts when you think of tall ship sailing:
In Bay City, paintings were hung from the lamp-posts to welcome in the tall ships. They were created by high school students, unfortunately I don't know which student wrote this quote, but it could not have been said any better, " Tall ships are the closest thing to heaven that hands have ever created."

Atlantic Coast 2007 - Matthew Maples

It is now 51 more days (at the time of this writing - 3/20) until my ASTA internship starts. Ugh! I mean Argh! Seems so far away. My imagination holds that this internship will be a time for challenges, satisfying success, and newfound friendships. An exploration of character, opportunities and the sea-lanes. It is an introduction into a new world. I am about to graduate college at age 22. This internship is undoubtedly the most exciting opportunity I could ask for as I am an aspiring photojournalist and I anticipate doing photography and writing on the side in addition to internship duties. This internship offers a unique photojournalistic opportunity. An event as exciting as the TALL SHIPS CHALLENGE® series begs to be photographed and written about!

/ Whoa! /

A week usually isn't considered a long length of time. My last week however, has felt as long as a month. This isn't because I'm bored. Certainly not. This past week and a day since our ASTA internship began has been an unprecedented amount of new and quite stimulating experiences. We have lived in an old home in colonial Newport, graciously hosted by a sailing notoriety everyone calls "The Commodore" (Mr. Harry Anderson, Jr.); traveled hundreds of miles of the Atlantic Coast; stayed at the best hotel I've ever been to - The Charleston Marina and Resort; seen Ft. Sumter (Lots of cannons! I'm a big fan); attended gala's and parties with notorieties of all types and have just today started our first real day of work with the Charleston Tall Ships® festival. We even went to "South of the Border" and saw the "Great Sombrero". It certainly has been a lot of fun. All signs however indicate that this is only a beginning and that really great things are yet in store.

Today we got our first real glimpse into what our sail training stint will be. We walked on the decks of our newest home, the *Picton Castle*. Beautiful vessel. It's darkened wooden decks, gleaming wooden surfaces, burnished brass, and tar-smelling lines and interior have a comfortable, homey feel. The vessel is very elemental, being composed of iron, wood and brass giving it an elegant simplicity while being simultaneously welcoming with all the signs of being a truly lived-in, communal home - The dishes and cups scratched from vigorous cleaning, the faded drapes among the bunks, the grainy texture of its surfaces grimed from work, the pasted papers with new rules. The crew, even while rushing to put their laundry up on deck, are able to pass a smile. They seem to be friendly and welcoming - even though they have surely greeted many more who have come and gone among the decks. The friendliest welcome we received was from the crew's two adopted puppies. That would be my first impression of the *Picton Castle* and I hope that it will be a lasting impression in the days to come.

So much done, and so much to do. There is plenty to elaborate on but its time to get back to work for ASTA.

Atlantic Coast 2007 - Heather Flanagan

I'm Heather. I'm 18 years old and a current student at the University of Rhode Island. Just like the URI school song goes "I'm Rhode Island born and Rhode Island bred and when I die I'll be Rhode Island dead..." Although I love my home state, I enjoy traveling and meeting new people. I am studying history and education which is why I love the idea of sail training. Last summer I was an intern sailing on the Continental Sloop Providence. As seasick as I was, I was bitten by the sailing bug (its not an actual bug) and fell in love. When I was put back on land for school, I missed my ship family. I couldn't wait for the 2007 season to begin, I'm getting so excited right now just thinking about May 11th. I look forward to meeting everyone I'll be working with.

And They Were Gone...

I am still mourning the loss of the tall ships in my life. I still find myself waking at peculiar hours of the night and I will eat my meals with my plate in my lap even though a table top is in front of me. I miss my friends.....who are now more like family. That is the great thing about tall ship sailing, within a week you have the same relationship with your crew mates as you do with friends of 15 years. I had a lot of fun. The events were great.

Charleston, SC was full of excitement and anticipation. I had never been to a Tall Ships® event like that. The event coordinators were very experienced and knew how to keep the event running smoothly. The hours were great. They weren't open too early and they didn't close too late.

Norfolk, VA was all about the ship's crews. There were laundry facilities near by and we were in the city so we were able to find our own fun, i.e mall, movies, and exploring the town. Every night there was something going on for the crew members after hours, such as concerts, BBQ's and tours. The walking parade was a blast. I fondly remember the day we were trained for the parade. The captain said that the military crews that we would be marching near are professional and are trained to march, we aren't. He told us to avoid straight lines and geometry. We needed to walk fast, walk slow and run. We needed to have various shapes, such as egg shaped blobs. We could wear whatever we wanted but it need to be full of color. The parade went over well. We were the brightest in the bunch. The greatest part of the Norfolk event was the location of the ships. They were in almost a straight line, stern to bow. You needn't walk far to get to any of the ships.

Newport, RI. Home sweet home! The docking situation for *Picton Castle* was a little hairy but we made it through with flying colors and then watched the caterers scramble. I still remember a waitress with a wheelbarrow standing on the dock trying to figure out how she would get the wheelbarrow of her goods onto the ship. I told her the easiest way was to do it like the crew, pass everything on-board one by one. Once I told her that, things moved along much more quickly. It was nice that Newport arranged free tours of the mansions for the crews but this event was certainly dedicated to the captains. Yes, the captains are important but if you asked the captains the people that make a lot of tall ships anything happen they'd say the crew first. Without us the ships wouldn't get anywhere.

Halifax, NS. That was an interesting event. The fog was so thick we could only see .02 nautical miles. That being said we had one near collision with a buoy and on the way to the event several other ships sustained injured crew and were heeled over.... A LOT ! The event itself was nice however and the city was wonderful. I really enjoy Canada.

The one thing each event had in common....great people watching.

- Heather Flanagan
2007 ASTA Intern

2005/2006 Sail Training Awards

Each year at the Annual Conference on Sail Training and Tall Ships, the ASTA membership honors a select group of sail trainers and supporters who have been chosen by their peers and fellow sail trainers for their outstanding accomplishments.

ASTA

Lifetime Achievement Award

Awarded to an individual who has dedicated his/her life's work to getting people to sea under sail and who has worked to preserve the traditions and skills of sail training.

2005 Lifetime Achievement Award Recipient: Captain David V. V. Wood

CAPT Wood had a celebrated 30 year career in the US Coast Guard including a four year tour of duty as Commanding Officer of the USCG Training Barque EAGLE, during which "America's Tall Ship" made a historic first visit to Leningrad, USSR in 1989, celebrated the Coast Guard's Bicentennial during 1989-90 in all ten of the original Revenue Cutter ports, and represented the US in the Columbus Quincentenary Regatta in 1992. Following retirement from active duty, CAPT Wood became a director of the American Sail Training Association and was its Chairman from 1998-2001. He also served as US National Representative to the International Sail Training Association, and was a Trustee of that organization from 1999-2002. He holds an unlimited USCG license as Master, Auxiliary Sail Vessels, Any Gross Tons, Oceans, and has occasionally returned to sea aboard sailing ships to keep his skills current.

2006 Lifetime Achievement Award Recipient: *Beth Bonds*

For her above-and-beyond work with ASTA, keeping the office going first as a volunteer and then as Executive Director, and for supporting many of the programs still being carried on today (like the directory, rallies, conference, etc.) and for volunteering countless hours and invaluable advice and experience to both ASTA and in her new homeport in Charleston, South Carolina.

2006 Lifetime Achievement Award Recipient: Captain David W. Hiott IV (1958-2006)

Captain David Hiott became master and commander of the *Kalmar Nyckel* - a replica of the ship that brought Delaware its first permanent European settlers in 1638 – upon the ship's completion and launch in 1997. His extensive knowledge - and enthusiasm interacting with crew and visitors - made him a presence on the ship and at its shipyard. He was considered an authority on the rigging and sailing of traditional ships. Hiott led the replica ship crew for all of its nine sailing seasons, with more than 1,000 volunteers training under his command and tens of thousands touring the ship. He was visited the day before his death by officials from the American Sail Training Association and, in a short ceremony, was presented with the association's Lifetime Achievement Award for dedication to sail training, living history and traditional seamanship. "With over 300 active crew and volunteers trained and ready, the Kalmar Nyckel Foundation intends to proceed with their program in the manner that Capt. Hiott intended," the foundation said. "We feel this is the best tribute we can make to him."

Sail Trainer of the Year

Awarded to an ASTA member whose contribution has been a demonstration of leadership by means of empowerment and inspiration.

2005 Sail Trainer of the Year Award Recipient: Captain Tim Pyron

Captain Pyron has gone far beyond the call of duty maintaining the sail training programs of Toronto Brigantine while mentoring the youth wardrooms of both T.S. *Playfair* and S.T.V. *Pathfinder*. His work has continued through the winter program where youth officers, aged 13 to 18, receive training in seamanship, leadership and safety and the summer program where the youth officers deliver the sail training program to trainees. After a period of debt management and cost control, the 2005 summer season saw the organization turn the corner. This success was in no small part due to the efforts and commitment of Captain Tim Pyron.

2006 Sail Trainer of the Year Award Recipient: Captain Walter Rybka

Due to the large crew that *Niagara* sails with each summer and after 15 consecutive summers of sailing her, it is reasonable to estimate that few captains in ASTA's currently-sailing membership have been responsible for training more professional crewmembers and novice trainees. Walter Rybka has earned this recognition for his achievements as an exemplary teacher and custodian of square-rig (and general) seamanship, and for his gift to the sailing community- his abundant knowledge and experience, which he graciously shares.

Sail Training Program of the Year

Awarded to a current ASTA member program, that significantly contributes to the development of seamanship, navigation skills, teamwork, and leadership skills. The program must be offered aboard a USCG-(or national equivalent) inspected vessel, must be offered by certified/qualified personnel, must have clear training goals and curriculum which is compatible to the ASTA sail training logbook and must offer students the opportunity to demonstrate knowledge at sea by participating as active trainees in the running of the vessel.

2005 Sail Training Program of the Year Award Recipient: Orientation at Sea Program onboard the *SSV Tabor Boy*

SSV *Tabor Boy's* more than 50 years of impacting students' lives is a remarkable record. Integrating the Orientation at Sea Program into the school experience and making it available to all incoming freshmen makes Tabor Academy unique among its peer institutions and other sail training organizations.

2006 Sail Training Program of the Year Award Recipient: *Picton Castle*

The *Picton Castle* has sailed four times around the world with trainees serving in every aspect of the ship's operation, learning all that a sailing ship has to teach. When not on a circumnavigation, the ship has participated in every ASTA-sponsored or supported event. Over 700 young people and adults have had comprehensive square-rig sailing ship experiences aboard the *Picton Castle* since her first voyage in 1997. The ships sole operational purpose is deep sea sail training and the proliferation of seamanship skills. There is no other auxiliary academic or scientific program. The program is the ship and the sea.

Sea Education Program of the Year

Awarded to a program offered by a current ASTA member which significantly contributed to the educational credibility of programs under sail. The program must be offered in conjunction with a school, school system, school group or other recognized educational institution, must have a clear curriculum of educational goals which are compatible with curriculum goals of traditional schools and must have qualified instructors on a certified vessel.

2005 Sea Education Program of the Year Award: Bayshore Discovery Project

The *A. J. Meerwald* has logged thousands of hours of sea time, providing education programs to more than 50,000 people each year. Her parent organization, the Bayshore Discovery Project, has a carefully-designed curriculum hand-in-hand with the local public school system, integrating the traditions of working sail with biological and ecological educational opportunities available only under sail, on the water. The schooner herself has been meticulously restored within the parameters of USCG regulations and maintained and operated as such.

2006 Sea Education Program of the Year Award: Tall Ships Education Academy, Tall Ship Semester for Girls

Since 1998, Tall Ship Semester for Girls has enrolled an ethnically diverse population of high school girls from the Bay Area. The majority of these students come from low-income families where the opportunity to participate in an experiential education program is beyond their financial means. Students work on a vessel at sea and build a community aboard the ship, where they grow personally, socially and academically. TSEA believes that youth who act with a sense of personal responsibility, interdependence and global awareness will lead productive lives and build strong communities.

Port City of the Year

Awarded to a city which has demonstrated significant support of ASTA or an ASTA Member Organization and who has furthered public recognition of sail training.

2005 Port of the Year Award: Tacoma, Washington

2006 Port of the Year Award: Bay City, Michigan

The Perry Bowl

Awarded to the top finishing ASTA member vessel in the TALL SHIPS CHALLENGE® Race Series.

2005 Perry Bowl: *Talofa*

2006 Perry Bowl: *Pride of Baltimore II*

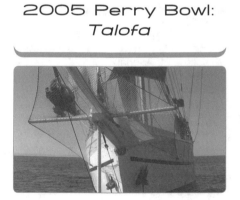

Volunteer of the Year

An ASTA individual member who has significantly advanced ASTA's overall mission.

2005 Volunteer of the Year Award: Captain Richard "Rusty" Rice

For close to ten years now, Rusty has volunteered countless hours in support of ASTA and ASTA programs, frequently volunteering at the ASTA conference, the TALL SHIPS CHALLENGE® Race Series and, through his company Wild Rice Adventure Consulting, running team building programs for ASTA staff and interns.

2006 Volunteer of the Year Award: Mr. Hal Barstow

As LAMI's (Los Angeles Maritime Institute) international relations volunteer, Hal has made friends for American sail training at every level, from cadets to captains, on ships small and tall. He is generous with his heart, his time, his networking and his own personal donations in support of sail training in local, national and international circles. He is an international treasure!

Special Recognition Awards

2005 Special Recognition Award: Mr. Steve Baker

ASTA Race Director from 1998 – 2005, Mr. Baker was largely instrumental in getting the American Sail Training Association's TALL SHIPS CHALLENGE® Race Series off the ground. In the fall of 2005, after completing five TALL SHIPS CHALLENGE® Series, '01 to '05, the 1998 Great Lakes series and the Tall Ships® 2000 series, Mr. Baker stepped down as ASTA's race director to pursue other goals.

2006 Special Recognition Award: Mr. Don Treworgy

Celestial navigation is a skill and tradition that is rapidly being forgotten in the sail training world and yet it remains an important tool in the traditional mariner's skill set. While institutions like the Coast Guard Academy are dropping celestial navigation course requirements, Don Treworgy is teaching, to full capacity, classes. There is no doubt that Don has dedicated his professional career to educating our young sailors and that he continues to positively impact the lives of young seafarers and the crews that are keeping them safe.

TALL SHIPS®
YOUTH ADVENTURE!

ASTA

Funded through a grant from the U.S. Department of Justice's (DOJ) Office of Juvenile Justice and Delinquency Prevention (OJJDP), The American Sail Training Association's Tall Ships® Youth Adventure program provides positive life changing experiences on ASTA Member tall ships and sail training vessels for youth in underserved communities through a series of scholarship and grant programs to make out of school time programs more accessible and affordable to young people. ASTA and ASTA Member affiliates identify at-risk youth and collaborate with other local youth serving organizations such as Boys and Girls Clubs, Girl Scouts, etc. ASTA and ASTA Member affiliates work with these local organizations in designing, delivering and monitoring after school or out of school sail training programs that foster self confidence and self efficacy. Program participants learn teambuilding and leadership skills that they will carry with them when they step ashore and into their transition to adulthood. Tall Ships® Youth Adventure provides young participants valuable experiences that prepare them to positively deal with the challenges that they will encounter throughout their lives.

Living Classrooms Foundation

Living Classrooms Foundation (LCF) is a non-profit organization providing hands-on education and job skills training for students from diverse backgrounds, with a special emphasis on serving at-risk youth. The Foundation uses maritime settings, community revitalization projects and other challenging learning environments. Their "learning by doing" education programs emphasize the applied learning of math, science, literacy, history, economics, and ecology. Key objectives of all Living Classrooms programs are career development, community service, elevating self-esteem, and fostering multicultural exchange.

LCF's Tall Ships® Youth Adventure "Fresh Start" students spent summer days learning sailing basics at the O'Brien Sailing Center as a prelude to their weeklong experience aboard the schooner *Lady Maryland*. Some of their journaling entries follow.

"The main thing about sailing is you have to work together to get somewhere."

"I got a close-up view of the Domino Sugar Company. I could actually smell the sugar. I saw fish jump out of the water and drop back in. I also saw ducks and their babies."

"We learned about the all the parts of the boat – starboard, port, boom, jib, stern, bow, halyards, sheets, etc. It felt good to know what we were doing and feel safe on the water. I thought it would be scary but it was fun."

"Every time we were on the water, the wind would blow different ways, so we would have to move the sails and sheets different ways to make the wind push us fast."

"I feel good about it because when me and the other guys are sailing, then that lets me know that we are doing good in the program and the staff trusts us."

"My experience with sailing was very fun. Baltimore looks like a different place when we are floating on the water."

Words From An Alum

*By Lulu Bernal, Girls Summer at Sea 2007 aboard the
SEAWARD (reprinted from Tall Ship Education Academy's
Enewsletter, the Pinrail)*

As soon as Nettie pulled out the Ziploc bag full of cell phones, I could see the smile and sparkle in every girl's eye. I could feel the excitement their bodies experienced as they knew they'd soon be able to speak to their loved ones.

We had arrived at our first stop, Catalina Island. It had been almost a week since we had left the city, about seven days since we had last spoken to our families. Everyone was anxious to call and let their loved ones know that they were safe and that they missed them a whole bunch. I, on the other hand, was excited as well, yet felt indifferent to calling home. As I held the pink Razor phone in my hand, my fingers didn't feel the immediate need to start dialing. I waited a couple of minutes before I dialed. First I had to pull myself together and put my emotions in order. Stepping on land for the first time after being in a boat for seven straight days just blows your mind. You're totally off balance and your world won't stop spinning. It's not a very pleasant feeling. As I looked around me and saw tears streaming down the eyes of my soon to be sisters, I thought to myself, why aren't I feeling this way, why am I not desperate to call home? I thought about it for a second but couldn't figure it out. As the days went by and we began experiencing more and more things the boat, everything in my mind began to settle. I realized that I loved the boat world too much to step out of it for even a second. As I embarked on this trip, I had made a commitment that this would be my life—my world--for the next nineteen days. Talking on the phone automatically pulls you back into your land life which is what I didn't want. Doing so, can bring one comfort yet it can also bring worries. I was perfectly fine with the comfort that the boat brought me and the love that my sisters provided for me. There's something about sailing that drives you crazy but in a good way. It plants a fire in your heart and brings peace to your mind. It takes you to the place you've always wanted to be. It sets you free! I had personally never been in such a peaceful environment. Along those lines I knew that not talking to my mom or dad would make me more independent than I already was.

When this was over, I would have to embark on another adventure, a little something called college. Independence is what I needed the most and doing this trip without my family was giving that to me. Learning how to build good relationships with complete strangers would be just as important as learning how to be independent.

Learning how to communicate would be just as crucial. I knew that the skills I'd learn on the boat would come in handy later on in life.

It's been a week since I've gotten back and my new found skills have already been put to use. I've been able to better handle problems that go on at home since I have a better understanding of how I come off to people, including my parents, and how I project things that I say. I take responsibility for my mistakes instead of always blaming someone else. I now feel confident stepping foot for the first time in my dorm and approaching my roommate with a warm hello just as I did with theses girls when I first walked into the classroom door at SF State. I stepped onto the boat with eleven strangers and got off with eleven sisters. If I was able to do this in a matter of nineteen days, I will for sure be able to make a sister out of my roommate, let's hope!

Overall this experience has changed my life but only for the better. Not only did it teach me about myself and others but it made me a stronger woman. I am extremely happy that I took on this challenge. It was meant to be.

A Week On The Sloop Providence

By Matthew Maples, ASTA 2007 Summer Intern

Last week, Heather and I had the opportunity to sail with the Sloop Providence to assist with the ASTA Tall Ships® Youth Adventure summer cadet program. While I was definitely excited to know I'd be spending time on the Providence. I didn't know what to expect or what the kids we would be working with would be like.

We arrived at the sloop Monday, with little time to spare before the kids arrived in their big yellow bus. Walking down the dock, they looked like a motley and diverse bunch. They were pretty excited initially as they came up the gangplank and congregated in a gibbering mass on the maindeck. That excitement promptly deflated when they were treated to a history lesson of the historical ship. Looking at their downcast faces and twitchy arms, it was evident that they didn't come onboard to get schooled. Following that was some initial knot-tying and belaying tutorials - skills they would become familiar with in the days to come. After lunch they all had a tour of Ft. Adams. When they finally came back several hours later they were all complaints - pleas of hunger and misgivings about the sun as they crowded in whatever little shade was available. They were, in general, relieved when the bus came to pick them up.

I was not really worried about them continuing to be apathetic throughout the week. I couldn't really blame them - I know I would want to be out in the bay sailing, not getting orientations and tours. I felt pretty confident that they would perk up once we got out on the water.

The next day we didn't waste much time before making preparations to head out into the bay. The kids had been split into two watches: Port and Starboard. The watch that won the "challenge" of the previous day chose between picking the course the ship would follow for the day or giving the ship a deckwash. Much to my surprise, the winning watch opted to do the deckwork over navigation! I don't think I'd have so willingly taken deckwash/domestics over navigation, but whatever the kids wanted is what they got. I have a feeling that they wanted the fun involved with using the fire hose.

In quick time we were steaming out into the bay. When we made some distance out from our berth we quieted the engine and raised the mainsail and headsails. Little did I know just how much sailhandling our cadet crew was in for that day and I doubt they had any more of a clue than I had. Apparently, the watch who got to choose the course decided to tack upwind and against the current. Needless to say, there was no real headway made. But that didn't matter because the kids got a lot of practice using the lines. It was interesting to watch them work, some of the kids were active and brought themselves up to the bow again and again to ease and haul the sheets as we tacked. Others were more timid. I believe that they were still getting over the new surroundings and the new world they found themselves in. A tall ship setting can be intimidating, not only because it is unfamiliar and complex in appearance, but also because of the sudden yelling of orders. I could tell they learned a lot but there was a bit of a gap between the kids who could be more easily engaged to sail the ship and the others who hung back.

Over the next two days I noticed a substantial improvement. The cadets got a lot of sailhandling practice in because of the constant tacking throughout our days of sail. There were a couple of days where we got a good sail in. On Wednesday however, despite a frenzy of tacking we were unable to beat the sloop upwind and against the current and ended up drifting backwards under the Pell Bridge with sail set. The cadets were not discouraged however, they were happy to have gone under the bridge. By the end of Thursday, when it came time to tack, the kids needed little to no encouragement to come forward to handle the lines. Sheet lines that used to flog wildly were now under better control, lines were not made fast counterclockwise and coils not hung over the pin. They were also not as shy to come forward to participate and some of them even waited nearby in anticipation.

I was talking to one of the quieter cadets on Wednesday and he told me that he was having a great time. When I asked him what his favorite part was he said it was doing the heavy work at line handling. When I asked him what his least favorite part was, he said it was lunch, because when he was at lunch he was not handling sail.

At the end of Thursday the challenge for the cadets was a pin-rail chase. While they were a bit stumped by some lines, they knew the lines that they had used to tack all week.

One cadet made very impressive progress. On the first day he was unenthusiastic and he could not be motivated to do anything besides tie a slipknot, which was the knot he decided to tie after giving up on tying a bowline. I would not have guessed that he would have been an enthusiastic watch leader midway through the week. I couldn't help but notice that he knew the lines during the pin-rail chase better than anyone else. He did very well when he applied himself. Another cadet on Thursday was allowed to steer the ship into the dock - I can imagine how proud she must have felt after that.

Then Friday arrived - the day that the kids were going to do as much of the sailing of the ship as possible - all done in front of the eyes of their parents. Even though it was a short sail, the kids did remarkably well and the professional crew did not have to lend much help at all. Compared to the first day when they could barely coil a line, the cadets were now easing and hauling and not hesitating to put their lines on the pins. I remember how demure, unenthusiastic and timid they were on their first day. By the end of Friday they were all smiles as they moved confidently about the deck to attend to their duties. A very different reaction from day one when I could see, by their bewildered and confused faces, that they were universally second-guessing their decision to come aboard.

As they received their graduation certificates, I could see that the kids felt that they had done something really cool. The program did a lot to raise their confidence in themselves and more than a few of them said that they would like to do it again.

The Sail Training Experience

"ASTA member vessels and programs foster opportunities
for intensive personal development -- intensive life
experience in order to advance leadership development,
an utter reverence for nature, a sense of time and
place, an appreciation for history, and teamwork ability.
Sail training really teaches the qualities of stewardship,
resourcefulness, pride, humility, bravery, strength and
grace. And we learn to sail, too."

 I have learned to take commands and to give them, to be tolerant, and to appreciate good weather and good crew when you've got them. I know what hard work is, and I'm not afraid of it. I know that a team is only as strong as its weakest member and that morale is more important than anything.

To Sea, Or Not To Sea?

By Diane Morgan

As much as I hate the idea of it, I may be settling down. I know, I know – I should resist, but I've fallen in love with a great guy and we're moving to New Zealand. And I'm going to get one of those cushy, clean, nine to five, office-type "real jobs."

I must say, after six or so years on and off boats, I find this term amusingly ironic. As if ensuring the safety of thirty-five people aboard a 110-foot ship with over seventy running lines and thirteen sails didn't qualify as "real"! Mom, Dad, sisters, brothers, aunts, uncles, jealous friends, wake up and smell the salt air! Just because I don't commute every day doesn't mean I don't have a "real job." But if you remain unconvinced, let's go furl the topgallant in forty knots of breeze, shall we?

In all seriousness, I got my first taste of tall ship sailing as a student at the Sea Education Association (SEA) in 2000. Compared with my often abstract liberal arts education, *Corwith Cramer's* intensely tangible learning environment was a refreshing change. Indeed, the hands-on nature of sail handling, scientific sampling and navigating provided a deep sense of satisfaction. And so, like many college students that leave SEA's tall ship sailor-spawning ground, I was thirsty for more.

I got my fix when I joined the Dutch Bark *Europa* in Seattle for the 2002 West Coast TALL SHIPS CHALLENGE® Race Series. Looking back on it now, I had no idea what I was getting myself into. But before I knew it, we were in San Diego stowing endless amounts of food, toilet paper, and fuel for voyages to places I had previously considered lunar. Antarctica? Were they nuts? As far as I was concerned, the continent only existed in National Geographic specials.

Soon we were casting off our dock lines and kissing land goodbye. You want to talk real? Well, it really took forty-one days to reach Easter Island, and we only saw terra firma on the first and last days of the trip. I can tell you the crew really got to know one another during that time and we were really excited to see those bizarre statues on the shore line.

Yes, sailing on *Europa* brought my imagination to life. Penguins did look as if they were ready for prom. Albatrosses had amazingly wide wingspans. And icebergs could sink ships – in fact, they could even stretch a mile wide.

As a deckhand aboard *Europa,* I did the dirty work side by side with my shipmates. We took turns steering, furling, cleaning, baking bread, and standing bow watch. Not one of us left the ship without hands that had hardened to leather from the rigors of sailing in the Southern Ocean. We even slathered our fingers in cow udder gel between watches so our knuckles didn't crack. And we kept each other company on the helm even when snow was blowing sideways.

Only a couple of years later, after studying for my first US Coast Guard license, I was hired to work as the first mate aboard the Los Angeles Maritime Institute's (LAMI) only floating brigantine, the *Exy Johnson.* Within days, I was operating that scary monster. I was untangling the octopus that was the bilge pumping system and jumping in the small boat to rescue pesky basketballs in man-overboard drills. (Couldn't I just be in charge of the Jacob's ladder?)

In the meantime, I was trying to gauge the strengths and weaknesses of every one of my deckhands, including those of LAMI's seemingly endless supply of energetic and enthusiastic volunteers. I was also considering how to approach a demographic I had never before encountered, inner-city kids from less fortunate neighborhoods. Graffiti in bunks was a problem.

As I begin to think about what sort of jobs I will apply for when I arrive in New Zealand, I know that my experiences aboard tall ships have prepared me for just about anything. I have learned to take commands and to give them, to be tolerant, and to appreciate good weather and good crew when you've got them. I know what hard work is and I'm not afraid of it. I know that a team is only as strong as its weakest member and that morale is more important than anything.

So if you're up for a fun, eye-opening challenge, sail on a tall ship. Just be aware that it might change your entire outlook on life. For the better.

As a North American society, we are constantly grappling with how to prepare our children for the future. The educational community is constantly trying to strike the balance between developing a student personally and academically so that they will become effective leaders and positive, contributing members to our communities in the future.

Class Afloat

By Caleb Pifer

Mark Twain once said, "Twenty years from now you will be more disappointed by the things you didn't do than by the ones you did do. So throw off the bowlines. Sail away from the safe harbor. Catch the trade winds in your sails. Explore. Dream. Discover."

Such a quote can be used to describe a modern sail training adventure onboard a tall ship. It has been said that a sail training experience is a powerful, formative event in a young person's life. The experience provides the young person with an unparalleled opportunity to grow socially, personally, and morally within the context of a small community onboard a tall ship that sails around the world. Now, imagine if this powerful social experience was combined with a challenging, intellectually stimulating academic program that pushed students to analyze and defend their scholastic knowledge. This highly unique and exceptional program does exist, known as Class Afloat, and I have the privilege of serving as the program's University Shipboard Director for the 2007-2008 voyage.

Class Afloat was founded in 1984 by Canadian educator and ASTA board member, Terry D. Davies. Inspired by a United Nations proclamation that declared 1984 as the

International Year for Youth, Davies set out to create the first Class Afloat. Through the UN proclamation themes of "Peace, Participation and Development", the program was born, and has since served over 1000 high school, GAP and university students, who have earned both high school and university credits while sailing around the world.

Class Afloat makes its home in Lunenburg, Nova Scotia, Canada, a town steeped in maritime tradition and charm. High school students may spend their junior or senior years, or both, with Class Afloat. Students rotate their time between one semester in the program's boarding school in Lunenburg, and the other semester on the floating campus, the square rigged tall ship, *Concordia*. University students have the option of spending either one semester or an entire year onboard and earn their university credits through Canada's leading liberal arts school, Acadia University.

Since my very first sail training experience as a teenager, I dreamed about working on a tall ship professionally. After finding out about the Class Afloat program, I set my sights on one day teaching for the program. This year the dream is a reality. I am leading the university program onboard *Concordia* as we engage in a ten month, twenty five country voyage of education and discovery. One of the hallmarks of the Class Afloat program is the land-based experiential education learning element that compliments the formal onboard classes. In each port we have planned a program that will engage students in the local culture and customs of the country that we are visiting. We strive to make the programs not only applicable to the curriculum, but also try to avoid the traditional tourist activities that often prevent students from truly

Cal Pifer

Cal has been sailing on ASTA member vessels since he was sixteen. He has served as crew on *Niagara, Elissa, Providence, Bounty,* and *Concordia*. Additionally, he spent two seasons with Thompson Island Outward Bound as a Lead Sailing Instructor. He also spent a short stint teaching for an Expeditionary Learning Outward Bound (ELOB) middle school in Boston.

Passionate about experiential education, Cal has spent the last five years working with various groups to bring progressive education reform to the traditional classroom. In addition to presenting at numerous education conferences, he has served on various committees and capacities for the Coalition of Essential Schools in San Francisco, the National Service Learning Partnership in Washington and the Kellogg Foundation in Detroit. A true believer in the power of sail training for young people, Cal attributes much of his success in high school and college to his time spent crewing on tall ships.

In 2006, Cal was elected to the ASTA Board of Directors, the youngest board member to serve. He is an active member of the Sail Training and Education Committee as well as the Marketing Committee.

engaging in the local flavor. A few examples of what we have planned this year includevisiting a traditional Amazonian village in Belem, Brazil and hearing a lecture on the "new Russian economy" in St. Petersburg, Russia. Additionally, all students will participate in Class Afloat's West African humanitarian service-learning project in Dakar, Senegal.

Students onboard *Concordia* maintain a busy daily schedule. In addition to taking a full load of classes, students participate in all facets of shipboard life, including daily maintenance, navigation, sail maneuvers, and of course, galley duty. Since students stand watch, it is not irregular to see a student completing his or her homework at three in the morning!

In addition to my administrative duties on board the vessel, I teach a high school level political science class, as well as a university level class on the Theories of Leadership. I can think of no better way to teach politics than to sail to foreign countries around the world where the students can truly see the political systems first hand. Additionally, the onboard marine biology classes engage students in a living classroom, where students conduct a plethora of experiments on the different waters that we visit.

As a North American society, we are constantly grappling with how to prepare our children for the future. The educational community is constantly trying to strike the balance between developing a student personally and academically so that they will become effective leaders and positive, contributing members to our communities in the future. Through a combination of rigorous academics, international travel, service, and blue water sailing adventure, Class Afloat strives everyday to cultivate and facilitate this positive growth in all students.

It is my hope that readers of this article will follow *Concordia's* voyage via the Class Afloat website (www.classafloat.com). Interested individuals can see our voyage chart and follow the day to day progress. The students will also be writing articles and posting many of their pictures. This way, even if you are no longer a high school or university student, you can be a part of our sailing adventure as we follow Mark Twain's directive: explore, dream, discover!

It's What You Make Of It

By Heather Flanagan , 2007 ASTA Summer Intern

A new friend of mine said to me on the last day of the Tall Ships® Nova Scotia event, "I never realized something so tiring, dirty, and difficult could be so addicting." I have found that many people who try out tall ship sailing share the same sentiment, myself included.

Tall ship sailing isn't fun and games, it is what you make of it. I am not going to lie and say that it is easy, because it isn't. The days are long, the nights are short, and the daily projects can be frustrating. Those that decide to be tall ship sailors don't go into it because the pay is that great either. Tall ship sailing is difficult because there is no experience required. Everything a trainee does is on the job training. Sail theory is learned and almost immediately put into practice. You pick up most of the theory as you go along. On *Picton Castle*, Captain Moreland would often ask "So, are you confused yet?" We'd nod yes and he'd reply "Good. Sailing a traditionally rigged vessel isn't easy. If it were, everybody would be doing it."

Tall ship sailing is tough. Your calloused and splinter-ridden hands will quickly attest to that. Those who stick with it really have their hearts in it. There were dozens of times when I wondered what I was doing on a ship. I did not really need to be awake at 2 am. I could be at home in my warm, cozy, and still bed. I didn't have to go 90 feet in the air to teach a new trainee how to stow a royal sail. I could be at home folding sheets. I didn't have to hand wash 26 place settings. At home we have a dishwasher.

Then I saw several shooting stars, the Milky Way, and the constellation Scorpio. The dolphins started swimming alongside the ship and whales were seen in the distance.

In port, the crew and trainees were treated like celebrities. I saw the most beautiful sunrises and sunsets. I met dozen of crew members from other tall ships from around the world, toured their ships, and went to their receptions. I worked every second to help the ship get to her next destination. It is an amazing feeling to give your all and then give a little more. It is the feeling of love, dedication, and reward.

Sailing on a tall ship has been one of the most exciting adventures of my life thus far. I started last summer on board the Continental Sloop *Providence* as an intern. I chose the internship, even though I knew nothing about sailing, because I didn't want to spend my summer working in a coffee shop. That summer was one of the most stressful, yet most rewarding, summers in my 19 years of life.

Aside from the few knots I vaguely remembered from Girl Scouts, I knew nothing about to sailing. I felt useless. I was sea sick at least once a week and to this day I feel bad for those who were witness. I was petrified to go on the head rig and even more fearful to go aloft. I was awoken at peculiar hours to work. My showers were limited and my clothes remained dirty. I lived with ten strangers, worked with ten strangers and ate with ten strangers. We did everything together. I remember saying to one of those strangers, "I can't wait to go home, I am never doing this again!".

He and I are really great friends now. Those peculiar hours in the night that I was woken up became apart of my normal sleeping habits. I would be the first to volunteer to go on the head rig and I started to warm up to being aloft. I laugh at the statement "I am never doing this again." I have to thank all of the *Providence* crew, they were great. Each one took the time to mentor me. I learned knots, navigation, setting courses, and cooking on a ship. I even learned about the generator and engine.

That summer, I helped teach students from the Bronx about sailing, some of them had never even been to a beach. Every day they were excited. They were the

greatest group of teenagers I had ever had the pleasure to work with. I actually knew enough by the middle of my internship to be a mentor to them. I no longer felt like an outcast among the more experienced and professional crew. And then, my internship was over.

When I moved into my dorm room at college, I met my two roommates and listened to their gripes about the small room that was to be shared between three people. I thought it was great. I had a bed, a dresser, and a desk...all to myself. On the *Providence*, I only had a bunk. I mourned the loss of my ship life and my ship board family. I had become accustomed to my early morning wake up and start to the working day, although I never missed cleaning the heads. I missed setting sails and teaching our cadets about tall ships. I am incredibly appreciative of my friends in the sailing world because I could chat with them about knots, rigging knives, and the best foul weather gear. My roommates were a little less than thrilled to discuss the numerous wonderful benefits of pine tar. My life consisted of checking the Billet Bank on the ASTA website weekly and then daily. That was when I found the ASTA internship, the most fun job anyone could have.

After getting the internship, I discovered that I would be sailing onboard the *Picton Castle* to the four ports in the American Sail Training Association's TALL SHIPS CHALLENGE® Race Series. *Picton Castle* was first on the list of ships I wanted to sail on so this experience was the greatest surprise of all. I did a little to prepare for the ship by reading up on the ship and making frequent visits to her website. The best you can do to prepare is pack smartly. No book can really prepare a person for what he or she will experience. The tall ship journey is different for everyone.

Some people try sailing to find something and some people sign on with no expectations. I only had three desires - learn new things, meet new people, and go to amazing places. I know that those aren't too exciting, but I knew that I wouldn't be disappointed.

I got exactly what I wanted. I learned to sail a 300 ton, three-masted barque. I traveled to places I had never been and I met the greatest people. This summer, my family grew by two dozen members. The people I sailed with started out as strangers, then co-workers, then friends, and eventually they all became family. We were a very diverse group of people when we stepped off of the ship and into the real world wearing our best (yet still tar and paint stained) clothing. Quite often we had to remind each other that we were in the real world and had to watch out for cars. We'd crowd restaurants and loudly exchange stories about each other. We'd listen to stories of injuries we sustained, disastrous yet hilarious mistakes we made, and how much we thought we were going to dislike one another. In time, we learned nearly everyone's life stories.

> "The greatest part about living and working on a tall ship is what you learn about yourself. You learn to deal with people and personalities you never dreamed of having to encounter on a daily basis. You learn your strengths and weaknesses. You learn what your breaking point is."

just like any family, we'd get each other's nerves. We'd frustrate each other and make fun of each other. However, by the time the sun was setting, moods were improved and disputes were settled. We were each other's therapists. A ship is no place for bottled anger or hidden emotions because those feelings are toxic to ship life. We'd express our feelings, sometimes tactfully and sometimes not so well, but grudges were never held.

Whenever I was asked by someone on the ship why I enjoy sailing, I would point to the after dinner scene. It was nice seeing people relaxing on deck reading books and playing card games. We'd laugh about the day's events and star gaze. Sometimes we'd sleep under the stars, I always did, unless there was foul weather in the midst. We would have dance parties on deck. I'd sit and wonder what my "normal" shore life would be like if I had never sailed and I could not imagine doing anything else.

The greatest part about living and working on a tall ship is what you learn about yourself. You learn to deal with people and personalities you never imagined you would have to encounter on a daily basis. You learn your strengths and weaknesses. You learn what your breaking point is. I learned that I had several, but after two seasons on a tall ship, I have found I can deal with more difficulties than I had ever imagined I could. I learned a little bit about what I want to do with my life. I want my history studies to focus on maritime history and I also want to teach in the inner city, specifically in the Bronx. I saw how happy those students were to be on the ship. I know I can't bring all of my students to ships, but I can bring ship life, stories, and photos to them and hope that the same curiosity that sparked in me will ignite a call for adventure for them.

 My character builds from a weenie pebble to a massive, two-ton boulder atop a mountain. I feel strong and proud and confident. I have found my place in this world. I am not lost, nor am I purposeless.

Ode to
Corwith Cramer

By Natalie Tarr

I am really happy to be a part of the history of Science at SEA (Sea Education Association), based in Woods Hole, Massachusetts. For ten days, my co-mates studied oceanography, navigation, and maritime studies and then we cruised on the SSV *Corwith Cramer* for ten days.

I enjoyed the journey aboard this ship a lot, and highly recommend it to anyone of any age. Whether you're a teenager like me, in your fifties like my mom, or in your eighties like my grandmother, being a part of a sailing crew, changes the way you see the world. You begin to conserve your resources, turning off lights, shutting faucets, cleaning dishes right away, and keeping your space organized and neat. The motto on my ship was: If you are idle and see another person working, it's your job to approach them and ask, "How can I help you?". I thought this was a brilliant motto. To get along better with each other, our leader told us to excuse anyone who snapped at you or suddenly got angry. He said you should forgive them because they were overtired. These were two excellent concepts I learned aboard that help me work with other people to this day.

Just after I left the dock on the last day, I jotted down this note in my notebook:

We were floating in our own little world. Nothing bothered us. Beneath and in between, everything was safe, calm and relaxed. Pieces were organized and put in place at the right time. It was a rolling dream of comfy clouds. How I wish my life could always be aboard the "Cramer girl."

In total, I've written sixty pages, completed numerous scientific labs, and taken about fifty pictures, all describing my journey around Cape Cod. If I could change the world, I'd hope for everyone to have an experience like I did. My confidence in myself grew in leaps and bounds. My teachers gave me knowledge of the oceans nobody had ever taught me. This was such a valuable learning experience for me. One that I hope many more young people around the world will have the opportunity to participate in.

LOG ENTRIES

I am on a boat now. It's not a cruise ship, sailing yacht or motor boat. Imagine! I'm on board a grand two-masted sailing ship named SSV Corwith Cramer- *voyager and explorer of the open seas.*

My journey began six months before today when my parents asked me if I wanted to be part of the crew of this 134-foot sail-training research vessel. I said, "Yes, ma and pa, I'd love to!"

Before I sailed, I studied oceanography, navigational studies, and maritime history with twenty other high school students I now call my shipmates. Based in Woods Hole, Massachusetts, the classes we took were fascinating. We had time to work, time for study halls, and free time. After ten jam-packed days of learning and exploring the National Seashore, a core lab and a whaling museum, I was finally ready. On the eleventh day I boarded SSV Corwith Cramer and instantly became part of a family. My "shipmates" are my brothers and sisters, the crew my mothers and fathers. Together, striving to survive one hundred miles off Cape Cod, we bond. My character builds from a weenie pebble to a massive, two-ton boulder atop a mountain. I feel strong and proud and confident. I have found my place in this world. I am not lost, nor am I purposeless. SSV Corwith Cramer has a place for me every moment of every day. Whether it's charting points, deploying nets, or scanning the horizon at bow, I am always wanted, needed and loved. I am important. For this, I thank you, Corwith Cramer.

LOG 07/19/07

I had one of the most amazing experiences in my life just a few hours ago. Dorinda Ostermann, a wonderful lady, gave us a lecture on paleontology and core sampling. She came to visit us and talked on and on about global warming and the government and ethanol, etc, etc, ad nausium. But when she took us to her lab at WHOI [Woods Hole Oceanographic Institute], Quisett Campus things got more interesting. She brought out five core samples. The first, from North America, resembled clay and was slimy (but dried out). The second, from the Bahamas, consisted of compacted calcium carbonate deposits, the stuff clam shells are made of. The Ceara Rise in the Atlantic Ocean was where the third core sample was from. It has an acute thin orange layer of rusted iron

deposits, where it eroded from the Andes Mountains out of the Amazon Basin. The fourth sample came from Antarctica. It was a light, chalky grey, which was mainly diatom oozes. But in a couple spots, there was some dark grey, which came from a volcano's ashes. My very favorite core sample came from the Red Sea. As Dorinda slid the core out I gasped. Boy was I surprised! There was a whole range of colors down the core! Metal ores and evaporation had made these layers of color. The Red Sea sample's number is Chn 100-3 9PC, in case I'd ever like to look it up on the WHOI website. This core has inspired me to go out and explore the Red Sea. Wahoo!

The core lab was super cool because it connected physical things with ideas Giora taught us in the classroom, that the Red Sea is splitting and growing. A long time ago it would fill with water (carrying sediments) and then get closed off. The water outside would then recede leaving a puddle. The puddle would evaporate leaving piles of these sediments. Some were iron and rusted. So that's why the Red Sea has many colorful deposits.

LOG 7/21/07

This afternoon we took out our charts, triangles, and compasses (compi?) and trooped to the Madden Center. Captain Terry was there with Laryssa, Scott and Cliff. Whenever I had a question, they helped me find the answer. First, I unrolled my chart and took a look. It was a chart of the Woods Hole area, Gayhead, and Crow's Neck. We used what we knew to plot the points at first. Then, as we progressed, we made point series to track our voyage. The answers were on the back and the longitudes and latitudes, too. I was good at plotting the points when they were by themselves. There are three methods to plot a fix, a compass bearing, a range (when 2 places line up) or a radar reading. I was good at that. But then it rapidly *got harder. We had to convert some compass readings to true degrees so we had to account for variation (or, why the reading would be inaccurate). At first, I plotted all the points, then realized I hadn't converted any of the compass readings to true. I needed to start over and I did. After plotting all the fixes again and not ending up at the right finishing fix, I gave up. After two or more hours of grueling, concentrating work, my brain was fried chicken. Man!*

LOG 7/23/07

Yesterday was an absolutely amazing day. Giorra took us an hour and forty five minutes to the National Seashore. I'd never been there before, but I absolutely loved it. The beach was large and secluded and there were big waves and grey seals. The topography, or incline, of the beach changed as you walked along it. At first the incline tended to be pretty smooth, it wasn't too steep. But then, this ridge grew. It was totally amazing because you could sit on the edge of the sand as if you were sitting on a bench and your feet could dangle. Further along, I came across a small island. Walking in my tennis shoes, I made my way over to the island but abruptly couldn't go any further. A giant wave came rushing towards me with a pile of brown algae and yellow nasty foam floating on top! I simply couldn't go any farther. I had to wait for the wave to go away so I could reach the island. I then remembered that the island I was aiming for was inundated with water when the wave came, so I decided not to go explore that island.

Meandering along, I found the steep sand eventually evened out. There lay a continuous fence posted as impassable. No trespassing could occur beyond the posts because endangered piping plovers and terns nested there. Needless to say, I didn't explore. But, I went the other way – to the water. In the water were mini starfish and one big starfish. Horseshoe crabs and sand eels popped their heads up every once in a while.

Eventually, I caught up with my friends Rachel, Molly, Alex and Lauren. Travis and Giorra came up from down the beach. Together we meandered to the end of the beach. Just before the end, Travis pointed out this mini ledge. He asked us why we thought the ledge was there and where the sand was moving with each wave. We observed and finally came up with the answer. Although the wave brought the sand up perpendicular to the shore, it dropped it down to the right as it receded back into the waves. It was quite interesting.

Before our trip, Mary had given us a reading. The author, Thoreau, described in great detail the sand, birds, seaweed, and emergency storm houses at that very beach. So I took one of his imageries of white horse chariots flying inland, their manes flying, as the waves curled and rushed up. I thought the white chariots looked like they had bangles dangling from their manes and hooves because the bits of brown seaweed left the white foam with brown specks. Boy, it sure was a gorgeous beach.

LOG 7/24/07

Today finished as quite an adventurous day. When I awoke, a concoction of bananas, strawberries, and cream cheese awaited me. Class was quite the norm. Giorra spoke much of phytoplankton and zooplankton and how they affect the oceans and marine environment. Captain Terry spoke of the sail layout, how to jibe and tack your sails, and how to control toward and away from the wind. What an adventure. The Cramer arrived today as we made my way to New Bedford on the bus...

The following is what I learned about whaling. The whaling ship is over 100 feet long with big arced wooden "U's" on the sides to hold boats. The watchman climbs up the shrouds and ratlines to the big circle at the top of the mast. When a whale is spotted he cries, "There she blows!" or "She blows!" and the men jump in a boat and row off toward the whale. It's six men a ship, four rowing, one up front, and one aft. The man at the front harpoons the whale and as the whale flees, the rope attached to the harpoon begins to unravel. As the cord gets scarce, either a nearby boat ties his supply of rope to it or the crew begins another step. The next step is to pull hand over hand, singing sea chantying all the while, while the front man and back man switch places. The new foreman or mate takes a hooked instrument and punctures the whale's lung. When the whale begins to spout blood, the mate knows he's got it. While the whale is dead and floating, the rowers head back to the ship. But sometimes, they can't find the ship and get lost at sea forever. But if they get back, the whale gets placed under a foot board and a man cuts a slice of blubber off him. The blubber gets boiled off to make wax and oil. It's great for candles and lamps. Baleen from the whales make the hoops for skirts. I found the whole process quite fascinating. Tonight we had pizza and ice cream sandwiches for dinner and watched "Moby Dick".

LOG 7/28/2007

At 2300, Will, Dave and I deployed the Neuston net. We had to let out the boom, which was resting upright so the net wouldn't hit the hull. Any noise against the hull will get heard in the bunks in the saloon and from the galley. So we let out the lines and I tied most of the bowline's (because I was the only person who knew how to tie them). We used a boom pusher (a pole with a metal "U" on it) to help ease the boom out. As soon as the net had been in water for 30 minutes (starting at 0000), I hauled it out with Will's help.

As I look up to the sky I think,
Who am I, Who am I am I?
I know I'm in Cape Cod,
Yes I know, I nod, I nod, I nod,
I think where am I where am I?
I know I'm in Cape Cod.

The Ocean's are a real beauty
And so I think it's my duty
Believe in her and all her jewels
Learn and listen,
Don't be a fool
For Cape Cod is one
beautiful place
Not some space for us to waste.

There is a little jar at the end of the net where all the zooplankton accumules. The zooplankton was dark grey and in little mounds. It shone and shimmered in the light. Will and Dave did phosphate samples and a chlorophyll sample. There were these little critters (black and sand worms) that were less than 2 cms. The zooplankton were copepods.

LOG 7/30/07

Last night was a good night. I got an almost full night's sleep. My watch started at 0300 and ended at 0700. The girl who woke me up told me it was cold and wet outside, so I put on all my foul weather gear. I went around and surveyed the boat and then I was called to deck duty. I don't really remember much of what happened… I think I made a lot of hourlies and did some boat checks and went on watches. Alex, a boy on my watch yelled, "Hey, we got some whales here!" I ran to port and sure enough there they were, blowing their spouts and showing off their beautiful black fins. After 0300-0700 duty, we had to clean the galley. I scrubbed the aft heads w/ bleach with both a two-cornered and one-cornered sponge. Then I scrubbed the showerhead. The soles got squeegeed too. After cleaning, we ate breakfast (honeydew and two slices of bacon). There are these mini hammocks of fruit hanging between the two masts filled with bananas, oranges, pineapples, watermelon, and honeydew. Finally, I got to go back to sleep and took a long, long nap. When I woke up, I helped the galley watch clean dishes. At around one o'clock, we ate lunch- mac and cheese with salad (yummy). After lunch, I read some of my Pi book and then went to the afternoon meeting where we learned about fog and direction. Giora taught us the relationship between depth and coastal range, temperature and the Gulf Stream. The best part was tying knots with Travis and Giora. One of them is called a butterfly knot. After knotting, I ran to take a cold sweater shower w/ dishwashing soap. Dinner was Mexican frijoles negros, arroz y pollo. Then my watch began. I learned how to winkle, or make seawater from various depths reveal the concentration of distilled oxygen they have. It's a long methodical drip process. Then, for two hours, we cleaned and scrubbed the galley soles, stoves and countertops. It was nasty icky. But after cleaning, it looked good, so I went back to winkling. I wrote up an hourly for science watch. Someone brought in a surface bucket sample. Today we reached our station (or the point we wanted to be at). I plotted our way there every half hour. I'm really tired now. Yesterday we tried to figure out which color of light penetrates first in the ocean. Red goes first, then green and blue last.

LOG 8/3/07

Woke up this morning and we were as still as land. We had morning meeting and it was announced we'd make our scientific hypotheses today. We grouped up into three groups – Soper Station 1, 2 and 3. All morning we spent looking at data from the deployed equipment. I was to research the meter net and compare our superstation's data to that of other meter nets. At 1030, everyone set out the graphs, pictures and charts they made and we had a conference. We went around and compared our data. Later, after spending the whole morning and lunch time drawing conclusions and finding general trends, SEA mates met again. In the afternoon, our hypotheses were presented along with any other data we collected. I had thought up an experiment we could do and other people had, as well. It was a conglomeration of the best scientific minds on the Cramer!

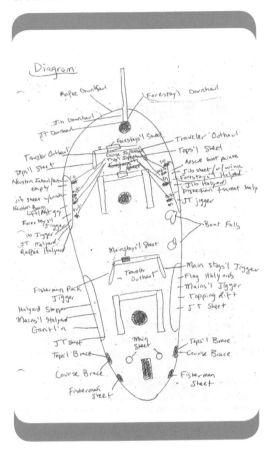

Diagram:

After the meeting, it was Field Day. A-watch cleaned the galley. We removed and wiped with bleach anything and everything possible. The soles, the counters, the shelves, pans, pots, dishes – every little thing! The stewards came around with costumes on and handed out candy like Halloween. The mates turned on iPod music and radios and we had a rockin' great time listening to oldies and newies. It was wicked awesome. The more effort we put into it, the shorter it would take and it did!

After hauling all the mats to the deck to rinse, and hauling them back down, it was time to pack. We packed our suitcases and wiped down our berths with bleach.

This concludes my story at SEA – a period in my life that tops the charts in all areas: in comfort, in relaxation, in interest, in hard work, in persevering, meeting new people, in success. Thank you, God, for bringing me and Science At Sea together in this vast, ever-changing world. What a wondrous fit!

Helping to make her SEA experience possible, Natalie Tarr was the recipient of a Henry H. Anderson, Jr. Sail Training Scholarship. For more information on the American Sail Training Association's Sail Training Scholarship Program please turn to page 354 or visit the ASTA website at www.sailtraining.org

Why the Tall Ships Matter (And To Whom)

By Nancy Richardson

A neighbor of mine just mentioned I was looking stressed. When I told her I was trying to meet a deadline for an article on "Why the Tall Ships Matter", she responded, "I love the swash-buckling era! Have you seen 'Pirates of the Caribbean'?" I don't think she saw me cringe or heard me say "We are not pirates", as she hurried off the elevator.

Although we can capitalize on this wave of popular pirate interest, we should add value by arming ourselves to highlight how today's tall ships are making the world a better place, with fleeting impact on millions at port events and even more lasting outcomes with individuals on lone ships doing 'sail training' out of sight of land.

Tall ships sail with a lofty mission and carry the valuable cargo of learning. Whether the learning is applied to students, ships, or the sea; for education, conservation or preservation; in the past, present or future, everything is connected. A goal of sail training emphasizes learning *from* sailing more than learning *to* sail.

A recent study on the value and effectiveness of sail training, was conducted by the University of Edinburgh, Scotland, for Sail Training International and its member national organizations around the world. It was based on the conviction that the wealth of anecdotal evidence available from these international organizations, and the few formal studies conducted, would be validated by much more comprehensive global research.

Among the three following findings is the conclusion that there are gains in teamwork that are lasting and universal. Young trainees who participate in off-shore sail training programs show measurable improvements in social confidence and their ability to work with others, the benefits are sustained over time after the voyage experience, and the positive value of the sail training experience transcends national and cultural boundaries.

Four ASTA members, Los Angeles Maritime Institute (LAMI), Ocean Classrooms, S.A.L.T.S., and Toronto Brigantines, Inc., were among the 16 organizations from 13 countries (USA, Canada, Australia, New Zealand and several in Europe) selected by the University of Edinburgh to complete shipboard observations and interviews on voyages in 2006, with follow up interviews early in 2007.

Pre-voyage reasons for participants to take part in an off shore voyage included looking forward to experiencing what they believed a tall ship sailing voyage would deliver: challenges, meeting new people, experiencing a different environment, and the idea of being on a boat. Their fears included "getting seasick" and "heights." Not only was it documented that all their positive expectations were met or exceeded, but also their fears were allayed by the overall experience, reflected in comments like "Even though I got seasick, it was worth it."

It is always gratifying to hear youth full of enthusiasm for the tall ship experience and the subsequent positive changes in their lives. In keeping with LAMI's commitment to 'use sailing the sea to educate for life,' the research identifies individual outcomes that the students themselves describe as life changing. Indeed, the study shows that they are using their "personal and social confidence" to improve their relationships with their families, friends and community. The tall ship experience strengthened these individuals. They tell us they do not join gangs and they stay in school. It really, really matters!

The report, as related to LA Maritime Institute's TopSail Youth Program, reinforces the "positive approach taken by staff, achieving good results in terms of the attitudes and learning experienced by participants." As the researchers reported from the LAMI data, "Young people are encouraged to have fun and to ask questions so that they learn about the vessel and the marine environment." And the researchers refer to TopSail crew as "closely integrated with trainees with little evidence of segregation aboard the vessels."

Answers to survey questions were written down by the interviewers as the participants responded. Responses were thoughtful, and their answers reflected that our Topsail goals are being fulfilled. They said their TopSail experience increased personal confidence, initiative and leadership; improved relationships with peers and adults, including parents/family; developed appreciation and skills for working as a team; motivated them to do better in school and to prepare for job skills; and encouraged a sense of responsibility, planning for future education, career and life success.

The STI-Edinburgh study reinforces real, credible results verifying that tall ship sail training experiences are "more than just a boat ride." Indeed, investing in tall ships yields measurable changes in participants' lives, gains that they retain and apply at home, in school and their communities, multiplying the value of tall ships.

What distinguishes sail training is a combination of three elements- students, ships and the sea. From their at sea experience, the students become better sailors, shipmates and stewards for our ocean planet, both out on the ocean and ashore.

The following answers the question, 'Why the Tall Ships Matter", in the words of the people involved with sail training.

Students: Trainees, Educators, Group/Crew/Watch Leaders, Program Developers, Curriculum Designers, Families, Friends, Communities

"The Big benefit to kids of ocean sailing is to mix adventure with education and to separate fantasy and instant gratification from dreams and goal setting..."

Captain Bill Pinkney

"My son has grown through other groups, sports, etc...but nothing comes close to the effectiveness -and fun- of sailing our tall ship, and the TopSail Youth Crew experience!"

Mother of LAMI Youth Crew member

"We're all shipmates, whether sailing or shore side aboard our spaceship planet. Whatever course you chart, you'll find that life is rarely more concentrated than on a ship and you can look forward to an authentic adventure, full of physical and personal challenges. The romance, as well as the demands and dangers, of the sea are genuine. No one is alone in facing waves of misery and fear, but there are higher crests of exhilaration and courage to be shared as well. Log entries from my shipmates show that they have pulled harder, climbed higher, grown faster, learned better, worked more closely with others and steered beyond more new horizons than they had ever imagined."

Nancy H. Richardson, Founding Editor, 1980-87 editions of 'Sail Tall Ships!'

Ships: Designers, Builders, Captains, Crews, Historians, Racers, Artists, Writers

On a ship, students find they need to pull together, literally and figuratively, to get anywhere. Raising, setting and trimming sail is a real hands-on/minds-on experience in doing the right thing at the right time to make everything easier. Whether for stark survival, comfortable cruising, or for speed in a race, on a safe ship well-sailed everything must be in harmony, the sails' set and trim and the crew's pulling together as a team, for peak performance in maximum efficiency and effectiveness.

Most of the world's navies and merchant marine academies operate tall ships for training under sail, since shiphandlers need to understand the forces of the wind to handle the hulls and superstructures of their superships that operate on engine power. Being responsive to the weather is imperative for safe decision-making and maneuvering. Therefore, the test of teamwork is put to the challenge when the progression of command and crew communication is utilized for both effective leadership and support in the complex demands of a sailing ship. Tall ships are revered as international friendship ambassadors in the context of Tall Ships Races and port events as well. In fact, many nations have built ships for the dual-purposes of training at sea and diplomacy ashore.

How wonderful that the original sister ship war-prizes from Germany have evolved such rich legacies of seamanship and friendship - US Coast Guard Bark *Eagle*, Portugal's *Sagres*, Romania's *Mircea* and the Russian *Tovarich*. And "ship" people are rewarded with educational and practical opportunities for historic preservation of traditional skills and the ships themselves.

> *"The traditional tall ship is the finest vehicle for learning ever devised by man...Why is it important? Because our wonderfully sophisticated society is enormously rich in technology-yet desperately poor in experience, that precious resource with which values are molded and leaders are made..."*
>
> Rafe Parker

Captain Irving Johnson's advice was "Pay attention to detail." In the Afterword of his book that compliments the film "Peking Battles Cape Horn", Irving went on to say, "The sea is still a place to learn and train and overcome. But I am glad that my education was aboard the *Peking* where the call for 'all hands' had its literal meaning. The ship had been our protecting home to a degree that no home on land could equal. We were trained not to waste or break things because no one could order up replacements --once damage occurred, we had to make it good by our own efforts. What a contrast to the casual way we now expand and dispose of material. But this self-reliance is still needed at times and where can it be learned now?". Captain Irving Johnson, with wife Exy, pioneered sail training by sailing *Yankee* around the world seven times with youth crew, 1935-58, famous for classic film he took in 1929-30, 'Around Cape Horn'.

Sea: Ocean and Aquatic Scientists, Marine Educators, Environmentalists, Ocean Literacy Specialists

The unfamiliar can be scary, and the scale and beauty of a tall ship daunting, especially to youth who say they've never seen the ocean. Interacting with the environment is rarely, if ever, more challenging than sailing in harmony with the wind and waves. being in the interface between the two major fluid systems of air and water. The great adventure on the seemingly 'tall' ship is dwarfed by the vast and overwhelming scale of the sea and sky.

Science, sustainability and stewardship come alive with the sea experience, as in the mission of the National Marine Educators Association, "*To make known the world of water, fresh and salt…*" The action step is environmental stewardship from ocean literacy, conveying understanding and application of the principles that there is one ocean and that the ocean and humankind are inextricably interconnected.

> *"We didn't know what we were starting and, of course, we were fitting in to what has been almost a world-wide phenomenon of people using beautiful boats, whether rowboats or schooners or whatever to tell, to give some kind of message. It might be an environmental message, but it was a message. Where people see the beauty of a boat and see the magic. Nobody can explain it in words what the magic is, in water and wind, and they will be saving the water where they are."*
>
> Pete Seeger

In the Girl Scout Gift of Water Projects for the GS 70th Anniversary in 1982, there was a national effort focused on water-related service in communities across the country, "in thought, word and deed from sea to shining sea…"

Shores: Port Event Organizers, Waterfront Developers, Community Leaders, Business People, Corporate Sponsors, Philanthropists, Social Workers, Law Enforcement Officers

> *Waiting for a connecting flight in Detroit airport recently, I was delighted to see tall ships framed on a front page from the Detroit Free Press July 23, 2001. The headline above schooners against the city skyline reads, "RIVER OF UNITY. Parade of tall ships is a testament to the city's heart and possibilities…"*
>
> *The day wasn't about ships at all, or musicians, or celebrities, or corn dogs. It was about possibility and green grass and a long smooth strip of sidewalk, free of trash, that now hugs a stretch of Detroit River shoreline downtown, where thousands stood in heat the past four days to celebrate the city's 300th birthday. On Sunday, the crowds came for the parade of Tall Ships. The mood was quiet, reflective, ponderous and sweltering.*
>
> *The ships were impressive, with their billowing sails and soaring masts and stubbornly casual pace, and argument against sound bites and cell phones. And they inspired applause and smiles and pointing and murmuring.*
>
> *"What the city has done is tremendous," said George Ford, 62, a Detroiter who watched the 24 tall ships but watched the crowd more. "What really felt good to me was how the people were together. Urban and suburban. Reticent and demonstrative. VIP and ordinary."*
>
> *"Family stuff," said Sharon Bender. "Not in the politician's sense, but in the human condition sense, with frailty and difference at the same table. This is what the city needs to do," she said.*
>
> *She was watching from the new Riverfront Promenade with her two nieces whom she brought from Port Huron, where they live. The three spent the afternoon against the rail, dressed in costumes from 1701, watching the ships…*
>
> By Shawn Windsor, Dan Shine and Erik Lords

We hear from port after port that Tall Ships® events attract more people to the waterfront than any other phenomenon. And the crowds are fascinated families and youth-of-all-ages who spend their money and, more importantly, their time and spirit relating to understanding why the tall ships matter . Dreams can be fulfilled just by watching these ships and having the opportunity to sail.

Many ports recognize the value of getting people aboard and sailing the visiting ships for an event—and then building (or acquiring) one of their own, for example Charleston's new *Spirit of South Carolina,* Bay City, Michigan's *Appledore IV* and *Appledore V,* Bermuda's *Spirit of Bermuda* and Baltimore's *Lady Maryland.*

Indeed, the tall ships bring us together in a multitude of wonder-filled and life-sustaining ways. In ASTA's by-laws we say, "ASTA is a bridge to the future, building on traditions of sailing, ships and the sea…" The tall ships matter. One and all are part of the mission to convey to others a state of fact, of mind and of heart about the benefits of sail training…and make the world a better place.

Of course, change happens on land, but I have never experienced a change as profound and in as short a time as I did at sea on a tall ship. I know I changed. I have become a much more confident, accomplished and worldly person from the experience.

Why Everything We Did Out There Mattered

By Matt Maples, 2007 ASTA Summer Intern

Night watch on the tall ship *Picton Castle*. The "longest" watch of the day. Coldest would have been just as appropriate. My gloveless hands were numb from the unexpected chill of early July. Apparently light was in as short a supply as warmth in these northern latitudes for we could not even see one another's faces as our watch fumbled to muster for duty on deck as midnight approached. In my nearly two months on board the *Picton Castle,* I could not remember a night as inky as this one - or one as cold. Glancing backward from my lookout post on the bow of the ship, I could not see anyone beneath our towers of gray sails. The ship would have looked abandoned had it not been for a handful of running lights.

The view forward was similarly stark. The seas were black, the skies pasted with a sticky cement-gray overcast that reduced the usual brilliance of the moon into a choked and ruddy dimness left to hang limply over the horizon. Everything was wearing shades of gray. To my eyes, the world looked as devoid of color as a black-and-white movie. As lookout, it was my responsibility to keep an eye out for dangers and to help spot navigational aids. A quick scan of the horizon revealed the same result as before- nothing but fog. There was no one out here but us, the handful of us manning the ship on her return to her homeport of Lunenburg, Nova Scotia.

Frost-tipped wind filled our sails from the port side, giving the ship the momentum it needed to rise on top of waves and then roll slightly to starboard before repeating the motion. The labyrinth of wavelets ahead of us led to a glowing horizon, the moon gave off just enough light to illuminate walls of fog. From my vantage point, it looked as if our solitary ship, with a jealous clutch of wind in her sails, was rolling through murky waters toward an illuminated horizon of feather-like fog where all the ghosts of the world would be found in expectation of our arrival.

A seemingly long solitary vigil passed before the slow clank of boots on metal steps tolled the passing of the hour and my relief from forward lookout. After a ship check below decks, I let my own ill-fitted and clumsy boots gravitate toward a source of light, heat and the cloying scent of burning diesel. My stiffened hand unbolted the door to the galley.

As the galley door swung open, I was instantly greeted by a breath of crisped hot air and a menagerie of tired but grinning faces. I soon had the source of their smiles, newly baked breadsticks (expertly twisted into knots) and still gooey Rice Krispies Treats, in hand. Our watch had clustered in the galley house to find refuge from eerie chills and busied themselves with creating baked goods, which were as much a relief for late-night stomachs as they were an excuse to fire up our 120-year-old diesel stove hours early for warmth. Many hours were passed in jovial company as we rotated out to complete our duties and ensure that the ship was safe and manned as we carried her through the night, en route to her home.

An hour after sunrise, the order came from the second mate to myself and two shipmates to go aloft and stow the royal and t'gallant, the two topmost sails on our fore and mainmasts, which were nearly one hundred feet in the air and still heavy from the rain. Placing my feet and hands on the slick, tarred ratlines, I clambered in full gear, heading for the top of a pitching foremast.

A handful of weeks earlier I was standing in line at a fluorescent-cast Baltimore 7-11, my arms cradling an assortment of junk food. As I stood in a stalled checkout line I scanned the magazine rack for news. Lindsey Lohan was acting out again, Paris Hilton was lamenting over a stint in prison and there were a half-dozen premature quips concerning an American election over a year away. I quickly realized that the only thing I had missed on shore while I had been away with the ship for several weeks previously was the pleasure food I held in my arms. As I left a convenience store populated by faces I did not recognize I thought, "Why is it that everything we [the crew] do out there [the sea] matters more than anything happening here [on land]?"

Of course, it would be unfair to try to pass such a statement off as a fact, but I did think that question in reference to my time sailing on the barque *Picton Castle* and I must have had a reason. I have done much contemplation to produce an answer to my own question but a truly fulfilling answer yet eludes me. However, I cannot deny a tangible fact, two months time beneath the masts of *Picton Castle* made a greater impression and change to me than any other experience in twenty-two years of my life thus far. I am a substantially more confident, accomplished and worldly person. Yet, at the same time, I feel humbled. If I was asked what caused these changes I would reply, "I crewed and sailed on a square-rigged tall ship." A deceptively simple answer because that statement entails much more than would be initially realized. The life associated with sailing a tall ship is rife with an assortment of challenges and unique experiences, especially for the beginner...

"Set headsails!" "Set the main topmast staysail!" "Set topsails!" The crew of the *Picton Castle* sprang into a frenzy of action as Captain Dan Moreland gave a series of orders from the bridge. A dense undergrowth of cast-off lines lay at the feet of tree-trunk-thick masts. Crew members grabbed handfuls of nameless, thick lines to haul down to the deck. As what appeared to be chaos unfolded around me, confusion must have re-arranged my face. Here I was on the deck of a tall ship during a parade of sail in Charleston, a place I had dreamed about being since childhood and had anticipated for months, and I had only a vague notion what the Captain was talking about and I had absolutely no clue about what to do! As I tried my best to make myself useful by helping haul on lines, I wondered, "What have I got myself into?"

I surely am not the first and almost certainly not the last person to think such words on a tall ship. A traditional sailing ship may as well be its own country, for its landscape is entirely foreign and it is populated by people who seem to have a different language, unique customs and a sleeping schedule surely considered peculiar by many on shore. Those new to tall ship sailing will likely (as I did) face a substantially significant learning curve before they can navigate (pun intended) this new world beyond the shore.

Enough generations have passed since the last tall ships carried cargo commercially. Enough time passed so that the skills once familiar to many of our ancestors for thousands of years are now largely alien to the average person. However, not enough generations have passed to render such skills lost to time. Thankfully, within the hulls of today's fleet of operating tall ships the skills of traditional seamanship are alive and available to be passed down to 21st century people ambitious enough to learn them. Working with lines, knots, and the maintenance of gear on a ship, navigation and sail theory, are some of the skills that need to be learned. I found that becoming relatively competent in them was a real challenge. It was hard, but I was ambitious and eager to learn.

When I first put my feet on the deck of the *Picton Castle,* I would have been at a loss to describe the purpose of a halyard. Seven weeks later I got a real test of my ability at sail handling. After docking in Lunenburg, Nova Scotia the *Picton Castle* let all its sails hang to dry to recover from a rainy day prior. I was on watch with two newer crewmembers while the rest of the crew was ashore or asleep. We expected our watch to be routine and uneventful, but then gusts of wind interrupted our expectations by filling our waiting sails with wind. Propelled by the wind, the ship strained at her dock lines that constrained her, hauling many of them bar-tight with awful creaking sounds. Fearing damage to our dock lines, the old dock itself or worse, we quickly contacted our bosun who told us to take in sails. For the first time ever, I had to direct others while we dropped headsails and took in many of the square sails with all the speed we could muster until enough wind was spilled to take the excessive strain off our dock lines.

While this event is not impressive or unusual to many, it was a benchmark for me. It proved to me that I really did learn how to handle the sails on *Picton Castle.* A goal I considered ambitious while looking at *Picton Castle's* 170 some lines in the weeks prior. Several weeks before I left *Picton Castle,* I was promoted from trainee to assistant deckhand – tangible proof that I had improved and was now a novice in seamanship, as opposed to clueless and uninitiated. It was not easy for me to learn, but I realized that learning the skills to sail a tall ship were attainable.

Learning the skills of the traditional mariner is only half of the challenge of tall ship sailing. The other half is adjusting and then thriving to a new lifestyle that bears little resemblance to the lifestyle of the contemporary westerner in the world today. Long hours of physical activity, constant exposure to the elements, living with a number of people in small spaces and no flushing toilets, all conspire against a new trainee. There were days for me where I had been working long hours, was constantly hungry, somewhat seasick, wet from a rain and dampness that had been perpetuating all week, working with disagreeable shipmates, while being a bit crabby myself.

Days like that were the exception, not the norm, but they did happen. Normally, I would never work that hard on land. On this tall ship however, I found myself going above and beyond what I normally would be willing to do. Why? I wanted to succeed and I believed that to succeed on a tall ship I needed to redefine my sense of self – this was probably the most significant adjustment from shore life. Contemporary society values "the individual." We are used to being able to make our own choices and prescribe ample time for our own privacy. On ship your personal wants and needs (within reason) become less important because you are part of a team that, in one aspect or another, needs to be available at all hours to run a ship as smoothly as possible. There is no place for selfishness, but ample need for selflessness. A crew needs to operate as cohesively as possible, thus hierarchy is as surely embedded in the foundation of the ship as the keel to ensure that everyone knows their place and responsibilities. A hierarchy taken much more seriously than most civilians are used to and for good reason, the waters can be dangerous. Even though your personal desires take a backseat to your responsibilities, your ability to carry out your duties actually increases your importance. Why? I found that I had much more responsibility on the ship then I ever had on land. Even seemingly routine duties like lookout, anchor watch and making fast or casting off dock

lines during docking maneuvers can have catastrophic consequences if such duties are neglected. I found it oddly interesting that I could have responsibilities on ship of a magnitude that would have never been given to me on land. Granted, these responsibilities are inherently simple to carry out, provided that one follows directions and remains aware of the situation, but nonetheless they can have serious consequences. On normal shore life however, I doubt that I, and many others near to my age, would be given the chance to carry out responsibilities with consequences as serious without substantial red tape. I am happy to report however, that by simply following directions and being aware, people on ship aged as young as fifteen to their elder years could, on a whole, fulfill their responsibilities successfully without a stifling amount of red tape.

It was challenging to overcome the learning curve and lifestyle changes on board the *Picton Castle*. I had plenty of help. The professional crew of the *Picton Castle* may as well have been saints for their patience in teaching us trainees. While many of the concepts and skills associated with tall ships are daunting at first, they are often quite simple when understood. I definitely respect them for being willing to show me how to do something that is simple to them three times, and then show me again! They taught well, for I did learn and in my last few weeks I found myself teaching newer trainees the pin rail, line handling and steering at the helm. There was much to learn from the professional crew and they were happy to show us, so long as we were engaged and willing to work just as hard to learn. Like all the other difficulties to overcome, I put substantial effort and will into learning. That effort, coupled with enthusiastic teachers, made it possible to achieve my goal of being a useful crewmember to my shipmates.

You might wonder, "If sailing on a tall ship is so hard, and full of responsibility, why would anyone want to do it?" It is hard, true, but the real motivation for me was the experiences and sense of accomplishment that makes the hard work more than worthwhile. Experiences like the thrill of scurrying up the ratlines to be the first on the fore royal yard or the tense moments of anxiety as the ship cautiously sails in a busy shipping lane where vessels and heavy buoys are concealed behind thick curtains of fog, only to be revealed at sudden, random moments. I remember my amazement one evening, as I was lying out in the head rig of the ship while dolphins swam off the bow, no more than fifteen feet underneath me. I remember the serenity of being at the helm on a moonless night, the sky above our swaying gray canvas towers lit with a multitude of stars that I had never seen before, the scene completed with a dash of the arm of the Milky Way Galaxy, a brilliant white belt studded with stars that seemed to slice the star field from horizon to horizon. Still, the best sights happened during my lookout shifts on the bow, when I could often scan from horizon to horizon and see (with some satisfaction) that there was no one out there but us. I would then spare a quick glance backwards to see all our canvas set, massive canvas spires with curves carved by the wind, a sight and viewpoint that few have seen in the generations since the waning years of great sailing ships.

Besides the fantastic sights and new scenery that one sees while sailing, there is the aspect of the floating community of a tall ship that is a remarkable experience unto itself. Separated from land, the amount of people that you have contact with is considerably smaller. Coming from many states and nationalities, we all lived, worked, ate and slept in close proximity with one another – privacy was limited to your bunk. Many would consider such conditions to be bothersome, as a member of modern society is accustomed to having ample amounts of space and privacy. Contrary to being a curse, this amalgamation of diverse people in a small space created a very sociable and close community. I never felt lonely, for chronic socializing was inevitable when small spaces are filled with adventurous people. We all learned a lot from each other, whether working hard on deck as a team or sharing bad jokes below decks. People that I knew for only a few weeks became close friends – we spent enough time together, relying on one another for that to happen. Our tall ship crew was more or less a close-knit community of friends, even if we had only known each other for a few short weeks. Living in such a community, sharing troubles, wonders and experiences as surely as we shared resources and stories created a unique community unlike any I had ever experienced on land. In so sharing our resources and living so closely together, I believe we got a feel for a different sort of self-sufficient community life, quite different from the more isolated and self-focused lifestyles that most 21st century westerners live. It is a different way of living, a different kind of society that is a worthwhile experience.

Yes, it is a hardworking lifestyle that I found quite challenging, especially at the beginning. But it can be learned and the lifestyle adjustments can be overcome. When I, for the most part, knew what I was doing I found the work to be enjoyable. Of course, for the experiences of the sights I saw on the ship, the people I met, the things I learned, and the altered world view that travel brings really made the moments that I remember. I am thankful for the challenges though, they made me push myself farther than I otherwise would have done. It is a hard but uniquely fun lifestyle.

Since I posed that question at the Baltimore 7-11, I have had some time to consider why that short time on the water, sailing on a tall ship meant more to me then what I had experienced on land. The best explanation that I've managed to appropriate is *change*. Of course, change happens on land, but I have never experienced a transformation as profound and in as short a time as I did at sea on a tall ship. I know I changed. I have become a much more confident, accomplished and worldly person from the experience. Why did I change though?

I believe it is because of the sea itself. The sea and the sailing ship are inextricably intertwined by change. The sea is in a perpetual flux. The weather, current and tide alter the conditions of a restless ocean. Therefore, the ship that uses sails must respond, she has no choice if she wants to be successful. To meet the whims of the ocean, the crew of the sailing ship have to be ready, willing and able to counter and take advantage of the ocean's alternating personalities at all times. In so meeting that challenge, those who choose to sail on a sailing ship and intend to be successful will change. They will be challenged at every step. They have to be, because the ocean itself is perpetually in motion.

Or maybe I felt that everything we did was more important because of the grand welcomes our ship received as we sailed into ports, the endless swarms of boats that would come near us just to gawk. It might have been my head swelling from our crew being a colorful attraction at crew parades in ports. Maybe because the thrills of working aloft at sea or the excitement of new sights at sea surpassed that of life on land. Or perhaps it was because the moments of complete serenity, whether sailing into a sunset at sea or underneath a brilliant canvas of stars, was more profound than any such similar moments seen from shore. It might have been because I shared these things and more with a fantastic menagerie of people.

Why Everything We Did Out There Mattered

Regardless, it would be ridiculous to say that everything we did out there, out at sea meant more then the things that were happening on shore. After all, we were just normal people sailing while very important business deals were closed on land, diplomacies written by politicians and famous, important celebrities were serving time in prison. If anything we must have been fools for missing out on all the glory-laden movies that will win the next Oscar's.

But...if two months sailing on a tall ship could mean more, and create more change in me and others than a lifetime thus spent on shore basking in the glow of such important things, if it created more positive change in me and others, then maybe, just maybe, it really was more important.

After that call to go aloft on that cold, wet July night, I moved as quickly as I could up the ratlines. It went much slower then usual. Barefoot and without hindering clothing was one thing, but foul weather gear with three layers underneath was another matter. By the time I reached the fore royal, I was breathing heavily, either from the excitement of being so far aloft or from the funny feeling of trying to push thick boots that didn't quite fit in between ratlines that seemed too small for feet in general. I stretched my left leg as much as possible, but the footrope for the royal was just out of reach – until I ripped a bigger hole in the inseam of my foul weather pants – then my now unrestrained legs could easily make it to the footrope. With a leg and two arms, I hauled my weight over to the wooden yard. To my right, my watch leader, Nadja, was already on the yard. My shipmate Shawn followed closely behind me, laying on to my left. We all knew what to do first, reaching down we brought in the first folds of wet, heavy canvas up to the yard underneath our stomachs.

As Nadja was fastening the buntline to hold up the middle section Shawn and I spared a glance at the scenery from our lofty position nearly one hundred feet up. We could see that the awful thick fog that seemed to be an institution of these waters did not follow us up the ratlines – it hugged the surface of the water, a wall about thirty feet high that spread out across the waves, leaving a fuzzy halo around our ship. I and then Shawn looked out to the port side, toward the horizon. Shawn spoke first, "Is that Nova Scotia?" Sure enough, there it was, from the distance it looked like a grayish-green silhouette on the horizon, barely jutting out of the fog. We finally got our first view of fabled Nova Scotia, our destination. I enjoyed the sight, Nova Scotia was the place I had been anticipating for months.

"Guys, you can look at it later!", said Nadja. She was right, we still had three more sails to furl before the next watch took the deck. Leaning over, I clutched another fold of canvas, and I did it again and again.

The color photographs on the following pages were taken by Matthew Maples over the course of his summer internship with the American Sail Training Association.

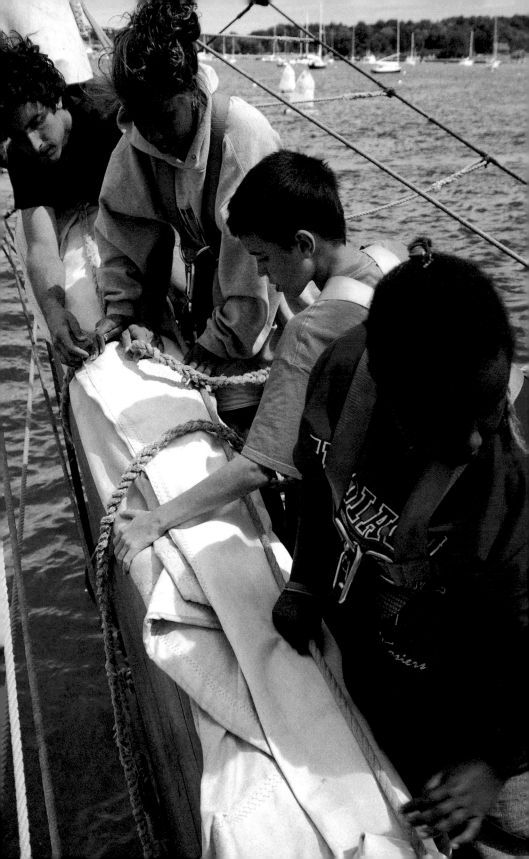

About Sail Training

"For some, sail training offers first time successes. For others, it is a much needed refresher course in life when we find ourselves, for instance, knocking hats off passerby's or staring too long at funeral processions -- which Herman Melville describes as "high time to get to sea" in Moby Dick. For all, sail training offers an absolutely unique experience."

Take Responsibility For Your Adventure!

By Michael J. Rauworth

One of the most important products of sail training is the development of a sense of judgment about what and whom you can rely on, and to what degree. This applies to: the compass, the weather forecast, your shipmates, the depths on the chart, the strength of the anchor cable, the vigilance of the lookout on the other ship, and many other things. Sail training also builds a reasoned sense of self-reliance. All of this starts from the moment you begin to think about a voyage. Use the information in this Directory to begin to evaluate and decide what might be the best sail training experience for you.

Recognize who you are dealing with and what is included. When you book a sail training trip, you are dealing with the vessel owner or its representatives—ASTA is not involved. You must evaluate whether the financial and business arrangements make sense for you. If there is connecting travel involved, for example, find out if you must make the arrangements, or if it is somehow tied into those you make with the vessel. What happens if you miss your ship because your plane is delayed, or vice versa? Do you need trip insurance? Have you confirmed with the vessel owner any possible customs or immigration issues? Will you need a passport or a pre-purchased air ticket? You must seek out the answers to these questions.

Make informed, responsible decisions about risk and safety, level of challenge, physical suitability and other important issues. One of the important reasons to embark on a sail training trip is to engage the world in a different, stimulating, and challenging way—if you want to stay warm and dry, you should stay at home by the fireplace. Much of the point is to come face-to-face with the elements. At the very least, this probably means that you will find yourself wet, chilled, or tired at some point in a challenging voyage. But everyone's threshold for this is different, and you need to find out what you are likely to be experiencing in order to find out if it is well matched for you.

Since the beginning of time, going to sea has been recognized as carrying an element of risk. These days, we more commonly think about risk in connection with highway travel or aviation, but the idea is the same: you get a pre-flight safety brief on an airliner, you get a lifeboat drill on a cruise ship. Part of the value of sail training is addressing these issues head on. You need to decide whether you are comfortable with the combination of risks and safety measures connected with your proposed sail training trip.

For example, will you be able to go aloft? Will trips in smaller craft be involved? Will you be expected to stand watch at night? Do the demands of the ship match your physical and health capabilities? Are you on medication that will (or may) become necessary during the voyage, or do you have a condition (for example, hemophilia or epilepsy) that may require special access to medical attention; if so, is the vessel operator aware of this? Will you be able to get up and down the ladders, in and out of your berth, and along a heeled-over deck? If there is an emergency, will you be needed to handle safety equipment or to help operate the vessel?

Remember that sail training is often not intended to be like a vacation. Some vessels, on the other hand, may offer leisurely voyages, where very little will be asked of you. You should arrive at a clear understanding of these issues prior to setting sail.

In short, you must satisfy yourself that the trip you are looking into is the right thing for you to do, considering safety, risk, suitability, challenge, comfort, convenience, educational value, cost, and any other factors you consider important.

Does the American Sail Training Association have a hand in any of this? In a word—no! ASTA is your "bulletin board" to introduce you to opportunities. However, the American Sail Training Association does not operate any vessels, and has no ability or authority to inspect, approve, or even recommend vessels or programs because programs are constantly evolving and changing.

> In short, you must satisfy yourself that the trip you are looking into is the right thing for you to do, considering safety, risk, suitability, challenge, comfort, convenience, educational value, cost, and any other factors you consider important.

The American Sail Training Association is a nonprofit organization with a limited staff. It serves as a forum for the sail training community, but it has no authority over what programs are offered, or how vessels are operated. The information in this Directory is supplied by the vessel operators, and ASTA can not possibly verify all the information, nor visit all the ships in order to evaluate programs. For these reasons, you must take the information in this Directory as a starting point only, subject to change and correction, and proceed directly with the vessel operator. The American Sail Training Association is not an agent or business partner for the vessel operators, and is not a travel agent.

ASTA believes in the value of sail training as a concept, but remember, from the moment you step beyond looking at this book, the decision and the resulting experiences rest with you.

Choosing a Sail Training Program

There are as many sail training programs as there are ships, and choosing the right one depends a great deal on your personal needs and desires. Sail training differs from going on a cruise ship, in that you are expected to take part in the running of the ship by handling sail and line and standing watch, as well as working in the galley (the ship's kitchen) or performing routine cleaning or maintenance duties. To what degree depends on the sail training program you select.

Do you want a program that specializes in marine biology or adventure travel? Would you like to ship out for a day, a week, a school semester—or, for as long as it takes to circumnavigate the world? Are you interested in maritime history? In celestial navigation? Whales? Do you want the unique challenge of climbing aloft in a square-rigger? A race across the Atlantic? Maine lobster dinners aboard classic windjammers? Exotic ports of call? Will you be bringing your wheelchair? Would you like to receive academic credit?

The answers to the above questions provide a profile for just some of the options available to you. As to what sail training programs require of you—beyond an eager willingness to get the most out of your voyage—the requirements are few:

SAFETY FIRST!
Take a close look at the vessel's credentials. In the US, check to see if the vessel operates under United States Coast Guard regulations. Does the vessel currently hold a USCG-issued Certificate of Inspection (see pg. 60 "Regulations for US Vessels") or comparable certification from the authorities of the country in which it is registered? If it is a non-US vessel you should ensure that the vessel operates in accordance with the maritime safety rules of that country. In most cases this is supervised by a government agency similar to the US Coast Guard. The resources section of the ASTA Web site lists the latest known web sites of some of these agencies.

Talk to the program provider! Ask questions! Read the organization or company's literature; check out their Web site. Most important: visit the ship if you can. Get a sense of the professionalism of the operation and the quality of its program. Find out about the experience level of the captain and officers. How long have they served the ship you are looking into? If you will be joining the vessel in a distant port, or if it does not hold a current USCG Certificate of Inspection, be especially diligent in your research. Ask the program operator for the names of past trainees or clients and give them a call and ask about their experience. The amazingly diverse range of opportunities featured in this book provides each of us with a variety of options.

EXPERIENCE

With very few exceptions, no prior sailing experience is required of trainees. Some programs do accept non-paying volunteers as crewmembers, but typically require experience in similar vessels or a long-term commitment—or both. Paying positions typically require a license—"Able-bodied Seaman" papers document a minimum of 180 days spent underway and successfully passing an exam administered by the US Coast Guard. Licenses are awarded to crew based on additional time underway, the tonnage of vessels served in, waters sailed, technical training, and additional testing. Trainees are encouraged to have the ability to feel comfortable in and around the water; however, many programs have no formal swimming requirements.

AGE

Most voyages are planned with a specific age group in mind. This varies from program to program, but many sail training programs start accepting unaccompanied trainees from the age of 14 (ninth grade). Ask what the composition of the ship's complement will be and, if you plan to send a young person on an extended voyage, what the in-port supervisory arrangements will be. Day sails and dockside education programs are readily available for elementary school students and overnight trips can be arranged for older school groups as well. There are a tremendous variety of adventure programs for adults of all ages, including "Elderhostel" voyages for seniors.

> The four essential components of any sail training program are a seaworthy vessel, a competent captain and crew, qualified instructors, and a sound educational program appropriate and suited to the needs of the trainees onboard.

ACADEMIC CREDIT

Some vessels are tied directly to academic institutions that grant academic credit to trainees who successfully complete sail training programs as part of a course of study or project in a wide range of subjects. Some educational institutions will also grant credit for on-board independent study.

CO-EDUCATION

Just about every sail training vessel in the US sails with both male and female professional crew and programs are typically co-ed. Others are designed specifically for groups such as the Girl Scouts or in conjunction with a single-gender school or affiliated program.

COST

Prices vary considerably depending on the nature and the duration of the program and the type of vessel. Some vessels have limited financial assistance available, and some trainees, Scouting, and school groups have successfully sought private, business, and/or community support . Check with the sail training program you are interested in to see what opportunities may be available. The American Sail Training Association offers sail training scholarships and criteria and applications can be found on the ASTA Website, or by calling the ASTA office.

Regulation of Vessels

Virtually all vessels are subject to some form of regulation by the national maritime authority of their "flag state"—the country in which they are registered. In the United States, these regulations are written and enforced by the US Coast Guard, pursuant to laws enacted by Congress. Under the Safety of Life at Sea (SOLAS) Convention, administered by the International Maritime Organization (IMO), vessels of any nation signatory to the convention and over a certain size or carrying more than 12 passengers and operating internationally must comply with the requirements of the Convention with regard to construction, safety equipment, manning, crew training, etc. Compliance is documented in a "SOLAS Certificate" issued by the ship's national maritime authority.

US-registered vessels listed in this directory will generally fall into one of the following categories: Small Passenger Vessel, Sailing School Vessel, Oceanographic Research Vessel, and Uninspected Vessel. For each category there is a comprehensive set of regulatory requirements governing construction and arrangement, watertight integrity and stability, lifesaving and firefighting equipment, machinery and electrical systems, vessel control and equipment, and operations.

With the exception of Uninspected Vessels, all categories of US-registered vessel are subject to Coast Guard inspection on an annual basis. Upon satisfactory completion of the inspection, a Certificate of Inspection (COI) is issued, and must be permanently displayed on board the vessel. The COI spells out what waters the vessel may operate in (its authorized route), how many passengers or sailing school students may be carried, how many crew must be carried and what qualifications the master and crew must have, the requirement for and location of lifesaving and firefighting equipment, and so forth. Although not inspected annually, Uninspected Vessels (which are generally vessels less than 65 feet in length and carrying 6 or fewer passengers for hire) must still comply with requirements for safety equipment and a licensed skipper. The type of COI to be issued to inspected vessels is determined by both the size and construction of the vessel and the operating intentions of the owner. Some vessels carry dual certification.

The Coast Guard also prescribes the qualifications for the officers and crew of inspected vessels, and requires both that they have certain minimum levels of experience and training and that they be examined and issued licenses or documents before they can lawfully serve on board. Following is a brief description of the various types of certifications governing the operation of US-flagged vessels:

Sailing School Vessels (SSV) are inspected under Title 46, Subchapter R of the Code of Federal Regulations (CFR). An SSV is a vessel of less than 500 gross tons carrying six or more sailing school students or instructors, principally propelled by sail, and operated by a nonprofit educational organization exclusively for the purpose of sailing education. Sailing School Vessels are required to pass regular inspection by the USCG in order to maintain their certification.

Passenger Vessels are certified according to size and number of passengers (not engaged in educational activities or in the operation of the vessel) carried under Title 46 of the CFR:

Subchapter C – Uninspected vessels which operate with no more than six passengers.

Subchapter T – Small passenger vessels of under 100 gross tons that carry more than six passengers and are required to pass regular USCG inspection of the ship and all onboard equipment.

Subchapter K – Small passenger vessels of under 100 gross tons that carry more than 150 passengers and are required to pass regular USCG inspection of the ship and all onboard equipment.

Subchapter H – Passenger vessels more than 100 gross tons that carry passengers for hire and are required to pass regular USCG inspection of the ship and all onboard equipment.

Attraction Vessel certification is required whenever a vessel is open to public boarding or conducts dockside programs. The vessel may be permanently moored to a pier, or it may also be certified under one or more of the above subchapters, but the Attraction Vessel COI (ATCOI) certifies its safety for dockside programs and visitation only. Oceanographic Research Vessels (ORV) are certified under Subchapter U of Title 46 of the CFR. An ORV is a vessel employed exclusively in either oceanographic (saltwater) or limnologic (freshwater) instruction and/or research, and is not necessarily equipped for passengers or other non-professionals. For more information, access the United States Coast Guard through the link on ASTA's Web site or contact the Government Printing Office for the above listed sections of the Code of Federal Regulations.

Shipping Out

The following list was provided to the ASTA 2007 summer interns, Matt and Heather, as they prepared to embark on their sail training adventure aboard the barque Picton Castle. While often similar, each sail training vessel has its own list of suggested items so be sure to ask for it! The list shown on these pages is intended as an example of what you might be expected to bring.

Barque PICTON CASTLE
2007 ASTA Tall Ship Challenge® East Coast Series
GEAR LIST

Your voyage is in the warm weather, so you will not need to bring much. The ship will visit several ports where you can buy everything extra you may need. It is best to bring only what you will absolutely need rather than everything you might wish for. While your personal storage space in the Picton Castle is ample when compared to other vessels, it is distinctly limited to what can fit in the shelves of your bunk or in your storage locker or sea chest. What we're saying is this: Think about bringing a lot less than you imagine. Here are the basics we recommend:

Valid Passport - (or photo ID and original birth certificate)

Luggage - A sea bag or duffel bag that can be rolled up and stowed.

Bedding - The ship provides blankets and sheets and pillow. Some folks prefer their own pillow. A lightweight sleeping bag and camping pad can be useful for sleeping on deck on hot nights.

Foul Weather Gear - You can buy this at marine supply stores in the U.S. and Canada and at most large ports. Bring jacket & trousers, Helly Hansens or the equivalent, in bright colors. Knee boots with heels are best.

Shoes - We often go barefoot on board. But thong sandals are popular along the way, as are running shoes or sneakers. A good pair of rubber-soled walking shoes will be valuable.

Clothes- One or two sets of get-dirty work clothes and one or two shore outfits are recommended. Lightweight carpenter-style jeans, blue or white, are popular for hot weather. Shorts and tee-shirts are obvious. Long-sleeve cotton work shirts are good for sun protection. A nice dress or skirt for the women and collar shirt with long pants for the men may come in handy for going ashore (foldable).

Warm Clothes- The nights and some sailing days may be cool, so bring clothes that layer—long underwear, tee shirt, flannel shirt, cotton sweater, wool sweater, windbreaker—and pile it on as needed.

Other Suggested Gear:

- Good sunglasses
- #15 or better sun block and sun hat
- 6-inch sheath knife with sheath to go on your belt
- Your own personal hygiene products for the time you are on board
- Talcum powder (former crew recommend Gold Bond® Medicated Powder)
- Camera and film
- Bathing suit
- Notebooks
- Insect repellent
- Towels and wash cloths (2)
- Small waterproof flashlight & spare batteries
- Battery-operated fan(s) for bunk
- Clothespins if you plan to do laundry on board
- Modest daypack for off-ship treks
- If you want a safety harness of your own, bring it.

What is a Tall Ship?

Full-Rigged Ship

A tall ship is not a strictly defined type of sailing vessel. Most of us use the term to mean a large traditionally rigged sailing vessel, whether or not it is technically a "ship". The United States Coast Guard's training ship Eagle, for example, is technically a "barque". A tall ship can also be a schooner, brigantine, barquentine, brig, ketch, sloop, or a full-rigged ship depending on the number of masts and the cut of the sails.

For the purposes of classification and race rating, the American Sail Training Association adheres to the descriptions found in the Racing and Sailing Rules and Special Regulations established by Sail Training International.

CLASS A
All square-rigged vessels and all other vessels over 40m (131 feet) length overall (LOA)

CLASS B
Traditional-rigged vessels with a LOA of less than 40m (131 feet) and with a waterline length (LWL) of at least 9.14m (30 feet).

CLASS C
Modern-rigged vessels with a LOA of less than 40m (131 feet) and with a LWL of at least 9.14m (30 feet), not carrying spinnaker-like sails.

CLASS D
Modern-rigged vessels with a LOA of less than 40m (131 feet) and with a LWL of at least 9.14m (30 feet), carrying spinnaker-like sails.

Ship Shapes

Sail training vessels are as varied as the programs operated on board them. Below are examples of the different rig configurations used by ASTA's Member Vessels. On the following page you will find a diagram of the different sails carried by a full-rigged ship as well as a glossary of terms commonly used in this book.

Two-Masted Schooner

Topsail Schooner

Three-Masted Schooner

Brigantine

Brig

Barquentine

Barque

Ship Rigging Identification

1. Bowsprit
2. Martingale
3. Figurehead
4. Flying Jib
5. Outer jib
6. Inner jib
7. Fore topmast staysail
8. Foremast
9. Fore royal
10. Fore upper topgallant sail
11. Fore lower topgallant sail

12. Fore upper topsail
13. Fore lower topsail
14. Foresail, Fore course
15. Main royal staysail
16. Main topgallant staysail
17. Main middle staysail
18. Main topmast staysail
19. Mainmast
20. Main royal
21. Main upper topgallant sail

22. Main lower topgallant sail
23. Main upper topsail
24. Main lower topsail
25. Mainsail, Main course
26. Mizzen royal staysail
27. Mizzen topgallant staysail
28. Mizzen middle staysail
29. Mizzen topmast staysail
30. Mizzen mast
31. Mizzen royal

32. Mizzen upper topgallant sail
33. Mizzen lower topgallant sail
34. Mizzen upper topsail
35. Mizzen lower topsail
36. Crossjack, Mizzen course
37. Jigger topgallant staysail
38. Jigger topmast staysail
39. Jigger staysail
40. Jigger mast
41. Gaff topsail
42. Spanker

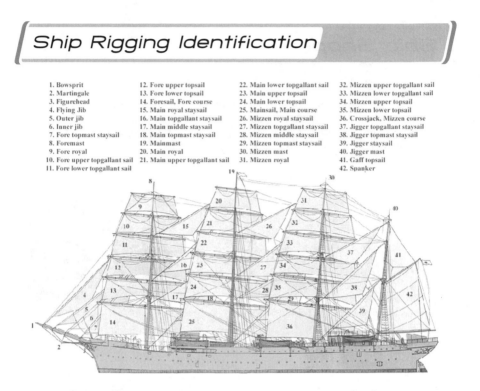

Sparred length - The length between the extremities of any spars that overhang the bow or the stern of a vessel, such as a bowsprit or a boomkin.

LOA- Length overall. The length between the forwardmost and the aftermost points on the hull of a vessel.

LOD - Length on deck. The length between the forwardmost and the aftermost points on a specified deck measured along the deck, excluding sheer.

Sheer - The fore-and-aft curvature of a vessel's main deck from bow to stern.

LWL - Length on the waterline. The length between the forwardmost and the after most points on a vessel's waterline.

DRAFT - The depth of water required to float a vessel.

BEAM- Width of a vessel at its widest part.

RIG HEIGHT - Maximum height of rig above waterline.

FREEBOARD - The vertical distance from the waterline to the freeboard deck, usually measured amidships.

FREEBOARD DECK - The uppermost deck that is designed to be watertight.

GRT - Gross registered tonnage. The volume, expressed in units of 100 cubic feet to the ton, of a vessel's total enclosed spaces below the weather deck and enclosed spaces above the deck including the bridge and accommodations.

ASTA Member Vessels

"From coastal cruising with gourmet cooking to blue water voyaging these ships are all in the business of enrichment. As diverse an agenda as this may seem at first glance, these ships all provide sail training. The common denominator is that each uses the wind and sea to teach us something else. Sail training, like reading, is not a subject in and of itself. It is a means to an end. We at ASTA often say that sail training is not learning to sail, it is learning from sailing. From the ship, from the sea, and perhaps most importantly, from yourself."

ADIRONDACK

SPECIFICATIONS

Flag: USA
Rig: Gaff schooner
Homeport: New York, New York
Normal cruising waters:
New York Harbor
Sparred length: 80'
LOA: 65'
LOD: 64' 6"
LWL: 58'
Draft: 8'
Beam: 16'
Rig height: 62'
Freeboard: 3' 4"
Sail area: 1,850 square feet
Tons: 41 GRT
Power: twin 65 HP diesels
Hull: wood

The schooner *Adirondack* is the third of five schooners to come out of the Scarano Boat Building yard, beginning with the 59-foot schooner *Madeline* and the 61-foot *Woodwind* in 1991, followed by the 105-foot schooner *America* in 1995 and a sister ship, *Adirondack II*, launched in 1999. *Adirondack* combines the virtues of turn-of-the-century schooner yachts with the latest in laminated wood technology. Offering an enviable combination of stability and speed, the *Adirondack* fulfills the builder and owner's ambition of providing a quality sail for people of all ages and experience.

Who sails: School groups from elementary through college, private and corporate charters, families, and individuals of all ages
Program type: Sail training with paying trainees, passenger day sails
Built: 1994: Albany, NY, Scarano Boat
Coast Guard certification: Passenger Vessel (Subchapter T)
Crew: 3 **Trainees-passengers**: 49 daysails
Contact: Sarah Greer, Manager, Classic Harbor Line, Chelsea Piers, Suite 5912, 23rd St. at Hudson River, NY, NY 10011 USA
Tel: 212-827-1825
Fax: 646-349-5963
E-mail: CaptSarah@Sail-NYC.com
Website: www.Sail-NYC.com

Flag: USA
Rig: Gaff schooner
Homeport: Newport,
Rhode Island
Normal cruising waters:
Narragansett Bay
Sparred length: 80'
LOA: 65'
LOD: 64' 6"
LWL: 58'
Draft: 8'
Beam: 16'
Rig height: 62'
Freeboard: 3' 4"
Sail area: 1,850 square feet
Tons: 41 GRT
Power: twin 60 HP diesels
Hull: wood

ADIRONDACK II

The schooner *Adirondack II* was launched in August of 1999. The near sister ship of the *Adirondack* joins the fleet of schooners known for their performance-oriented design/construction, combined with classic traditional aesthetics. With its wide-open cockpit, *Adirondack II* can comfortably accommodate groups of up to 65 trainees/passengers. While dockside, spacious cockpit doghouses double as serving space for food and beverages or classroom navigation paperwork. *Adirondack II* affirms that modern wood composite construction and 19th century elegance blend seamlessly to the benefit of all.

Who sails: Private charters, families, and individuals of all ages
Program type: Sail training with paying trainees, passenger day sails
Built: 1999: Albany, NY, Scarano Boat
Coast Guard certification: Passenger Vessel (Subchapter T)
Crew: 3 **Trainees-passengers:** 65 daysails
Contact: Audrey Singsen, Manager, Sailing Excursions, Inc., Bowens Wharf, PO box 1155, Newport, RI 02840 USA
Tel: 401-862-8441; 401-847-0000
Fax: 518-463-3403
E-mail: Audrey@Sail-Newport.com
Website: www.Sail-Newport.com

ADVENTURE

SPECIFICATIONS

Flag: USA
Rig: Gaff topsail schooner
Homeport: Gloucester, Massachusetts
LOA: 122'
LOD: 122'
LWL: 109'
Draft: 13' 6"
Beam: 24' 6"
Rig height: 110'
Sail area: 6,500 square feet
Tons: 130 GRT
Hull: wood

The schooner *Adventure* is one of the last of the Gloucester fishing schooners, an icon of our nation's fishing industry and Gloucester's heritage. Gloucester's fishing schooners, known as "Gloucestermen", were famous throughout the world. Built in 1926, the 122-foot *Adventure* represents the pinnacle of schooner design, embodying grace, speed, and functionality. Fast and able under sail, and carrying 14 dories, *Adventure* was the "highliner" of the North Atlantic fleet, earning more money than any other fishing vessel of her era. After retiring from fishing in 1953, *Adventure* was refitted as a windjammer and carried passengers along the coast of Maine until 1987. In 1988 she was given to the people of Gloucester to be preserved as Gloucester's historic tall ship. Today *Adventure* is being restored as a 1926 Gloucester fishing schooner and will resume sailing once work is completed. She will serve as a community resource for educational programming, focusing on maritime, cultural, and environmental issues, and will sail as a living symbol of Gloucester's maritime heritage.

Program type: Dockside interpretation; educational programs for schools
Designer: Tom McManus
Built: 1926: Essex, MA, John F. James & Son Yard
Coast Guard certification: Moored Attraction Vessel (dockside)
Contact: Sally Curry, Gloucester Adventure, Inc, PO Box 1306, Gloucester, MA 01931-1306 USA
Tel: 978-281-8079
Fax: 978-281-2393
E-mail: scurry@schooner-adventure.org
Website: www.schooner-adventure.org

Flag: USA
Rig: Gaff topsail schooner
Homeport:
Port Townsend, Washington
Normal cruising waters:
Puget Sound and San Juan
Islands
Sparred length: 133'
LOD: 101'
LWL: 71'
Draft: 12'
Beam: 21'
Rig height: 110'
Sail area: 5,478 square feet
Tons: 82 GRT
Power: 250 HP diesel
Hull: wood

ADVENTURESS

The 1913 schooner *Adventuress* sails to increase awareness of the majesty and vulnerability of Puget Sound. Since 1989, the non-profit environmental education organization, Sound Experience, provides hands-on education aboard *Adventuress* to thousands of young people annually and partners with youth-serving organizations to reach Puget Sound area at-risk teenagers. Volunteer and paid crew receive environmental and sail training. The ship's apprentice program for youth 14 – 18, and month-long internships for adult sailor/educators also feature extensive sail training. The non-competitive environment fosters cooperation, teamwork, and leadership skills. A National Historic Landmark and a Puget Sound treasure, the *Adventuress* is truly a boat for the people, providing empowering, life-changing experiences to more than 3,500 youth and adults each year.

Who sails: Schools and other groups from elementary through college, individuals and families
Program type: Sea education in marine science, maritime history, and ecology; passenger day and overnight sails; dockside interpretation during port visits
Season: March - October
Designer: B. B. Crowninshield
Built: 1913: East Boothbay, ME, Rice Brothers
Coast Guard certification: Passenger Vessel (Subchapter T)
Crew: 4-5, with an additional 8-10 instructors **Trainees-passengers:** 45 daysails, 25 overnight
Contact: Catherine Collins, Executive Director, Sound Experience, PO Box 1390, Port Townsend, WA 98368 USA
Tel: 360-379-0438 **Fax:** 360-379-0439
E-mail: mail@soundexp.org
Web site: www.soundexp.org

A. J. MEERWALD

A. J. MEERWALD

SPECIFICATIONS

Flag: USA
Rig: Schooner
Homeport: Bivalve, NJ
Normal Cruising waters:
Delaware Bay, Delaware River, NJ
Coastal Waters
Sparred length: 115'
LOA: 85'
LOD: 81' 7"
LWL: 78' 3"
Draft: 6'
Beam: 22' 1"
Rig height: 67' 8"
Sail area: 3,560 square feet
Freeboard: 3' 6"
Tons: 57 GRT
Power: 225 HP diesel
Hull: wood

The Bayshore Discovery Project operates the schooner *A. J. Meerwald*, New Jersey's official tall ship, as an experiential classroom. This authentically restored 1928 Delaware Bay oyster schooner sails from her homeport of Bivalve, New Jersey as well as annual visits to cities and coastal towns throughout New Jersey, Pennsylvania and Delaware and occasional special trips into the Chesapeake and the Northeast Atlantic Seaboard. Students range from fourth graders to senior citizens; subject matter ranges from the history of Delaware Bay oystering to present water quality issues. Motivating people to take care of the environment, the history and the culture of New Jersey's Bayshore region are the primary goals of all activities on the *A. J. Meerwald,* regardless of their target audience, length of program, and/or port of origin. The Bayshore Discovery Project also conducts shore-based programs, lecture series, hosts Delaware Bay Day (the first Saturday in June), and provides leadership on watershed issues throughout the Delaware Estuary. Members and volunteers are the lifeblood of the organization and are always welcome.

Who sails: School groups 4th grade through college, private and corporate charters, and individuals of all ages
Program type: Sail training for professional crew, volunteers, and paying trainees; three hour educational sails, summer camp, family sails, teacher workshops, overnight programs, team building, and theme sails; sea education in marine science, maritime history, ecology, and watershed awareness in cooperation with accredited institutions and other groups and as informal, in-house programming
Season: April 1 - November 1
Designer: Charles H. Stowman & Sons Shipyard **Built:** 1928: Dorchester, NJ, Charles H. Stowman & Sons
Coast Guard certification: Passenger Vessel (Subchapter T)
Crew: 11, augmented by volunteers **Trainees-passengers:** 45 daysails, 6 overnight
Contact: Meghan E. Wren, Executive Director, Bayshore Discovery Project, 2800 High Street-Bivalve, Port Norris, NJ 08349 USA
Tel: 856-785-2060 **Fax:** 856-785-2893 **E-mail:** info@bayshorediscoveryproject.org
Website: www.bayshorediscoveryproject.org

SPECIFICATIONS

Flag: USA
Rig: Gaff schooner
Homeport:
Vineyard Haven, Massachusetts
Normal cruising waters:
Southern New England
Sparred length: 126'
LOA: 90'
LOD: 85'
LWL: 78'
Draft: 12' 6"
Beam: 21'
Rig height: 94'
Freeboard: 5'
Sail area: 5,000 square feet
Tons: 85 GRT
Power: twin diesels
Hull: wood

ALABAMA

The ex-pilot schooner *Alabama* is an authentic example of a typical Gloucester fishing schooner of the early 1900s. She was built for the Mobile Bar Pilot Association in Pensacola, Florida in 1926 and designed by the greatest New England designer of Gloucester schooners, Thomas F. McManus. After a major three-year reconstruction, the summer of 1998 marked her first year sailing the waters of southern New England joining the *Shenandoah* in The Black Dog Tall Ships fleet of Martha's Vineyard. The *Alabama* runs 6-day sailing trips for youth ages 9 to16 from late June through late August and is available for day and sunset sails and private charter each year from June 1 through late June and late May through mid October.

Who sails: School groups elementary through college, private and corporate charters, and individuals of all ages
Program type: Sail training for paying trainees ages 9 - 16; private charters and public days sails
Designer: Thomas F. McManus
Built: 1926: Pensacola, FL, Pensacola Shipbuilding Company
Coast Guard certification: Passenger Vessel (Subchapter T)
Crew: 6 **Trainees-passengers:** 49 daysails, 27 overnight
Contact: Captain Robert Douglas, Coastwise Packet Co., dba The Black Dog Tall Ships, PO Box 429, Vineyard Haven, MA 02568 USA
Tel: 508-693-1699
Fax: 508-693-1881
Website: www.theblackdogtallships.com

ALCA i

SPECIFICATIONS

Flag: USA
Rig: 3-masted marconi schooner
Homeport: Portsmouth, NH
Normal cruising waters: East Coast U.S./Canadian Maritimes
Sparred length: 75'
LOA: 64' 6"
LOD: 63'
LWL: 59'
Draft: 6'
Beam: 17'
Freeboard: 4'
Rig height: 63' 6"
Sail area: 1,200 square feet
Tons: 50 GRT
Power: 180 HP Cummins diesel
Hull: oak/epoxy composite

R/V *Alca i.*, launched in 2003, was designed as a research vessel, supporting SCUBA, for rocky inshore work in the Subarctic and Arctic. The hull of *Alca i.* is plank-on-frame, heavy construction, with frames and floors of epoxy-laminated white oak backed up with monel or 316 stainless fastenings. The white oak, 2-3 foot square cross section keel, is straight and bears a 4000 lb., steel I-beam shoe with 8000 lbs. of lead ballast. The hull is strip-planked of two-inch red oak, using bronze, grip- fast nails and epoxy, and is double sheathed, inside and out with epoxy saturated glass mat (four layers at the water line). The hull has eight, water tight bulkheads, with both independent and central bilge-pumping. The aft cabin is a combination laboratory and dive facility. The schooner rig provides an easily handled means of range extension in remote waters as well as stability. Although the basic crew is professional, the vessel typically caries 2-3 students/technicians that provide SCUBA and lab support; the students receive sailing and general maritime training.

Program type: Research vessel
Designer: George Buehler Yacht Designs
Built: 2003: Bay Meadows Boatyard, Gloucester, VA
Crew: 6
Coast Guard certification: Yacht (documented or state-numbered) Documented No. 1138386 Ocean
Contact: Walter & Karen Adey, Ecological Systems Technology, Inc., 600 Waverly Road, Reedville, Virginia 22539 US
Tel: 804-453-3932
Fax: 804-453-5106
E-mail: klfilms@aol.com

SPECIFICATIONS

Flag: USA
Rig: 3-masted gaff topsail schooner
Homeport: Yorktown, Virginia
Normal cruising waters: Chesapeake Bay (summer), Caribbean (winter)
Sparred length: 105'
LOA: 105'
LOD: 80'
LWL: 65'
Draft: 8'
Beam: 20'
Rig height: 63'
Freeboard: 5'
Sail area: 2,778 square feet
Tons: 85 GRT
Power: 130 hp John Deer
Hull: steel

ALLIANCE

Four centuries ago, Capt. John Smith explored the waters around Yorktown aboard a small sailing vessel while trading with the Powhatan Indians. Join him in spirit when you sail the 105', three-masted gaff-rigged schooner *Alliance*. As you pass Yorktown Battlefield and the Victory Monument along the banks of the York River, you'll relive sailing's golden age, when a young America clambered aboard vessels similar to *Alliance* to find adventure. If you like, lend a hand hoisting a sail the traditional way-no electric winches here, just block, tackle and a little elbow grease. *Alliance* is so much more than a sailing ship-it's an opportunity to experience an exciting and unique time in America's history.

Who sails: Groups and individuals of all ages
Program type: Daysails and weekly charters
Designer: Tom Colvin
Built: 1995: Palm Coast, Florida, Treworgy Yachts
Coast Guard certification: Passenger Vessel (Subchapter T)
Crew: 3 - 4 **Trainees-passengers:** 49 daysails, 10 overnight
Contact: Laura Lohse, Yorktown Sailing Charters, 505 Monroe Ave., Cape Charles, VA 23310 USA
Tel: 757-639-1233
E-mail: info@schooneralliance.com
Website: www.schooneralliance.com

ALMA

SPECIFICATIONS

Flag: USA
Rig: Schooner, two-masted
Homeport:
San Francisco, California
Normal cruising waters:
San Francisco Bay
Sparred length: 88'
LOA: 62'
LOD: 61' 4"
LWL: 59' 5"
Draft: 3' 6"
Beam: 23' 6"
Rig height: 76'
Freeboard: 4'
Sail area: 2,684 square feet
Tons: 47 GRT
Power: twin diesels
Hull: wood

The last of approximately 400 scow schooners that carried cargo in the San Francisco Bay area at the turn of the century, *Alma* was built at Hunter's Point in San Francisco Bay in 1891. Today she is owned and operated by the San Francisco Maritime National Historical Park, and docked at Hyde Street Pier near Fisherman's Wharf. From March to November, the *Alma* sails with a crew of volunteers, representing and interpreting a time when commerce moved by boat around the Bay. The volunteer program enables trainees to learn about traditional sailing and wooden boat maintenance. No fees are required as all crew volunteer to sail and maintain the *Alma* and other park vessels. The park will offer visitors a ranger-led interpretive program (under sail) aboard *Alma* in 2008.

Who sails: Adult education groups, families, students, and individuals of all ages
Program type: Sail training for professional crew and apprentices; sea education based on informal in-house programming focused of maritime history; dockside interpretation; ranger-led interpretative program under sail; affiliated groups include the San Francisco Maritime National Park Association, San Francisco Maritime National Historical Park, and National Park Service
Designer: Fred Siemers
Built: 1891: San Francisco, CA, Fred Siemers
Crew: 6 **Trainees-passengers:** 40 daysails, 28 overnight
Contact: Lynn Cullivan, Management Assistant, San Francisco Maritime National Historical Park, Building E, Fort Mason Center, San Francisco, CA 94123 USA
Tel: 415-561-7006 **Fax:** 415-556-1624
E-mail: lynn_cullivan@nps.gov
Website: www.nps.gov/safr/historyculture/alma.htm

SPECIFICATIONS

Flag: Republic of Vanuatu
Rig: Main topsail schooner
Homeport:
Port Vila, Republic of Vanuatu
Normal cruising waters:
Tropical waters worldwide
Sparred length: 126'
LOA: 92'
LOD: 92'
LWL: 87'
Draft: 10'
Beam: 19'
Rig height: 85'
Freeboard: 2' 6"
Sail area: 5,700 square feet
Tons: 87 GRT
Power: Wichmann 2-cycle diesel 160 HP
Hull: riveted steel

ALVEI

Underway since 1995, *Alvei* makes both long Trade Wind passages using the old sailing ship routes and shorter passages among the islands of the South Pacific. During December through April, *Alvei* sails coastal waters of Australia or New Zealand. From April to December, there is a long, deep-sea passage north to the tropics, followed by inter-island passages among the islands between Tahiti and New Guinea. *Alvei* will be working with Project MARC, (Medical Aid to Remote Communities). From June to October we will carry Doctors, medical supplies, technicians and materials to Islands in Vanuatu. *Alvei* operates as a non-profit sailing co-operative. Everyone contributes both work and money toward the operation of the vessel. There are no paid positions. Duties include steering, lookout, standing watch, sail handling, anchoring and docking along with maintenance projects such as painting, tarring, sewing, cooking and rigging. Lessons on seamanship, boat handling and navigation are provided. The purpose of our endeavour is to provide the crew with a low-cost, self-sufficient lifestyle on the worlds oceans and to provide Project MARC with a means of carrying out their medical aid program.

Who sails: Adults 18 and over
Program type: Sail training for volunteers and paying trainees; sea education based on informal in-house participation; coastal and offshore passages
Season: Year-round
Designer: Hull unknown, accommodations and rigging, Evan Logan
Built: 1920: Montrose, Scotland
Certification: Vanuatu Maritime Authority, Charter Vessel (pending final topsides inspection)
Crew: 6, volunteer crew and 12 paying trainees **Trainees-passengers:** 36 daysails, 18 overnight
Contact: Evan Logan, Owner/Operator, Alvei Sail Training Cooperative, PO Box 415, Nelson, New Zealand
Tel: 6421-111-8501
Fax: 643-546-8505
E-mail: alvei@yahoo.com
Website: www.alvei.com or www.alvei.de

AMERICAN PRIDE

SPECIFICATIONS

Flag: USA
Rig: Schooner, three-masted
Homeport: Long Beach, California
Normal cruising waters:
Southern California
Sparred length: 129'
LOA: 105'
LOD: 101'
LWL: 92'
Draft: 10'
Beam: 22'
Rig height: 98'
Freeboard: 6'
Sail area: 4,900 square feet
Tons: 203 GRT
Power: diesel
Hull: wood

Built in 1941 as a two-masted "schooner-dragger", the *American Pride* spent over 40 years commercially fishing the Grand Banks and George's Banks. In 1986, completely restored and with a third mast added, she operated as a charter boat out of Bar Harbor, Maine. She was purchased by the American Heritage Marine Institute (AHMI) in 1996, and sailed to her new home in Long Beach, California. Aboard the *American Pride*, the AHMI offers hands-on educational programs stressing science, marine biology, history, and sail training. Programs encourage teamwork, good communication, problem solving and leadership. Actively engaged in sharing the thrill of sailing with people of all ages, the AHMI frequently donates sails to child welfare groups, fundraising guilds, and others. A professional crew and strong volunteer group generously give time, talents, and resources in support of the programs.

Who sails: School groups elementary through college, private and corporate charters, and individuals of all ages
Program type: Scientific or living history educational programs, sail training, team building, sailing adventures
Season: Year-round
Built: 1941: Brooklyn, NY, Muller Boatworks
Coast Guard certification: Passenger Vessel (Subchapter T)
Crew: 6 (paid and volunteer) **Trainees-passengers:** 100 daysails, 48 overnight
Contact: Helen H. Clinton, Director, American Heritage Marine Institute, 21520 "G" Yorba Linda Blvd. #444, Yorba Linda, CA 92887 USA
Tel: 714-970-8800
Fax: 714-970-8474
E-mail: americprd@aol.com
Website: www.americanpride.org

Flag: Italy
Rig: Full-rigged ship
Homeport: La Spezia, Italy
Normal cruising waters:
Worldwide
Sparred length: 330'
Draft: 23' 6"
Beam: 50' 9"
Hull: steel

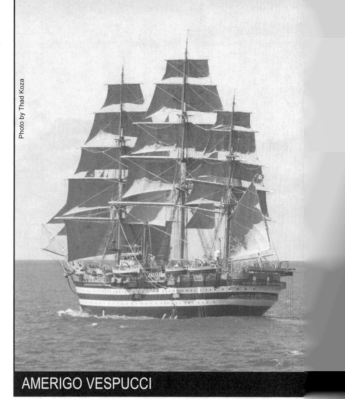

Photo by Thad Koza

AMERIGO VESPUCCI

The pride of the Italian Navy, *Amerigo Vespucci* conjures up memories of men-of-war from two centuries ago. Riding high in the water, with triple decks indicated by painted stripes, *Amerigo Vespucci* is a gracious twentieth-century goodwill ambassador, as well as a symbol of Italy's global maritime heritage and tradition. Named for the great explorer and cartographer of the seventeenth century, this elegant, full-rigged ship is a grand visitor to many ceremonial parades of sail. Since her launch, *Amerigo Vespucci* has been used to train junior officers of the Italian Navy.

Who sails: Junior officers of the Italian Navy
Program type: Sail training
Season: Year-round
Built: 1931
Contact: Embassy of Italy, 3000 Whitehaven Street, NW, Washington, DC 20008 USA
Tel: 202-612-4400
Fax: 202-518-2151

AMISTAD

SPECIFICATIONS

Flag: USA
Rig: Topsail schooner
Homeport:
New Haven, Connecticut
Normal cruising waters:
East Coast of the United States
Sparred length: 129'
LOA: 85'
LOD: 81'
LWL: 79'
Draft: 10' 6"
Beam: 23'
Rig height: 100'
Sail area: 5,200 square feet
Power: cat 3304 x 2, 135
Hull: wood

AMISTAD America, Inc. is a national, non-profit educational organization. We promote improved relationships between races and cultures by acknowledging our common experiences and encouraging dialogue that is based on respect. The inherent lessons and legacies of freedom, justice, perseverance, cooperation and leadership arising from the historic Amistad Incident of 1839 are symbolized by the re-created *Amistad*, Connecticut's Flagship and Tall Ship Ambassador. The Freedom Schooner visits ports nationally and internationally as an ambassador for friendship and goodwill. It serves as a floating classroom, icon and as a monument to the millions of souls that were broken or lost as a result of the insidious Transatlantic slave trade. The vessel offers an important message for all Americans about our collective history and future. The home port for Freedom Schooner *Amistad* is Long Wharf Pier in New Haven, Connecticut.

Who sails: School groups elementary through college
Program type: Sail training for crew and apprentices and paying trainees; maritime history and a full range of programming are expected; sea education in cooperation with accredited institutions and other groups; passenger day sails and dockside interpretation during home and port visits
Designer: Tri-Coastal Marine
Built: 1998 – 2000: Mystic Seaport, Mystic, CT
Coast Guard certification: Passenger Vessel (Subchapter T), Sailing School Vessel (Subchapter R)
Crew: 8, combination paid and volunteer **Trainees-passengers:** 49 daysails
Contact: AMISTAD America, Inc., 746 Chapel Street, Suite 300, New Haven, CT 06510-3102 USA
Tel: 203-495-1839 or 866-AMISTAD
Fax: 203-495-9647
E-mail: operations@amistadamerica.org
Website: www.amistadamerica.org

SPECIFICATIONS

Flag: USA
Rig: Gaff topsail schooner
Homeport: Camden, Maine
Normal cruising waters:
Maine to the Florida Keys
Sparred length: 86'
LOA: 82'
LOD: 65'
LWL: 53'
Draft: 10' 6"
Beam: 18' 9"
Rig height: 75'
Freeboard: 8'
Sail area: 2,815 square feet
Tons: 63 GRT
Power: 210 HP diesel
Hull: wood

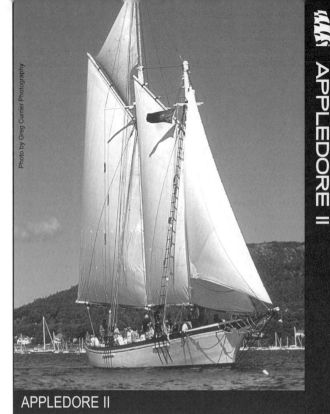

Photo by Greg Currier Photography

APPLEDORE II

The *Appledore II* is a traditional gaff-rigged schooner designed for ocean sailing. Launched in 1978 she circumnavigated the world on her maiden voyage. From her homeport of Camden, Maine, the *Appledore II* makes day sails from late June through mid-October. During the winter months, she operates out of Key West, Florida, offering day sails, snorkeling trips on North America's only living coral reef, and sunset cruises. Committed to sail training, the crew of the *Appledore II* are trained in sailing and marlinspike seamanship through operation of the vessel on day sails as well as two 2,000-mile offshore voyages yearly. Those interested should contact the *Appledore II* for possible payroll and/or volunteer positions.

Who sails: School groups elementary through college, families, and individuals of all ages
Program type: Sail training for crew and apprentices; sea education based on informal in-house programming; passenger day sails
Season: June – October (Maine) December – May (Florida)
Designer: Bud McIntosh
Built: 1978: South Bristol, ME, Gamage Shipyard, Herb Smith
Coast Guard certification: Passenger Vessel (Subchapter T)
Crew: 7 **Trainees-passengers:** 49 daysails, 26 overnight
Contact: John P. McKean, President, Schooner Exploration Associates, Ltd. (summer) "O" Lily Pond Drive, Camden, ME 04843 USA (winter) PO Box 4114, Key West, FL 33041-4414 USA
Tel: 207-236-8353 (year round); 305-304-9222 (winter only)
E-mail: sail@appledore2.com

APPLEDORE IV

SPECIFICATIONS

Flag: USA
Rig: Topsail schooner
Homeport: Bay City, Michigan
Normal cruising waters:
Saginaw Bay and Lake Huron
Sparred length: 85'
LOA: 65'
LOD: 65'
LWL: 53'
Draft: 8' 6"
Beam: 18' 5"
Rig height: 76'
Freeboard: 6'
Sail area: 3,560 square feet
Tons: 48 GRT
Power: 135 HP diesel
Hull: steel

The schooner *Appledore IV* is owned and operated by BaySail, a 501(C) 3 non-profit corporation. Tall ship adventures aboard the *Appledore IV* further BaySail's mission: "To foster environmental stewardship of the Saginaw Bay watershed and the Great Lakes ecosystem and to provide personal development opportunities for learners of all ages through shipboard and land based educational experiences." BaySail's environmental education program, Science Under Sail, begins and ends in the classroom with materials designed to prepare students for their sailing experience and reinforce the lessons learned while on board the *Appledore IV*. During the three-and-a-half-hour excursion, trained volunteer teachers lead small groups of students through hands-on activities including collecting and analyzing water, sediment, and plankton samples. Land use, maritime history, navigation, and weather observation are also discussed. To date over 24,000 K-12 students have taken part in BaySail's award winning education programs. *Appledore IV* is also available for private charter to companies, organizations, and other groups of up to 48 people, and for weekend public sails from May through October.

Who sails: School groups elementary through college and individuals of all ages.
Program type: Half-day K-12 marine science and ecology education; public sails and private charters.
Affiliated institutions include: Saginaw Valley State University, Delta College, and the Boy's and Girl's Clubs of Michigan.
Season: April – October
Designer: Bud McIntosh
Built: 1989: Palm Coast, FL, Treworgy Yachts
Coast Guard certification: Passenger Vessel (Subchapter T)
Crew: 4 **Trainees-passengers:** 48 daysails, 7 overnight
Contact: Roger Nugent, Executive Director, BaySail, 107 Fifth Street, Bay City, MI 48708 USA
Tel: 989-895-5193
Fax: 989-460-1472
E-mail: info@baysailbaycity.org
Website: www.baysailbaycity.org

Flag: USA
Rig: Gaff topsail schooner, 2-masted
Homeport: Bay City, Michigan
Normal cruising waters: Great Lakes
Sparred length: 65'
LOD: 58'
LWL: 49'
Draft: 7' 6"
Beam: 14'
Rig height: 63' 6"
Tons: 34 GRT
Power: 90 HP diesel
Freeboard: 4'
Hull: steel

APPLEDORE V

Through the summer months, the *Appledore V* delivers BaySail's youth sail training program "Windward Bound". During the five to ten day Windward Bound voyages, *Appledore V* is sailed by a professional captain and mate, two youth officers, and eight youth trainees. On their regular watches trainees are involved in every aspect of running the ship, from navigating and steering, to galley duty and manning the oars in *Appledore's* tender on trips ashore. Trainees who successfully complete a summer training voyage become eligible to join the year-round program and train to qualify as youth officers. In the fall, *Appledore V* sails Lake Huron's beautiful Cheneaux Islands and the North Channel on three to five day training voyages for adults. The *Appledore V* is owned and operated by BaySail, a 501(C) 3 non-profit corporation.

Who sails: Youth ages 14 – 18.
Program type: Youth Sail Training. Affiliated with Boy's and Girl's Clubs of Michigan.
Season: April to October
Designer: Bud McIntosh
Built: 1992: Palm Coast, FL, Treworgy Yachts
Coast Guard certification: Passenger Vessel (Subchapter T)
Crew: 2 **Youth Officers:** 2 **Trainees-passengers:** 29 daysails, 8 overnight.
Contact: Roger C. Nugent, Executive Director, BaySail, 107 Fifth Street, Bay City, MI 48708 USA
Tel: 989-895-5193
Fax: 989-460-1472
E-mail: info@baysailbaycity.org
Website: www.baysailbaycity.org

ARGIA

Flag: USA
Rig: Gaff topsail schooner
Homeport: Mystic, Connecticut
Normal cruising waters:
Fishers Island, Block Island and
Long Island Sounds
Sparred length: 81'
LOD: 56'
LWL: 48'
Draft: 7' 6"
Beam: 20'
Rig height: 75'
Freeboard: 5'
Sail area: 1,800 square feet
Tons: 20 GRT
Power: 100 HP diesel
Hull: Honduran mahogany
on white oak frames

Voyager Cruises operates the *Argia* out of Mystic, Connecticut during the months of May through October. She is a replica of a 19th century schooner, designed and built by Captain Frank Fulchiero for the day passenger trade. She carries 49 passengers on the waters of Block Island and Long Island Sounds for two to three hour day sails, charters, and marine science/ coastal ecology programs. The Coastal Ecology Program utilizes various sampling and testing techniques to provide students with a better understanding of marine and coastal ecosystems. Volunteer and intern positions are available for this program which runs in spring and fall. Paid crew positions include: deckhand, 1st and 2nd mate, and licensed captain.

Who sails: All ages
Program type: Sail training for paying trainees and passengers; sea education in marine science, maritime history, and ecology in cooperation with accredited institutions and other groups; passenger day sails
Season: May – October
Designer: Frank Fulchiero
Built: 1986: Reedville, VA and Mystic, CT, Frank Fulchiero and Jennings Boat Yard
Coast Guard certification: Passenger Vessel (Subchapter T) Inland
Crew: 5 **Trainees-passengers:** 49 daysails
Contact: Captain Amy Blumberg, Voyager Cruises, 15 Holmes Street, Schooner Wharf, Mystic, CT 06355 USA
Tel: 860-536-0416
Fax: 860-536-0416
E-mail: alblumberg@voyagermystic.com
Website: www.voyagermystic.com

SPECIFICATIONS

Flag: UK
Rig: Schooner, two-masted
Homeport: Road Town Harbour, Tortola
Normal cruising waters: Worldwide
Sparred length: 112'
LOA: 101'
LOD: 94'
LWL: 71'
Draft: 10'
Beam: 25'
Rig height: 102'
Freeboard: 6'
Sail area: 4,700 square feet
Tons: 130 GRT
Power: 425 HP diesel
Hull: steel

ARGO

S/Y *Argo* is a two-masted staysail schooner that measures 112-ft overall and accommodates twenty six students and seven professional crew on ocean voyages around the globe. She is certified and inspected by the British Maritime and Coastguard Agency as a Category "0" vessel, allowing her unrestricted operation in the world's oceans. Sailing under the Sea|mester flag, *Argo* circumnavigates the globe offering students the chance to cross oceans while furthering their educational and personal goals in a highly experiential college-level academic setting.

Who sails: 12th grade high school students (fall semester), high school graduates and college age students (fall, spring, and summer)
Program type: Experiential education semesters for high school graduates and college students; accredited academics with sail and scuba training and adventure travel
Season: Year-round
Designer: Langan Design Associates
Built: 2006: Marsun Shipyard, Thailand
Certification: MCA (UK) inspected Small Commercial Vessel up to 24 meters Load Line, Category "0"unrestricted ocean service
Crew: 7 **Trainees-passengers:** 26
Contact: Sea|mester, PO Box 5477, Sarasota, FL 34277 USA
Tel: 941-924-6789 or 800-317-6789 **Fax:** 941-924-6075
E-mail: info@seamester.com **Website:** www.seamester.com

ARUNG SAMUDERA

SPECIFICATIONS

Flag: Indonesia
Rig: Schooner
Homeport: Jakarta, Indonesia
Normal cruising waters:
Worldwide
Sparred length: 129'
Draft: 9'
Beam: 22'
Hull: steel

Photo by Thad Koza

In 1995, the Indonesian government celebrated their golden anniversary of independence by hosting a conference, heralded the Arung Samudera '95, to draw attention to the archipelago nation. At the conclusion of the conference, a 129-foot staysail schooner purchased in New Zealand was commissioned as Indonesia's first sail training ship. Know originally as *Adventurer*, the schooner was built in 1991 to serve as a sail training vessel based in Auckland, New Zealand. She was renamed Kri *Arung Samudera* to reflect her new home and service. The honorific "kri" is used just as "HMS" is used in Britain to designate a ship in service of the Royal Navy. Together the words "arung" and "samudera" in this context mean "cruise the ocean" a fitting goal for this adventurous schooner. *Arung Samudera* embarked on a circumnavigation of the globe as her first assignment.

Program type: Sail training vessel of the Indonesian Navy
Built: 1991
Contact: Embassy of the Republic of Indonesia, 2020 Massachusetts Avenue, NW, Washington DC 20036 USA
Tel: 202-775-5200
Fax: 202-775-5365

Flag: USA
Rig: Gaff topsail schooner
Homeport: Newport,
Rhode Island
Normal cruising waters:
Narragansett Bay
Sparred length: 101'
LOD: 80'
Draft: 8'
Beam: 17' 6"
Rig height: 82'
Sail area: 2,800 square feet
Tons: 53 GRT
Hull: wood

AURORA

Formerly known as the *Francis Todd*, the *Aurora* is a two-masted schooner built in 1947 for work in the fishing industry. She retired from fishery work in 1991 and has since been rebuilt to offer ample seating, a spacious deck plan, and amenability to charter arrangements. Perfect for entertaining and special occasions, the *Aurora* is inspected and certified by the US Coast Guard as a Passenger Vessel. She is stable, seaworthy, and professionally maintained for comfort and safety. Based in Newport, Rhode Island, the *Aurora* sails New England waters and Narragansett Bay and is available for day sails and private charter.

Who sails: School groups elementary through college, individuals, families, corporate and social groups
Program type: Passenger day sails and informal sail training
Designer: Newbert & Wallace
Built: 1947: Thomaston, ME, Newbert & Wallace
Crew: 3 **Trainees-passengers:** 75 daysails
Contact: IDC Charters, Inc. Goat Island Marina, Newport, RI 02840 USA
Tel: 401-849-6683
Website: www.newportexperience.com

BAGHEERA

SPECIFICATIONS

Flag: USA
Rig: Gaff rigged schooner
Homeport: Portland, Maine
Normal Cruising Waters:
Casco Bay
Sparred length: 72'
LOA: 55' 6"
LOD: 54'
LWL: 44'
Draft: 7' 6"
Beam: 14' 6"
Rig height: 65'
Freeboard: 4'
Tons: 21 GRT
Power: 72 HP diesel
Hull: wood

The schooner *Bagheera* was designed by John G. Alden and built in 1924 in East Boothbay, Maine. Shortly after launching, she sailed in the Bermuda Race, and then spent the next 50 years sailing in the Great Lakes. *Bagheera* was entered in the Chicago Mackinac Race numerous times, winning in 1930. The vessel was sailed to the Caribbean in the 1970s, eventually finding her way to the Galapagos Islands. She was converted to the passenger trade in the 1980s. She then sailed out of Los Angeles, San Diego and San Francisco before being shipped to Maine in 2002 to serve Portland Schooner Co., her current stewards. Today, *Bagheera* sails Memorial Day through Columbus Day from the Old Port in Portland, Maine, offering a variety of educational courses, public sails, and private charters.

Who sails: Schools, camps, organizations, families and individuals of all ages
Program type: Sea education based on in-house programming
Season: Memorial Day through Columbus Day
Designer: John G. Alden
Built: 1924: East Boothbay, ME, Rice Brothers
Coast Guard certification: Passenger Vessel (Subchapter T)
Crew: 2 **Trainees-passengers:** 48 daysails
Contact: Scott Reischmann, Portland Schooner Company, Box 111, Pears Island, Portland, ME 04108 USA
Tel: 207-766-2500 or (toll free) 1-87-SCHOONER
Fax: 866-319-5736
E-mail: scott@portlandschooner.com
Website: www.portlandschooner.com

Flag: USA
Rig: Full-rigged ship
Homeport:
San Francisco, California
Sparred length: 301'
LOD: 256'
Draft: 22' 7"
Beam: 38' 6"
Rig height: 145'
Tons: 1,689 GRT
Hull: steel

BALCLUTHA

The three-masted, riveted steel ship *Balclutha* was built in Glasgow, Scotland, in 1886 "to the highest class in Lloyd's Registry." As a deepwaterman, *Balclutha* and a 26-man crew rounded Cape Horn with grain for Great Britain, and later ran Pacific Coast lumber to Australia. Each year as a salmon packet, the vessel carried hundreds of men (with boats and supplies) to the salmon fishing grounds of Alaska. She was rescued from decay by the San Francisco Bay Area community in 1954, and has been restored as a memorial to the men and times of the grand days of sail. Today the vessel hosts a slate of unique school education programs presented by the San Francisco Maritime National Park Association and is open to the public as part of the San Francisco Maritime National Historical Park.

Program type: Dockside sea education in maritime history
Designer: Charles Connell
Built: 1886: Scotland, Charles
Contact: Lynn Cullivan, Management Assistant, San Francisco Maritime National Historical Park, Building E, Fort Mason Center, San Francisco, CA 94123 USA
Tel: 415-561-7006
Fax: 415-556-1624
E-mail: lynn_cullivan@nps.gov
Website: www.nps.gov/safr/historyculture/balclutha.htm

Photo from the Port of LA Collection

BILL OF RIGHTS

SPECIFICATIONS

Flag: USA
Rig: Gaff topsail schooner, two-masted
Homeport: Los Angeles, California
Normal cruising waters: Coastal California and other offshore islands
Sparred length: 136'
LOA: 129'
LOD: 94'
LWL: 85'
Draft: 10'
Beam: 23'
Rig height: 100'
Sail area: 6,300 square feet
Freeboard: 5' 8"
Tons: 95 GRT
Power: 210 HP diesel
Hull: wood

As this is written, *Bill of Rights* is for sale. After considerable restoration work at Los Angeles Maritime Institute (LAMI) in 2007 and Grays Harbor Historical Seaport in 2005, *Bill of Rights* is fully certified as a passenger vessel under USCG Subchapter T. *Bill of Rights* is a beautiful learning environment for 'youth-of-all-ages,' creating real-world challenges in the sea-world setting. Inquiries about subsequent use may be directed to LAMI. Los Angeles Maritime Institute, current owner of *Bill*, operates the TopSail Youth Program, character-building sail training adventures for youth aboard the twin brigantines *Irving Johnson* and *Exy Johnson*, and the schooner *Swift of Ipswich*. TopSail can be adjusted to fit the age, interests, and abilities of virtually any participants. LAMI is eager for *Bill of Rights* to find a new home and continue making a difference through sailing adventures.

Who sails: Open opportunities to suit new owner. TopSail aboard *Bill* served 'youth-of-all-ages.'
Program type: Educational
Season: Year-round
Designer: McCurdy, Rhodes & Bates
Built: 1971: South Bristol, ME, Harvey F. Gamage Shipyard
Coast Guard certification: Passenger Vessel (Subchapter T)
Crew: 5 (day), 8 (overnight), 5 instructors **Trainees-passengers:** 52 daysails, 39 overnight
Contact: Captain Jim Gladson, Los Angeles Maritime Institute, Berth 84, Foot of Sixth Street, San Pedro, CA 90731 USA
Tel: 310-833-6055
Fax: 310-548-2055
Website: www.lamitopsail.org

Flag: Canada
Rig: Brigantine
Homeport: Ottawa, Ontario, Canada
Normal Cruising Waters: Upper Ottawa River
Sparred length: 90'
LOA: 87'
LOD: 68'
LWL: 57'
Draft: 6'
Beam: 15'
Rig height: 60'
Sail area: 2,300 square feet
Freeboard: 3'
Tons: 42 GRT
Power: 235 HP diesel
Hull: steel

Photo by Cal Vandergeest

BLACK JACK

On May 2, 1904, *G. B. Pattee II*, a steam tugboat, was launched in Quyon, Quebec, Canada. She worked the logging industry for 50 years on the Upper Ottawa River. In 1952 the hull was purchased by the late Captain Thomas G. Fuller and converted into a tall ship brigantine, *Black Jack*, for a family yacht. On May 2, 2004, after a major refit, *Black Jack* was re-christened and launched at Britannia Yacht Club by Her Excellency, the Right Honorable Adrienne Clarkson, Canada's Governor General. At the same time, the vessel was designated Ottawa's Signature Vessel by the City of Ottawa. Bytown Brigantine was founded by the Thomas G. Fuller Family as a charitable foundation to provide opportunities for youth to experience adventure in the time honored traditions inherent in square rigged sailing. *Black Jack* is now the centerpiece of the Black Jack Island Adventure Camp, a 10 day program where youth 12-15 sail this tall ship or one of our 27' navy whalers as well as participating in other various camp activities.

Who sails: Middle school 12 – 15 year olds
Program type: Sail training for paying trainees, overnight voyages, Island Adventure Camp
Season: Summer and fall
Built: 1904: Scotland
Certification: Sailing School Vessel, Inland/Minor Waters
Crew: 6 high school and university officers **Trainees-passengers:** 30 daysails,18 overnight
Contact: Bytown Brigantine, 2700 Queensview Drive, Ottawa, Ontario K2B 8H6 Canada
Tel: 613-596-6258
Fax: 613-596-5947
E-mail: tallshipinfo@tallshipsadventure.org
Website: www.tallshipsadventure.org

BONNIE LYNN

BONNIE LYNN

SPECIFICATIONS

Flag: USA
Rig: Schooner
Homeport: Islesboro, Maine
Normal cruising waters:
New England (summer),
Caribbean (winter)
Sparred length: 72'
LOA: 57'
LOD: 57'
LWL: 49'
Draft: 7'
Beam: 15' 3"
Rig height: 63'
Sail area: 2,500 square feet
Tons: 32 GRT
Power: 220 HP diesel
Hull: steel

Bonnie Lynn is one of the most unique of the Maine Windjammer Fleet. She is a modified version of designer Merrit Walter's *Trade Rover*, the hull being built by Treworgy Yachts and then the interior and rigging completed in Maine. Being a serious offshore cruising vessel, she is built to very high standards. The steel hull is 57-feet on deck, with an overall length of 72-feet. She was completed in July of 1998 and has been actively chartering since then. *Bonnie Lynn* made a transatlantic voyage to the Azores, Ireland, Scotland and Portugal in the summer of 2005 and returned to the Caribbean via Madeira and the Canaries. She is Coast Guard certified for 36 passengers for day sails and 6 for ocean. Although she has a very traditional look, passengers rest in the serenity and luxury of modern day technology and amenities. Extraordinary means have been taken to make the *Bonnie Lynn* a most comfortable and seaworthy vessel. *Bonnie Lynn* is presently available for charter, June through October, in New England.

Who sails: Families and groups
Program type: Sail training for volunteer crew and for volunteer and paying trainees; dockside interpretation during port visits
Designer: Merrit Walter
Built: 1997: Palm Coast, FL, Islesboro, ME, Treworgy
Coast Guard certification: Passenger Vessel (Subchapter T)
Crew: 3 **Trainees-passengers:** 36 daysails, 6 overnight
Contact: Captains Bonnie and Earl MacKenzie, PO Box 41, Islesboro, ME 04848 USA
Tel: 401-835-3368
E-mail: mack@bonnielynn.com
Website: www.bonnielynn.com

Flag: USA
Rig: Full rigged ship
Homeport: Greenport,
Long Island, New York
Normal cruising waters:
East Coast US, Canada, Florida
and Europe (upon request)
Sparred length: 180'
LOD: 120'
Draft: 13'
Beam: 32'
Rig height: 115'
Sail area: 10,000 square feet
Tons: 412 GRT
Power: (2) twin 375 John Deere
diesel
Hull: wood

BOUNTY

HMS *Bounty* was built for the 1962 movie "Mutiny on the Bounty" by MGM Studios in Lunenburg, Nova Scotia to tell the story of the famous maritime mutiny that occurred in the South Pacific in 1789. Now owned and operated by the HMS Bounty Organization LLC, she makes Greenport, Long Island, New York her homeport. In an effort to return *Bounty* to the condition of her Hollywood film days, the famous ship completed an extensive renovation from 2006-2007 in Boothbay Harbor, Maine. In August 2007, *Bounty* returned to England and will spend 2008 traveling around the world, culminating in the 220th anniversary of the original *Bounty's* first arrival in Tahiti in 1788. The ship carries 18 full-time paid crewmembers working side by side with our sail trainees and passengers. When docked in port, the *Bounty* is open for dockside tours, private functions and educational programs. She offers day sails for individuals and groups, sail passages, and corporate sail training and is available for private functions, film production, commercials and documentaries. Strongly dedicated to the educational development of today's youth, *Bounty* works closely with universities and other non-profit organizations to provide leadership learning and youth education-at-sea programs. The mission of the *Bounty* is to preserve the skills of square rigged sailing in conjunction with youth education and sail training.

Who sails: Students, individuals, and groups of all ages
Program type: Sail passages, dockside interpretations, school groups
Season: Year-round
Designer: British Admiralty
Built: 1960: Lunenburg, Nova Scotia, Smith & Rhuland
Coast Guard certification: Moored Attraction Vessel
Crew: 18 **Trainees-passengers:** 12
Contact: Margaret Ramsey, Executive Director, HMS Bounty Organization, LLC, 548 West Jericho Turnpike, Smithtown, NY 11787 USA
Tel: 631-588-7900
Fax: 631-584-7901
E-mail: mramsey@tallshipbounty.org
Website: www.tallshipbounty.org

Photo by Captain Wendell Corey

BOWDOIN

SPECIFICATIONS

Flag: USA
Rig: Schooner
Homeport: Castine, Maine
Sparred length: 100'
LOA: 88'
LOD: 83'
LWL: 72'
Draft: 10'
Beam: 20'
Rig height: 70'
Sail area: 200 square feet
Freeboard: 4'
Tons: 66 GRT
Power: 190 HP Diesel
Hull: wood

The schooner *Bowdoin* is the flaghip of Maine Maritime Academy (MMA) sail training fleet, and the official sailing vessel of the state of Maine. Built in 1921 for exploring the Arctic waters, she is one of the strongest wooden vessels ever constructed. Between 1921 and 1954 she made 26 voyages above the Arctic Circle under the command of explorer Donald B. MacMillian. Today, *Bowdoin* serves the students of MMA, the state of Maine, and New England. She is the flagship of MMA's Sail Training Curriculum (http://bell.mma.edu/~bowdoin/sailtraining/) in which students learn to sail and manage traditional and modern sailing vessels. *Bowdoin's* sailing grounds include New England, Nova Scotia, Newfoundland, Labrador, and Greenland. Training afloat is performed on the Academy's fleet of over 100 vessels, including a 500-foot training ship, a 35-foot schooner, a Tugboat, 5 Colgate 26's, and numerous other sailing and power vessels from 15 to 50 feet.

Who sails: Students of the Maine Maritime Academy
Program type: Sail training
Season: June to October
Designer: William Hand
Built: 1921, East Boothbay, ME, Hodgdon Brothers Shipyard
Coast Guard certification: Sailing School Vessel (Subchapter R), Passenger Vessel (Subchapter T), Ocean
Crew: 6 **Trainees-passengers:** 40 daysails, 11 overnight
Contact: Tim Leach, Marine Operations Manager, Castine, ME, 04421 USA
Tel: 207-326-2364
Fax: 207-326-2377
E-mail: tleach@mma.edu
Website: http://bell.mma.edu/~bowdoin/

Flag: USA
Rig: Cutter/sloop
Homeport:
Wickford, Rhode Island
Normal cruising waters:
Narragansett Bay, Rhode Island
Sparred length: 63'
LOA: 58'
LOD: 55'
LWL: 53'
Draft: 2' 6"
Beam: 18'
Rig height: 59'
Sail area: 1,317 square feet
Freeboard: 4' 6"
Tons: 60 GRT
Power: 135 HP Ford
Hull: riveted iron

BRANDARIS

Brandaris, the 63-foot Dutch-design sailing vessel, was launched in 1938 as the private yacht of William De Vries Lentsch, Jr., shipyard owner and famous Dutch designer. After a colorful escape from German occupation in WWII, *Brandaris* participated in the evacuation of Dunkirk. Now berthed in Wickford, Rhode Island, she is available for excursions, sailing charters, and special occasion functions from weddings to funerals. *Brandaris* also offers a Classroom Afloat program featuring educational field trips and curriculum-based experiential learning programs. Many of these programs have received sponsorship from corporate and grant-based underwriters at no charge to schools.

Who sails: School groups from elementary through college; individuals and families; charter groups
Program type: Sail training for volunteer and paying trainees; sea education in marine science, maritime history, and ecology, in cooperation with organized groups; passenger day sails and overnight voyages
Designer: William De Vries Lentsch, Jr.
Built: 1938: Amsterdam, The Netherlands, Amsterdam Shipyard
Coast Guard certification: Passenger Vessel (Subchapter T) Inland, Near Coastal
Crew: 2 **Trainees-passengers:** 32 daysails
Contact: Captain Douglas Somers, Owner, Brandaris Sailing Charters/Friends of Brandaris, 7 Main Street, Wickford, RI 02852 USA
Tel: 401-294-1481
Fax: 401-294-1938
E-mail: brandaris@earthlink.net

BRILLIANT

SPECIFICATIONS

Flag: USA
Rig: Gaff schooner, two-masted
Homeport: Mystic Seaport, Mystic, Connecticut
Normal cruising waters: New England
Sparred length: 74'
LOA: 61' 6"
LOD: 61' 6"
LWL: 49'
Draft: 9'
Beam: 14' 8"
Rig height: 81'
Tons: 30 GRT
Power: 97 HP diesel
Hull: wood

Winner of the Tall Ships 2000® transatlantic race from Halifax to Amsterdam, captained by ASTA's 2000 "Sail Trainer of the Year", George Moffett, *Brilliant* is the traveling ambassador of Mystic Seaport, our nation's leading maritime museum. In service for nearly 50 years, the oldest sail-education program in the nation, *Brilliant* has introduced more than 9,000 people to the lessons a sailing ship teaches naturally. Board this classic schooner and become the crew; steer, handle sails, cook and clean as you learn the venerable maritime tradition of "for the good of the ship." *Brilliant* has two other ASTA awards to her credit: "First in Class" in the 2000 Boston to Halifax race and "Sail Training Vessel of the Year" in 1996. She also won the 1997 Nantucket Lighthouse Opera Cup.

Who sails: Teens ages 15–19 and adults 20+; participants must be physically fit, agile, and competent swimmers; affiliated institution is Mystic Seaport
Program type: Sail training with paying trainees; sea education in cooperation with organized groups such as Scouts, based on informal, in-house programming
Season: May through October
Designer: Sparkman & Stephens
Built: 1932: City Island, New York, Henry B. Nevins
Coast Guard certification: Sailing School Vessel (Subchapter R), Passenger Vessel (Subchapter T)
Crew: 2-3 **Trainees-passengers:** 10 daysails, 8 overnight
Contact: Mystic Seaport, Brilliant Program, PO Box 6000, Mystic, CT 06355-0990 USA
Tel: 860-572-5323
Fax: 860-572-5355
Website: www.mysticseaport.org

SPECIFICATIONS

Flag: Canada
Rig: Barquentine
Homeport:
Halifax, Nova Scotia, Canada
Normal cruising waters:
North American waters and
the Caribbean
Sparred length: 245'
Draft: 15'
Beam: 30'
Rig height: 132'
Sail area: 17,000 square feet
Power: 1500 HP Deutz diesel
Hull: steel

CALEDONIA

Canadian Sailing Expeditions (CSE) has developed the concept of a traditional tall ship cruise product for Atlantic Canada and the Caribbean. The square-rigged *Caledonia* hosts corporate clients and leisure travelers in old world charm onboard a traditional tall ship, with new world amenities including local gourmet cuisine prepared by our onboard chefs and finely appointed cabins with queen size berths, ensuite toilet and shower, A/C and heat. While onboard, guests enjoy a Reading Room, Saloon, and Dining Salon, as well as large open spaces on deck. Three large Zodiacs, mountain bikes, and sea kayaks are available for the guests use. CSE is currently developing academic programming which will be carried out in the early spring and late fall onboard *Caledonia*. Become part of the crew of a traditional sailing ship and participate in the highly challenging and rewarding life on board a tall ship at sea. *Caledonia* is designed to enable guests to have a unique and personal experience with the ship, the crew, and the cruising destination. CSE's product, offers a high level of education, accommodation, adventure, and scenery.

Who sails: Groups and individuals of all ages
Program type: Sail training for paying trainees, day sails, overnight passages, adventure travel cruises
Season: Year-round
Built: 1947: Beverley, United Kingdom
Trainees-passengers: 40
Contact: Captain Doug Prothero, Canadian Sailing Expeditions, PO box 2613, Halifax, NS B3J 3N5 Canada
Tel: 902-429-1474
Fax: 902-429-1475
E-mail: doug@canadiansailingexpeditions.com
Website: www.canadiansailingexpeditions.com

Photo by Steve Danford

C.A.THAYER

SPECIFICATIONS

Flag: USA
Rig: Schooner, three-masted
Homeport: San Francisco, California
Sparred length: 219'
LOD: 156'
Draft: 11' 3"
Beam: 36'
Rig height: 105'
Tons: 453 GRT
Hull: wood

Built in 1895, the *C. A. Thayer* was part of a mighty Pacific Coast fleet of sailing schooners that carried lumber to San Francisco from Washington, Oregon and the California Redwood Coast. Later, the vessel supplied the Alaskan salt-salmon canneries, anchoring out during the summer and returning in September with the season's catch packed in her hold. From 1925 to 1950, *C. A. Thayer* carried men north to the Bering Sea cod fishing grounds. She was purchased by the State of California in 1957, and transferred to the National Park Service in 1977. Now a National Historic Landmark, the *C. A.Thayer* is a rare survivor from the days when strong canvas sails billowed over tall deckloads of freshly milled fir and redwood. Today, the *Thayer* is open to the public daily as a part of the San Francisco Maritime National Historical Park. Visit the vessel's web page for photos and movies about *Thayer's* recent, extensive preservation project.

Program type: Dockside sea education programs in maritime history
Designer: Hans Bendixsen
Built: 1895: Fairhaven, CA, Hans Bendixsen
Contact: Lynn Cullivan, Management Assistant, San Francisco Maritime National Historical Park, Building E, Fort Mason Center, San Francisco, CA 94123 USA
Tel: 415-561-7006
Fax: 415-556-1624
E-mail: lynn_cullivan@nps.gov
Website: http://www.nps.gov/safr/historyculture/c-a-thayer.htm

Flag: USA
Rig: Topsail schooner
Homeport: San Diego, California
Normal cruising waters:
Southern California and the
California Coast
Sparred length: 145'
LOA: 93' 4"
LWL: 84'
Draft: 9' 5"
Beam: 24'
Rig height: 95'
Freeboard: 6'
Sail area: 7,000 square feet
Tons: 130 GRT
Power: 140 HP diesel
Hull: wood

CALIFORNIAN

Californian was launched in celebration of the 1984 Summer Olympics in Los Angeles. In 2003, *Californian* was designated the official tall ship of the State of California. She is the only ship to carry this prestigious title. A 145-foot topsail schooner, *Californian* is a replica of a mid-19th century revenue cutter. She has played host to thousands of adventure travelers, sailing enthusiasts, students and history buffs during her career. In 2003, she underwent an extensive refit including a haul out, re-stepping the masts, replacing the standing rigging, new sails and mechanical systems and a re-design and re-furbishing of the areas below deck. The Maritime Museum of San Diego uses her for a variety of educational programs and public adventure sails. Her annual coastal tour offers residents and visitors throughout California an opportunity to enjoy the state of California's official tall ship.

Who sails: Groups and individuals of all ages
Program type: At sea and dockside education programs in maritime history and programs for at-risk youth in cooperation with area schools and social services agencies, passenger day sails and overnight passages
Season: Year-round
Designer: Melbourne Smith
Built: 1984: San Diego, CA, Nautical Heritage Society
Trainees-passengers: 60 daysails
Contact: Peter Durdaller, San Diego Maritime Museum, 1492 N. Harbor Drive, San Diego CA 92101 USA
Tel: 619 234 9153 x 120
E-mail: pdurdaller@sdmaritime.org
Website: www.sdmaritime.org

Photo by Thad Koza

CAPITAN MIRANDA

SPECIFICATIONS

Flag: Uruguay
Rig: Staysail schooner
Homeport: Montevideo, Uruguay
Normal cruising waters:
Worldwide
Sparred length: 205'
LOA: 198'
LOD: 172'
LWL: 147' 5"
Draft: 12'
Beam: 27'
Hull: steel

Built in 1930 in the Matagorda Shipyard and factory located in Cadiz, Spain, the *Capitan Miranda* originally served as a hydrographic vessel. As such, she carried out an outstanding and extensive career, performing countless cartographical surveys which were, and still are, highly useful to seamen. The ship honors the memory of Captain Francisco P. Miranda (1869 – 1925), who was not only a bright professional but also an exceptional teacher, particularly remembered for his research in sea subjects. In 1977, the vessel underwent a major refit and in 1978 was rededicated as a sail training vessel for the Uruguayan navy teaching newly graduated midshipmen to apply the knowledge acquired at the Naval Academy.

Who sails: Midshipmen, civilian students, foreign guests
Program type: Sail training vessel of the Uruguayan Navy.
Built: 1930: Cadiz, Spain, Astiueros Matagorda
Crew: 12 officers, 39 enlisted **Trainees-passengers:** 35
Contact: Embassy of Uruguay, 1913 I Street, NW, Suite 419, Washington, DC 20006 USA
Tel: 202-331-1313
Fax: 202-331-8142
E-mail: navyofuruguay@yahoo.com
Website: www.armada.mil.uy

Flag: USA
Rig: Gaff rig sloop
Homeport: Oyster Bay, New York
Normal cruising waters:
Long Island Sound
Sparred length: 60'
LOA: 52'
LOD: 40'
LWL: 35' 6"
Draft: 3'
Beam: 15' 2"
Rig height: 50'
Freeboard: 18"
Sail area: 960 square feet
Tons: 11 GRT
Power: 63 HP diesel
Hull: wood

CHRISTEEN

The *Christeen* is the oldest remaining oyster sloop in North America and a National Historic Landmark. She was originally built in 1883 for Captain William Smith in Glenwood Landing, New York to harvest oysters in nearby Oyster Bay and Cold Spring Harbors. Over her 121 years, *Christeen* served not only as an oyster dredge but also as a cargo carrier and live-aboard between Connecticut, New York and New Jersey. After surviving 16 major hurricanes, numerous nor'easters, two sinkings and severe neglect, *Christeen* was returned home to Oyster Bay in 1992 and completely restored in 1999. *Christeen's* new mission is to serve as a floating classroom. Her Coast Guard Certified Captain's and experienced crew will instruct passengers about maritime history, marine science, coastal ecology and aquaculture. The *Christeen* is available for education, member and public sails, special events, and corporate charters.

Who sails: Students of all ages, individuals, families, and groups
Program type: Marine science, maritime history, marine trades (ie. commercial fishing, oystering)
Season: April through October
Designer: Traditional
Built: 1883: Glenwood Landing, NY
Coast Guard certification: Passenger Vessel (Subchapter T)
Crew: 3 **Trainees-passengers:** 20 daysails
Contact: The Waterfront Center, One West End Avenue, Oyster Bay, NY 11771 USA
Tel: 516-922-7245
Fax: 516-922-2901
E-mail: info@thewaterfrontcenter.org
Website: www.thewaterfrontcenter.org

Photo by Thad Koza

SPECIFICATIONS

Flag: Brazil
Rig: Full-rigged ship
Homeport: Rio de Janeiro, Brazil
Normal Cruising Waters: Worldwide
Sparred Length: 254'
LOA: 249'
LOD: 205'
LWL: 183'
Draft: 15' 9"
Beam: 34' 6"
Rig Height: 152'
Sail Area: 23,627 square feet
Freeboard: 5' 3"
Tons: 703 GRT
Power: 1001 HP Diesel
Hull: steel

CISNE BRANCO

The *Cisne Branco* (White Swan) is a Brazilian navy tall ship which was built in Amsterdam, Netherlands, by Damen Shipyard. Its keel was laid on November 9th, 1998, launched and christened on August 4th, 1999, delivered to Brazilian Navy on February 4th, 2000 and commissioned as a Brazilian Naval vessel on March 9th, 2000. *Cisne Branco* made its maiden voyage across the Atlantic Ocean to Brazil, celebrating the 500th anniversary of the discovery of Brazil by the Portuguese Admiral Pedro Alvares Cabral. The ship's project is inspired in the design of the 19th century clippers. The *Cisne Branco* is normally used in national and international activities as a representative of the Brazilian Navy and for Brazilian culture. Also, it is used as an instructional sailing ship to the cadets of Brazilian Naval Academy, Academy of Merchant Marine and other naval schools.

Who sails: Sail Training for Officers and Cadets from Brazilian Navy, Academy of Merchant Marine and other Naval schools.
Program type: Sail training, goodwill ship and representation for Brazilian Navy
Season: Year-round
Designer: Gerard Djikstra
Built: 2000: Amsterdam, Holland, Damen shipyards
Certification: Brazilian Naval Vessel
Crew: 52 **Trainees-passengers:** 31
Contact: Oficial de Relações Públicas, Marinha do Brasil, Centro Postal da Marinha - Praça Barão de Ladário, s/nº - Centro, Rio de Janeiro 20091-000 Brasil
Tel: 0021871762149980 **Fax:** 0021871762149982
E-mail: msgcisnebr@uol.com.br or msgcisnebr@yahoo.com.br
Website: www.cisnebranco.mar.mil.br

Flag: USA
Rig: Gaff topsail sloop
Homeport: Poughkeepsie, New York
Normal cruising waters: Hudson River, New York Harbor, Long Island Sound
Sparred length: 106'
LOA: 76' 6"
LOD: 76' 6"
LWL: 67'
Draft: 6' 6"
Beam: 24'
Rig height: 108'
Sail area: 4,350 square feet
Tons: 69 GRT
Power: 190 HP diesel
Hull: wood

Photo by Chris Bowser

CLEARWATER

The *Clearwater* is the only full-sized replica of the 18th and 19th century merchant vessels known as Hudson River sloops. Owned and operated by the Hudson River Sloop Clearwater, Inc., a non-profit membership organization dedicated to defending and restoring the Hudson River and related waterways, the *Clearwater* has served as both a platform for hands-on environmental education and as a symbol for grassroots action, since 1969. She sails seven days a week, carrying as many as 50 passengers for three- to five-hour educational programs. Adults and children take part in a range of activities involving water life, water chemistry, sail raising, steering, piloting and more. A USCG licensed captain is in charge, and an education specialist directs the program. The permanent crew is composed of apprentices, ages 16 and older, an education assistant, and volunteers.

Who sails: Students of all ages, individuals, families, and groups
Program type: Sail training for crew and apprentices; sea education in marine science, maritime history, and ecology; passenger day sails; dockside interpretation during port visits
Season: April through November
Designer: Cy Hamlin
Built: 1969: South Bristol, ME, Harvey Gamage Shipyard
Coast Guard certification: Passenger Vessel (Subchapter T)
Crew: 6 **Trainees-passengers:** 50
Contact: Captain, Hudson River Sloop Clearwater, Inc., 112 Little Market St., Poughkeepsie, NY 12601 USA
Tel: 845-454-7673
Fax: 845-454-7953
E-mail: captain@clearwater.org
Website: www.clearwater.org

USS CONSTELLATION

SPECIFICATIONS

Flag: USA
Rig: Full-rigged ship
Homeport:
Baltimore, Maryland
Sparred length: 282'
LOA: 200'
LOD: 176'
LWL: 179'
Draft: 21'
Beam: 42'
Rig height: 165'
Freeboard: 16'
Sail area: 20,000 square feet
Hull: wood

The last all-sail warship built by the US Navy, the *USS Constellation* was launched in 1854 at the Gosport Naval Shipyard in Portsmouth, Virginia. *Constellation* served the country for over 90 years in both military and non-military roles. Before the Civil War, she was the flagship of an international squadron charged with the mission of intercepting vessels engaged in the illegal trade of slaves along the coast of West Africa. During the Civil War, *Constellation* saw duty in the Mediterranean Sea protecting American interests there, and as part of the Gulf Coast blockading squadron. During her later years, she sailed as a training ship for the US Naval Academy and then as a stationary training ship at the Naval War College in Newport, Rhode Island. She was last under sail in 1893. Her final role as a commissioned vessel came during World War II when *Constellation* served as flagship of the Atlantic Fleet. In 1955, *Constellation* was brought to Baltimore to be preserved as a national shrine. The ship has recently undergone a nine million dollar reconstruction that has restored her to her original 1854 configuration. She is now open for public tours, offering a wide array of living history and educational programs under the management of the Living Classroom Foundation.

Program type: Dockside interpretation and educational programming
Designer: John Lenthall
Built: 1854: Portsmouth, VA, US Navy
Contact: USS Constellation Museum, Pier 1, 301 East Pratt Street, Baltimore, MD 21202 USA
Tel: 410-539-1797
Fax: 410-539-6238
E-mail: rowsom@constellation.org
Website: www.constellation.org

SPECIFICATIONS

Flag: USA
Rig: Full-rigged ship
Homeport: Charlestown, Massachusetts
Normal cruising waters: Boston Harbor
Sparred length: 306'
LOA: 204'
LOD: 174' 10" (gun deck)
LWL: 175'
Draft: 22'
Beam: 43' 6"
Rig height: 189' 2"
Freeboard: 15'
Sail area: 42,710 square feet
Tons: 2,200 GRT
Hull: wood

USS CONSTITUTION

"Old Ironsides" is the oldest commissioned warship afloat in the world. One of six ships ordered by President George Washington to protect America's growing maritime interests in the 1790s, *Constitution* earned widespread renown for her ability to punish French privateers in the Caribbean and thwart Barbary pirates of the Mediterranean. The ship's greatest glory came during the War of 1812 when she defeated four British frigates. During her first engagement against HMS *Guerriére* in 1812, seamen nicknamed her "Old Ironsides" when they saw British cannonballs glance off her 21-inch thick oak hull. In the 1830s, the ship was going to be to be disassembled, but the public outcry, sparked by the publication of an Oliver Wendell Holmes poem, saved her. Over the following century, the ship undertook many military assignments and served as a barracks and as a training ship. She was restored in 1927, and after a coast-to-coast tour, *Constitution* was moored in the Charlestown Navy yard in 1934 where she is now open year-round to the public for free tours.

Program type: Dockside interpretation; US Naval history
Built: 1797: Boston, MA, US Navy, Edmond Hartt Shipyard
Certification: Commissioned Naval Vessel
Crew: 75
Contact: Commanding Officer, USS Constitution, Charlestown Navy Yard, Charlestown, MA 02129-1797 USA
Tel: 617-242-5670
Fax: 617-242-2308
Website: www.ussconstitution.navy.mil

Photo by Wojtec Wacowski

CONCORDIA

SPECIFICATIONS

Flag: Barbados
Rig: Barquentine, three-masted
Homeport: Bridgetown, Barbados
Normal cruising waters:
Worldwide
Sparred length: 188'
LOA: 154'
LOD: 152' 6"
Draft: 13' 1"
Beam: 31'
Rig height: 115'
Freeboard: 8'
Sail area: 10,000 square feet
Tons: 495 GRT
Power: 570 HP diesel
Hull: steel

West Island College – Class Afloat is an international experiential education boarding school located in Lunenburg, Nova Scotia, Canada. Its mission is to broaden student understanding of international issues while preparing them for responsible global citizenship in the 21st century. The concept of "taking the classroom to the world" is intended to encourage self-sufficiency, cooperation, and a clear awareness of other cultures. Each academic year, 96 qualifying students spend one semester at the historic land-based boarding school and one semester working as crew and studying aboard the *Concordia*, a modern tall ship. A fully certified faculty instructs students in a full curriculum including social studies and global issues, anthropology, marine biology, maths, sciences and physical education. Optional non-credit enrichment courses are also offered in seamanship, celestial navigation, and the history and traditions of the sea. Over 1000 students have joined Class Afloat and sailed the world for an academic semester or full year program. Applications from 11th and 12th grade coeds are encouraged and accepted year-round.

Who sails: 11th and 12th grade students
Program type: Full-curriculum academics and marine biology for high school students
Season: Year-round
Built: 1992: Poland
Certification: Sailing School Vessel (Subchapter R), Lloyds 100A1 and LMC
Crew: 8 **Instructors:** 8 **Trainees-passengers:** 48
Contact: Doug Prothero, Chief Operating Officer/Vice President, West Island College International – Class Afloat, 97 Kaulbach Street, PO Box 10, Lunenburg, Nova Scotia B0J 2C0 Canada
Tel: 902-634-1895 or 800-301-7245
Fax: 902-634-7155
E-mail: dprothero@classafloat.com
Website: www.classafloat.com

Flag: USA
Rig: Gaff topsail schooner
Homeport:
Newport, Rhode Island
Sparred length: 190'
LOA: 133'
LOD: 133'
LWL: 125'
Draft: 12'
Beam: 27'
Freeboard: 6'
Sail area: 8,300 square feet
Tons: 174 GRT
Hull: wood

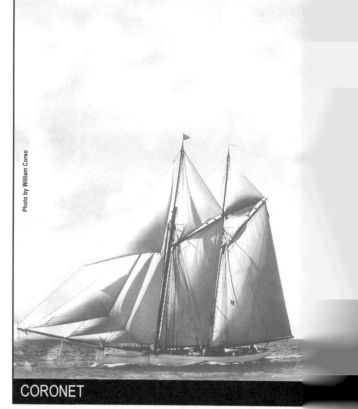

Photo by William Corso

CORONET

Built in 1885, *Coronet* is America's most historic yacht, and the last remaining grand yacht from the gilded age. She has voyaged far and wide during her career, twice circumnavigating the globe. In 1995 *Coronet* was acquired by the International Yacht Restoration School (IYRS), in Newport, Rhode Island. Founded in 1993, IYRS teaches the skills, history, and related sciences needed to restore classic yachts. IYRS will carry out a comprehensive and well-documented restoration to return *Coronet* to her late-19th century condition. She will have no engines, electricity, or modern equipment. When completed, she will sail as the school's flagship and a living museum of yachting history. *Coronet* is open to visitors, dockside from May to October each year.

Program type: Walk-on visitation and dockside interpretation for groups and individuals of all ages
Season: May to October
Designer: Smith & Terry, Christopher Crosby, William Townsend
Built: 1885: Brooklyn, NY, C & R Poillon
Contact: International Yacht Restoration School, 449 Thames Street, Newport, RI 02840 USA
Tel: 401-849-1995
Fax: 401-842-0669
Website: www.iyrs.org

CORWITH CRAMER

Flag: USA
Rig: Brigantine
Homeport: Woods Hole, Massachusetts
Normal cruising waters: Worldwide
Sparred length: 134'
LWL: 87' 6"
Draft: 13'
Beam: 26'
Sail area: 7,380 square feet
Tons: 158 GRT
Power: 500 HP diesel
Hull: steel

The *Corwith Cramer* was the first ship built to the USCG's regulations for Sailing School Vessels. The Sea Education Association (SEA), working through ASTA, was instrumental in helping the Coast Guard shape these regulations. The *Corwith Cramer* was built in Bilbao, Spain, and it took the largest floating crane in northern Spain to launch her. She is a safe, stable vessel and a platform for SEA's educational and oceanographic research missions. Along with the *Robert C. Seamans*, the *Corwith Cramer* is owned and operated by the Sea Education Association of Woods Hole, Massachusetts.

Who sails: Educators and students who are admitted by competitive selection; over 150 colleges and universities award credit for SEA programs
Program type: Marine and maritime studies including oceanography, nautical science, history, literature, and contemporary maritime affairs
Season: Year-round
Designer: Woodin & Marean
Built: 1987: Bilbao, Spain, ASTACE
Coast Guard certification: Sailing School Vessel (Subchapter R)
Crew: 6 professional mariners and 4 scientists **Trainees-passengers:** 25
Contact: Sea Education Association (SEA), PO Box 6, Woods Hole, MA 02543 USA
Tel: 508-540-3954 OR 800-552-3633
Fax: 508-546-0558
E-mail: admission@sea.edu
Website: www.sea.edu

Photo by Thad Koca

SPECIFICATIONS

Flag: Mexico
Rig: Barque
Homeport: Puerto de Acapulco, Mexico
Normal cruising waters: Worldwide
Sparred length: 270'
LWL: 220' 4"
Draft: 17' 1"
Beam: 39' 4"
Sail area: 25,489 square feet
Power: 1,125 HP engine
Hull: steel

CUAUHTEMOC

The sail training ship *Cuauhtemoc*, "tireless navigator", has covered 378,725 nautical miles and trained officers of the Mexican Navy for nearly 20 years. Through almost two decades, its accomplishments have been acknowledged and praised by other navies in the world. The ship has participated in important regattas like the Colón Regatta, the Cutty Sark Tall Ship Races, and the Centenary of Osaka Port Modernization Regatta, among others. The sail training ship *Cuauhtemoc* is undoubtedly a living symbol of the sailor spirit that characterizes the personnel of the Mexican Navy, who are always ready to serve their country.

Who sails: Captains, officers, cadets, and sailors of the Mexican Navy
Program type: Sail training vessel
Season: Year-round
Built: 1982: Bilbao, Spain, Celaya Shipyards
Crew: 123 (officers and sailors)
Contact: Rear Admiral Conrado Aparicio Blanco, Naval Attache of Mexico, Embassy of Mexico, 1911 Pennsylvania Avenue, NW, Washington, DC 20006 USA
Tel: 202-728-1760
E-mail: navalmx@msn.com or buquetemoc@hotmail.com

SPECIFICATIONS

Flag: USA
Rig: Gaff topsail schooner
Homeport: Destin, Florida
Normal cruising waters:
Northern Florida's Emerald
Coast
Sparred length: 75'
LOA: 53'
LOD: 53'
LWL: 48'
Draft: 3' 2"
Beam: 18'
Rig height: 61'
Freeboard: 4' 2"
Sail area: 2,000 square feet
Tons: 32 GRT
Power: 150 HP diesel
Hull: yellow pine

DANIEL WEBSTER CLEMENTS

The gaff rigged topsail schooner *Daniel Webster Clements* was constructed as a replica of a "Biloxi" design Gulf Coast fishing and trading schooner that evolved in the late 1800s and remained active through the I930s. Launched in I996, her shallow draft and plentiful sail area make her ideal for the shallow coastal waters and light airs that prevail much of the time on the Gulf Coast. The *Daniel Webster Clements* is operated by Sailing South Charters of Destin, Florida, in the heart of Florida's Emerald Coast. She offers an onboard nautical classroom for school groups of up to 47 participants and two overnight sail training programs for up to 20 participants. A structured youth adventure program emphasizes character education and an adult teamwork program provides leadership training for organizations and businesses. Both overnight programs feature an effective combination of team instruction on the schooner and in traditionally rigged skiffs. Practical sailing skills best learned on these smaller vessels are applied with ease to the operation of the larger vessel. The *Clements* specializes in service to youth scouting groups and meets all requirements for sailing merit badges.

Who sails: Students grades elementary through college, groups and individuals of all ages
Program type: Sail training for paying trainees; sea education in maritime history, ecology, and marine science in cooperation with accredited institutions and other organized groups
Season: Year-round
Designer: Gene Zirlott
Built: 1996: Coden, AL, Nathanial Zirlott Yard
Coast Guard certification: Passenger Vessel (Subchapter T)
Crew: 4 **Trainees-passengers:** 47 daysails, 20 overnight
Contact: William Campbell, Manager, Sailing South Charters, 600 Highway 98 East, Destin, FL 32541 USA
Tel: 850-837-7245
E-mail: schoonerdwc@cox.net
Website: www.sailingsouth.com

Flag: Poland
Rig: Full-rigged ship
Homeport: Gdynia, Poland
Normal cruising waters:
Worldwide
Sparred length: 360'
LOD: 311'
Draft: 20' 7"
Beam: 45' 9"
Rig height: 162'
Sail area: 32,453 square feet
Tons: 2,385 GRT
Power: Cegielski - Sulzer type 8
AL 20/24, 2 * 750 PS (552 kW)
Hull: steel

Photo by Thad Koza

DAR MLODZIEZY

Dar Mlodziezy, "gift of the children", is a full-rigged ship designed by the distinguished Polish Naval architect Zygmunt Choren and is the flagship of the Merchant Marine Academy in Gdynia, Poland. *Dar Mlodziezy* was funded in part by contributions of elementary school children during the 1960s and 1970s. Commissioned in 1982, she replaced the venerable *Dar Pomorza,* "gift of Pomoraze" (a reference to the coastal region of Poland), which served Poland for more than six decades before her retirement. *Dar Mlodziezy's* distinctive design served as the prototype for a class of vessels (five in all) built in Gdansk for the Russian confederation of the 1980's. Four of the five vessels – *Mir, Druzhba, Pallada, and Nasheba* – now fly the Russian flag, while *Khersones* flies the flag of Ukraine. These are true sister ships and vary only slightly in dimensions and configuration.

Who sails: Students of the Gdynia Maritime University
Season: Year-round
Designer: Zygmunt Choren
Built: 1982: Gdansk, Poland
Crew: 40 **Trainees-passengers:** 150
Contact: Gdynia Maritime University, Morska 81-8, 81-225 Gdynia, Poland
Tel: 48 58 621-70-41
Fax: 48 58 620-67-01
Website: www.wsm.gdynia.pl/

DENIS SULLIVAN

DENIS SULLIVAN

SPECIFICATIONS

Flag: USA
Rig: Schooner, three-masted
Homeport:
Milwaukee, Wisconsin
Normal cruising waters:
Great Lakes, Florida,
Bahamas
Sparred length: 137'
LOA: 99'
LOD: 98'
LWL: 88' 4"
Draft: 8' 9"
Beam: 24'
Rig height: 95'
Sail area: 5,916 square feet
Tons: 99 GRT
Power: twin 180 HP diesels
Hull: wood

The S/V *Denis Sullivan*, owned and operated by Discovery World Ltd., was completed by over 900 volunteers in 2000. This replica of a Great Lakes schooner, and Flagship of Wisconsin, operates as a floating classroom and goodwill ambassador for the State of Wisconsin. From her homeport in Milwaukee on Lake Michigan, the schooner offers educational day sails and private charters for people of all ages from May through September and is committed to re-establishing the historical, cultural and environmental bonds between the community and one of its most valuable resources, the Great Lakes. She winters in Florida, the Bahamas and Caribbean. Three hour LakeWatch Expeditions and Dockside Discovery educational programs are offered for 5th through 12th graders. High school and college students can partake in five to fourteen day Science Under Sail ™ programs in the Great Lakes, Bahamas and Caribbean.

Who sails: Students and the general public
Program type: Sail training for crew, volunteers, and paying trainees; sea education in maritime history, ecology, and marine science; professional development for educators; "themed" sails and passenger day sails; dockside interpretation while in port
Season: Year-round
Designer: Timothy Graul
Built: 2000: Milwaukee, WI, Rob Stevens
Coast Guard certification: Passenger Vessel (Subchapter T), Sailing School Vessel (Subchapter R)
Crew: 10 **Trainees-passengers:** 50 daysails, 16 overnight
Contact: Hugh Covert, Senior Captain, Pier Wisconsin, 500 North Harbor Drive, Milwaukee, WI 53202 USA
Tel: 414-765-8640 **Fax:** 414-765-0311
E-mail: hcovert@discoveryworld.org
Website: http://voyage.discoveryworld.org or www.discoveryworld.org

SPECIFICATIONS

Flag: Indonesia
Rig: Barquentine
Homeport: Surabaya, Indonesia
Normal cruising waters:
Indonesian waters, Indian Ocean,
Pacific Ocean
Sparred length: 191'
LOA: 165'
LOD: 163' 1"
LWL: 138' 4"
Draft: 13'
Beam: 31'
Rig height: 119' 7"
Freeboard: 15' 1"
Sail area: 11,738 square feet
Tons: 847 GRT
Power: 986 HP diesel
Hull: steel

Photo by Benson Lee

DEWARUCI

KRI *Dewaruci,* the beautiful barquentine flying the red and white Indonesian flag, is the largest tall ship in the Indonesian Navy. She was built in 1952 by H. C. Stulchen and Son of Hamburg, Germany and launched in 1953. Since then, the ship has served the Indonesian Navy as a sail training vessel and as a successful ambassador of goodwill for the people of Indonesia. *Dewaruci's* name and figurehead represent the mythological Indonesian god of truth and courage.

Who sails: Cadets of the Indonesian Naval Academy
Program type: Sail training and sea education for Indonesian Naval cadets
Season: Year-round
Built: 1952: Hamburg, Germany, H.C. Stulchen & Sohn
Crew: 70 **Trainees-passengers:** 80
Contact: Indonesian Naval Attaché, Defense Attaché Office, 2020 Massachusetts Avenue NW, Washington, DC 20036 USA

DREAM CATCHER

SPECIFICATIONS

Flag: USA
Rig: Schooner
Homeport: Key West, Florida
Normal cruising waters:
Florida Keys, Bahamas
Sparred length: 75'
LOA: 69'
LOD: 65'
LWL: 62'
Draft: 5'
Beam: 20'
Rig height: 73'
Freeboard: 5'
Sail area: 1,700 square feet
Tons: 49 GRT
Power: 130 John Deere
Hull: steel

Designed by marine architects Woodin and Marean from Maine, and built by Treworgy Yachts in Palm Coast, Florida in 1996, *Dream Catcher's* conception, design factors, and interior design came from Captain John Duke. John grew up on the waters of Biscayne Bay in Miami, Florida, has been USCG licensed since 1979, and has been sailing the waters of the lower Florida Keys, South Florida, and the Bahamas for 30 years. During this time, he has worked with scientific research groups, environmental groups, and has introduced hundreds of marine enthusiasts to the many wonders of the sea. The *Dream Catcher* provides sailing adventures designed to be informative for both environmental professionals and individuals interested in marine habitat. Ideal for large families and groups interested in participating in and learning all aspects of sailing and navigation, *Dream Catcher* is looking for groups that want to be part of an adventure!

Who sails: Students, families, groups and individuals of all ages
Program type: Sail training for volunteer crew and paying trainees; sea education in cooperation with accredited institutions and other organized groups; longboat rowing aboard *Aida*, a 32' longboat that is used on *Dream Catcher's* extended voyages
Designer: Woodin and Marean
Built: 1996: Hammocks, FL, Treworgy Yachts
Coast Guard certification: Passenger Vessel (Subchapter T)
Trainees-passengers: 49 daysails, 19 overnight
Contact: Captain John Duke, Coastal Sailing Adventures, Inc., 28555 Jolly Roger Drive, Little Torch Key, FL 33042 USA
Tel: 305-304-5100
E-mail: saildreamcatcher@mindspring.com
Website: http://www.sailingkeywestflorida.com

SPECIFICATIONS

Flag: USA
Rig: Barque, three-masted
Homeport: New London, Connecticut
Normal cruising waters: Atlantic Ocean, Pacific Ocean, Caribbean
Sparred length: 295'
LOA: 266' 8"
LWL: 231'
Draft: 17'
Beam: 40'
Rig height: 147' 4"
Sail area: 22,245 square feet
Tons: 2,186 GRT
Power: 1,000 HP diesel
Hull: steel

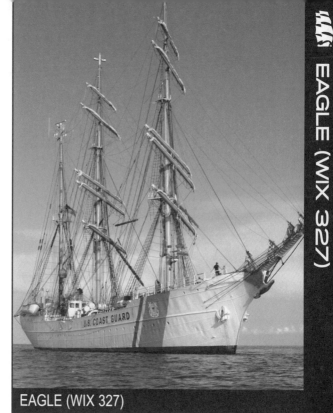

EAGLE (WIX 327)

One of five sister ships built for sail training in Germany in the 1930s, *Eagle* was included in reparations paid to the United States following World War II and the Coast Guard took her over as a training ship. Aboard the *Eagle*, cadets have a chance to put into practice the navigation, engineering, and other skills they are taught at the Coast Guard Academy. As underclassmen, they fill positions normally taken by the enlisted crew of a ship, including watches. They handle the more than 20,000 square feet of sail and more than 20 miles of rigging. Over 200 lines must be coordinated during a major ship maneuver, and the cadets must learn the name and function of each. As upperclassmen, they perform officer-level functions. For many, their tour of duty aboard the *Eagle* is their first experience of life at sea and it is here that they learn to serve as the leaders they will one day become in the Coast Guard. *Eagle* is safely maintained and operated by six officers and 49 crew who are stationed on board for two to three years at a time. This experienced core provides leadership and coaching to over 700 trainees and 60 short term temporary crew each year.

Who sails: US Coast Guard Academy cadets, US Coast Guard Officer candidates, and other USCG personnel
Program type: Seamanship training
Season: Year-round
Built: 1936: Hamburg, Germany, Blohm & Voss
Contact: Commanding Officer, USCGC EAGLE (WIX-327), 45 Mohegan Ave., New London, CT 06320 USA
Tel: 860-625-0831
Fax: 860-436-1659
Website: www.uscga.edu

ELISSA

SPECIFICATIONS

Flag: USA
Rig: Barque, three-masted
Homeport: Galveston, Texas
Normal cruising waters:
Coastal waters near Galveston
Sparred length: 205'
LOA: 155'
LOD: 150'
Draft: 10'
Beam: 28'
Rig height: 110'
Freeboard: 10'
Sail area: 12,000 square feet
Tons: 411 GRT
Power: 450 HP diesel
Hull: iron

In 1975, a rusted iron hulk lay in the waters of Piraeus, Greece. Nearly 100 years earlier, she had sailed the world's oceans as a proud square-rigged sailing ship. Cut down, leaking and decrepit, she waited a cable's length from the scrap yard. Today, *Elissa* remains one of the hallmarks of maritime preservation. Lovingly restored and maintained, she sails again, continuing a far longer life than most ships are ever granted. She tests her readiness annually in a series of sea trials amid the oil rigs and shrimpers off Galveston Island. Working under professional officers, her volunteer crew completes an extensive dockside-training program. As funds allow, she makes longer voyages.

Who sails: School groups from middle school through college; individuals of all ages
Program type: Sail training for crew and apprentices; sea education in maritime history based on informal,
in-house training; dockside interpretation
Season: April to November
Built: 1877: Aberdeen, Scotland, Alexander Hall and Sons Yard
Coast Guard certification: Cargo and Miscellaneous Goods (Subchapter I)
Crew: 40 **Trainees-passengers:** 85 daysails
Contact: Texas Seaport Museum/Galveston Historical Foundation, Pier 21, No. 8, Galveston, TX USA
Tel: 409-763-1877
Fax: 409-763-3037
E-mail: elissa@galvestonhistory.org
Website: www.tsm-elissa.org

SPECIFICATIONS

Flag: USA
Rig: Barque, three-masted (lateen mizzen)
Homeport: Manteo, North Carolina
Normal cruising waters: Inland sounds of North Carolina
Sparred length: 78'
LOA: 68' 6"
LOD: 55'
LWL: 59'
Draft: 8'
Beam: 16' 6"
Rig height: 65'
Sail area: 1,920 square feet
Tons: 97 GRT
Hull: wood

ELIZABETH II

Built with private funds to commemorate the 400th Anniversary of the English colonization of the America's, *Elizabeth II* is named for a vessel that sailed from Plymouth, England on the second of the three Roanoke voyages sponsored by Sir Walter Raleigh between 1584 and 1587. She probably carried marines, colonists and supplies to establish a military garrison to support England's claim to the New World. *Elizabeth II's* sail training program teaches volunteer crew about America's 16th century maritime heritage. In addition to classroom instruction and dockside training, crewmembers participate in the care and maintenance of the vessel. Voyages are scheduled during the spring and fall seasons. Sponsorship for the volunteer crew program is provided by the nonprofit Friends of *Elizabeth II*, Inc.

Who sails: Volunteer crew
Program type: Sail training for volunteer crew and apprentices; dockside interpretation
Season: Spring and fall
Designer: W. A. Baker and Stanley Potter
Built: 1983: Manteo, North Carolina, O. Lie-Nielsen, Creef-Davis Shipyard
Contact: Scott Stroh, Executive Director, Roanoke Island Festival Park, One Festival Park, Manteo, NC 27954 USA
Tel: 252-475-1500
Fax: 252-475-1507
E-mail: scott.stroh@ncmail.net
Website: www.roanokeisland.com

ERNESTINA

SPECIFICATIONS

Flag: USA
Rig: Gaff topsail schooner, two-masted
Homeport: New Bedford, Massachusetts
Normal cruising waters: dockside during restoration until 2009
Sparred length: 156'
LOA: 112'
LOD: 106'
LWL: 93'
Draft: 13'
Beam: 24' 3"
Rig height: 115'
Freeboard: 4'
Sail area: 8,323 square feet
Tons: 98 GRT
Power: 259 HP Cummins diesel
Hull: wood

Launched on February 1, 1894 in Essex, MA as the *Effie M. Morrissey,* the schooner became famous as a Gloucester Grand Banks fisherman, as an Arctic expeditionary vessel under the command of Captain Robert Abrams Bartlett, and as a World War II survey and supply vessel under Commander Alexander Forbes. After a fire in 1946, the *Morrissey* was raised and then purchased by Capt. Henrique Mendes who renamed her *Ernestina* to serve in the transatlantic Cape Verdean packet trade. In 1982 she was gifted by the Republic of Cape Verde to the U.S. The essence of *Ernestina's* educational mission today extends from the vessel's phenomenal and unique history. Aboard *Ernestina*, students of all ages use the ship as a platform to study the marine environment and human impacts during structured dockside programs. The *Ernestina* is presently raising funds to continue its restoration to so she can sail again in 2009.

Who sails: School groups from elementary through college and individuals of all ages
Program type: Dockside interpretation and educational programs and restoration projects
Season: dockside until 2009
Designer: George M. McClain
Built: 1894: Essex, MA, James and Tarr Shipyard
Crew: 11 **Trainees-passengers:** 65 - 80 daysails, 24 overnight
Coast Guard certification: Moored Attraction Vessel (while under restoration)
Contact: Paul J. Brawley, Executive Director, Schooner Ernestina Commission, State Pier, P.O. Box 2010, New Bedford, MA 02741-2010 USA
Tel: 508-992-4900
Fax: 508-984-7719
E-mail: Paul.Brawley@state.ma.us
Website: www.ernestina.org

Flag: Chile
Rig: Barquentine, 4-masted
Homeport: Valparaiso, Chile
Normal cruising waters:
Worldwide
Sparred length: 371'
Draft: 19' 8"
Beam: 42' 8"
Hull: steel

Photo and text by Thad Koza

ESMERALDA

The pride of the Chilean Navy, *Esmeralda* was built in Cadiz, Spain from plans used to build Spain's *Juan Sebastian de Elcano*. Both vessels were constructed from Camper & Nicholson design at the same yard, though some twenty-seven years apart. The only difference between these two elegant four-masters are the additional fore-and-aft sail on the *Sebastian's* foremast, designating her as a topsail schooner, and the slightly flatter angle of *Esmeralda's* bowsprit. Esmeralda was completed in 1954. Her distinctive figurehead represents a giant Andes condor, the national bird of Chile.

Program type: Sail training vessel of the Chilean Navy
Design: Camper & Nicholson
Built: 1952 – 1954, Cadiz, Spain
Contact: Embassy of the Republic of Chile, 1732 Massachusetts Avenu, NW, Washington, DC 20036 USA
Tel: 202-785-1746
Fax: 202-887-5579

Photo and text by Thad Koza

Flag: France
Rig: Topsail schooner
Homeport: Brest, France
Sparred length: 124'
Draft: 12'
Beam: 24'
Hull: wood

ETOILE

Along with her sister ship *La Belle Poule*, the schooner *Etoile* serves the French Navy in the training of future officers. Designed with the hull shape and the rigging of fishing vessels from Breton, *La Belle Poule* and *Etoile* were built in 1932 in the fishing port of Fecamp in northern Normandy, France. During World War II, both vessels relocated to Portsmouth, England, where they served the Free France Forces. They are permitted to fly the French ensign with the imposed Cross of Lorraine in recognition of their service during the war.

Program type: Sail training vessel of the French Navy
Built: 1932: Fecamp, Normandy, France
Contact: Embassy of France, 4101 Resevoir Road, NW, Washington, DC 20007 USA
Tel: 202-944-6000
Fax: 202-944-6166

SPECIFICATIONS

Flag: The Netherlands
Rig: Barque
Homeport: Amsterdam, The Netherlands
Normal cruising waters: Worldwide
Sparred length: 185'
LOA: 150'
LOD: 143'
LWL: 132'
Draft: 12'
Beam: 24'
Rig height: 109'
Freeboard: 4'
Sail area: 11,000 square feet
Tons: 303 GRT
Hull: steel

EUROPA

Europa was launched in Hamburg in 1911. Her construction had been ordered by the city of Hamburg for use as a lightship. In the seventies, she was bought by a German from Rendsburg and spent years lying at rest waiting to find out if a new owner had the financial means to pay for her costly face-lift. This new owner materialized as Harry Smit. The gutting and reconstruction of the barque *Europa* took eight years to complete. In the years since 1994, when she recommenced sailing, *Europa* has become famous among tall ship lovers as a ship which really *sails*. The crew of 10 to 12 professional seafarers tries to involve the passengers as much as possible in running and sailing the ship. With the motto "anything you may, nothing you must", the ship is sailed with or without the help of the passengers, many of whom have no seafaring experience. They stand watches, take turns at steering or as lookout, make up or set sails, bake bread, scrub the decks and practice traditional seafaring/seamanship skills. For a few weeks of each year, the ship sails as the training ship of the "Enkhuizen Nautical College" which trains people as mates and captains of coastal and ocean sailing vessels.

Who sails: Youth trainees, individuals, families, and groups of all ages
Program type: Sail training for paying trainees; fully accredited sea education in maritime history; special expeditions; dockside interpretation during port visits
Season: Year-round
Built: 1911: Hamburg, Germany, Stülcken
Crew: 12 **Trainees-passengers:** 100 daysails, 50 overnight
Contact: Rederij Bark EUROPA, PO Box 23183, 3001 KD Rotterdam The Netherlands
Tel: +31 (0) 10 281 0990
Fax: +31 (0) 10 281 0991
E-mail: info@barkeuropa.com
Website: www.barkeuropa.com

Photo by Lee Uran

EXY JOHNSON

EXY JOHNSON

SPECIFICATIONS

Flag: USA
Rig: Brigantine
Homeport:
Los Angeles, California
Normal cruising waters:
Southern California and offshore islands
Sparred length: 110' 8"
LOA: 90'
LOD: 81' 7"
LWL: 72' 6"
Draft: 11'
Beam: 21' 9"
Rig height: 87' 8"
Sail area: 4,540 square feet
Tons: 99 GRT
Power: 315 HP diesel
Hull: wood

The Los Angeles Maritime Institute (LAMI) launched the twin brigantines, *Exy Johnson* and *Irving Johnson,* in 2002 for the TopSail Youth Program. With ships named in honor of sail training pioneers and seven-time circumnavigators and with youth crew aboard their shi,*Yankee,* TopSail recognizes that the shipboard environment is challenging yet nurturing, encouraging exploration and self-reliance. TopSail is notably effective with youth who are not yet coping well with the demands of society and are at risk of dropping out of school and giving up. The 2007 research findings from the University of Edinburgh-Sail Training International study describe TopSail as "highly successful, developing personal and social confidence, and the ability to work together with others." With the premise that 'school is where the kids are...' , TopSail youth engage in building cooperation, courage, confidence and character in the real-world classroom of the sea. LAMI is a volunteer-driven, youth-focused, educational 'family' organization. We welcome the skills and enthusiasm of people of all ages and all walks of life to sail with youth, maintain the tall ships, and be involved in many other ways.

Who sails: Youth/school groups from diverse communities, mostly from middle schools in urban areas
Program type: Educational sailing adventures for youth and adult groups
Season: Year-round
Coast Guard certification: Sailing School Vessel (Subchapter R), Passenger vessel (Subchapter T)
Contact: Captain Jim Gladson, President, Los Angeles Maritime Institute, Berth 84, Foot of Sixth Street, San Pedro, CA 90731 USA
Tel: 310-833-6055
Fax: 310-548-2055
Website: www.LAMITopSail.org

Flag: Canada
Rig: Brigantine
Homeport: Ottawa, Ontario, Canada
Normal cruising waters: Great Lakes and East Coast (summer), Caribbean (winter)
Sparred length: 110'
LOD: 82'
LOA: 62'
Draft: 6'
Beam: 24' 6"
Rig height: 80'
Freeboard: 8'
Sail area: 4,000 square feet
Tons: 124 GRT
Power: 235 HP diesel
Hull: fiberglass on steel

FAIR JEANNE

Designed and built in 1982 by the late Captain Thomas G. Fuller, *Fair Jeanne* was first sailed as a private yacht. Captain Fuller was one of Canada's most decorated WWII naval war heroes, earning the name "Pirate of the Adriatic". His wartime experience taught him the value of instilling confidence and resourcefulness in our youth while at sea. More than 100,000 nautical miles and, 22 years later, *Fair Jeanne* is now in service as a sail training vessel for Bytown Brigantine, a non-profit charitable organization dedicated to providing adventure through the time honored traditions inherent in square rigged sailing. During the summer months we provide programs for youth 14-19 years old, and during the spring and fall we also provide programs for school groups, adults, and Elderhostel.

Who sails: Middle school, high school, college, adults, Elderhostel
Program type: Sail training for paying trainees; overnight voyages; sea education in maritime history with formal organizations and as informal, in-house programming; dockside interpretation
Season: Spring, summer and fall (winter sailing in 2006/2007)
Designer: Captain Thomas G. Fuller
Built: 1982: Ottawa, Ontario, Canada, T. G. Fuller
Certification: Sailing School Vessel, inland/near coastal
Crew: 6 high school and university officers **Trainees-passengers:** 50 daysails, 24 overnight
Contact: Bytown Brigantine, Inc., 2700 Queensview Drive, Ottawa, Ontario K2B 8H6 Canada
Tel: 613-596-6258
Fax: 613-596-5947
E-mail: tallshipinfo@tallshipsadventure.org
Website: www.tallshipsadventure.org

Photo by Thad Koza

FALKEN

SPECIFICATIONS

Flag: Sweden
Rig: Schooner
Homeport: Karlskrona, Sweden
Sparred length: 129'
Draft: 13' 9"
Beam: 23'
Hull: steel

Falken and her sister ship *Gladan* are twin schooners built in 1947, in the same yard and according to the same plans. Differentiated only by their sail numbers, these two vessels train future officers of the Swedish Royal Navy, as they have since their commissioning.

Program type: Sail training vessel of the Swedish Royal Navy
Built: 1947
Contact: Embassy of Sweden, 1501 M Street, NW, Suite 900, Washington, DC 20005-1702 USA
Tel: 202-467-2600
Fax: 202-467-2699

SPECIFICATIONS

Flag: USA
Rig: Chebacco schooner
Homeport: Salem, MA
Sparred Length: 70'
LOA: 60'
LOD: 52'
LWL: 49'
Freeboard: 5'
Draft: 6'4"
Beam: 15'
Rig Height: 70'
Sail Area: 1200 square feet
Tons: 29 GRT
Power: 160 HP diesel
Hull: white oak

FAME

Fame is a replica of a successful Salem privateer from the War of 1812. The original *Fame* was a Chebacco-style fishing schooner that was converted to privateering at the outbreak of war. She was one of the first American privateers to put to sea, and one of the first to bring back a prize. She captured 21 vessels — both British merchantmen and American smugglers — before being lost in the Bay of Fundy in 1814. Her captured crew was involved in the infamous Dartmoor prison riot of 1815. Our *Fame* is a traditional double-sawn-frame vessel, framed and planked in native white oak by Harold Burnham of Essex, MA in 2003. *Fame* is now based at Pickering Wharf in Salem, where she carries the paying public on 90-minute cruises around historic Salem Sound. For much more information on *Fame*, please visit our website at www.SchoonerFame.com.

Who sails: Everyone
Program Type: Public day sails; private charters; summer day camp for children; sail training; sea education in maritime history; dockside interpretation
Season: May through October
Designer: H. A. Burnham
Built 2003: Essex, MA, H.A. Burnham
Coast Guard certification: Passenger Vessel (Subchapter T)
Crew: 2 **Trainees-passengers:** 40 daysails
Contact: Captain Mike Rutstein, Pennant Enterprises, 73 Middleton Road, Boxford, MA 01921 USA
Tel: 978- 729-7600
Fax: 978- 561-3021
E-mail: SchoonerFame@aol.com
Website: www.SchoonerFame.com

FAREWELL

FAREWELL

SPECIFICATIONS

Flag: USA
Rig: Topsail schooner
Homeport: Dundalk, Maryland
Normal cruising waters:
Chesapeake Bay,
East Coast of US
Sparred length: 47'
LOD: 40'
LWL: 30'
Draft: 4' 9"
Beam: 10' 6"
Sail area: 1,000 square feet
Tons: 9 GRT
Power: 25 HP diesel
Hull: fiberglass

Peter Van Dine designed *Farewell* and traded the design with Andy Merrill for guitar lessons for he and his wife. Over a two-year period Andy built *Farewell* in his backyard in Annapolis, MD and launched her in 1972. *Farewell* was home to Andy and his family until 1982. The second owner purchased *Farewell* in 1994 to use as a coastal sail training vessel for three pre-teen sons. In 1996, the owner and the three boys cruised from Annapolis, MD to Camden, ME. The ship competed in the Great Chesapeake Bay Schooner Race each year from 1994 to 1998. In early 1999, her present owners, Captain Linda Meakes and her husband, Mike, purchased *Farewell*. During the past several years, they have participated in ASTA events and several maritime festivals and celebrations, including the homecoming of the USS *Constellation*, the Baltimore Preakness Schooner Race, and the Leukemia & Lymphoma Society Bridge to Bridge race. They also continued the tradition of competing in the Great Chesapeake Bay Schooner Race, placing no less than third with stiff competition in very close races. Future plans include participating in ASTA events as well as other educational programs to promote sail training and maritime traditions and history.

Who sails: Groups and individuals of all ages
Program type: Sail training for paying trainees; sea education in maritime history; passenger day sails and overnight passages; dockside interpretation
Season: April through November
Designer: P. Van Dine
Built: 1972: Andy Merrill
Crew: 6
Contact: Captain Linda Meakes, 4414 Falls Bridge Drive, Unit K, Baltimore, MD 21211 USA
Tel: 410-961-4054
E-mail: schoonergirl@comcast.net
Website: www.geocities.com/schoonerfarewell

Flag: USA
Rig: Brig
Homeport:
Gloucester, Massachusetts
Sparred length: 72'
LOA: 55'
LWL: 49'
Draft: 6'
Beam: 18'
Rig height: 55'
Sail area: 3,000 square feet
Hull: wood

Photo by Thad Koza

FORMIDABLE

Formidable is inspected by the Coast Guard and permitted to carry up to 49 passengers on day trips. They offer an extensive day charter schedule, including fund-raising for charities. *Formidable* is rigged as a brigantine. Her main mast carries the spanker and her foremast carries square sails, fore tops'l, and fore course, as well as several jibs and stays'ls.

Program type: Day sails including fundraising trips for nonprofit organizations; military reenactments
Contact: Captain Keating Wilcox, Longmeadow Way, Box 403, Hamilton, MA 01936-0403 USA
Tel: 866-921-9674
Fax: 978-468-1954
E-mail: kwillcox@shore.net
Website: www.tallshipformidable.com

FRIENDS GOOD WILL

SPECIFICATIONS

Flag: USA
Rig: Square topsail sloop
Homeport:
South Haven, Michigan
Normal cruising waters:
Upper Great Lakes
Sparred Length: 101'
LOD: 56' 3"
Draft: 8' 9"
Beam: 16' 10"
Rig Height: 82'
Sail area: 3,180 square feet
Tons: 49.2 GRT
Power: diesel
Hull: wood

"We have met the enemy and they are ours..." -Commander Oliver Hazard Perry, U.S.N., Battle of Lake Erie, September 10, 1813. This famous dispatch, dashed off within an hour after the great guns fell silent, went on to reference a merchant sloop turned man-o-war. That sloop was *Friends Good Will.* The Michigan Maritime Museum launched a replica of this fateful vessel in 2004. Scarano Boatbuilding, Inc. of Albany, New York, designed and built *Friends Good Will*, to be rigged and sailed by Museum volunteers. The vessel serves as an historic flagship for the preservation of traditional maritime skills. The Michigan Maritime Museum is developing programs and curriculum, utilizing its Padnos Boat Shed as a rig shop and its ample exhibit space so to assist in educating members, visitors, school groups of all ages and special tours about Michigan's maritime history and culture. Combining these resources with dockside interpretation and a day sail program throughout the summer, *Friends Good Will* employs traditional materials and skills to keep Michigan's rich maritime heritage alive.

Who sails: Museum members, school groups, individuals and families
Program Type: Sail Training for museum members and crew; passenger day sails; dockside interpretation, historical reenactment at home port and during port visits; education in history, geography, navigation, marine science for school groups of all ages. Affiliated with Sea Scout Ship #5191, South Haven, Michigan.
Designer: Scarano Boatbuilding, Inc.
Built: 2004: Albany, NY, Scarano Boatbuilding, Inc.
Coast Guard certification: Passenger Vessel (Subchapter T)
Crew: 13 **Trainees-passengers:** 28 daysails
Contact: Ellen Sprouls, Executive Director, Michigan Maritime Museum, 260 Dyckman Avenue, South Haven, Michigan 49090 USA
Tel: 269-637-8078 **Fax:** 269-637-1594
E-mail: ellen@michiganmaritimemuseum.org
Website: www.MichiganMaritimeMuseum.org

SPECIFICATIONS

Flag: Rig: Full-rigged ship
Homeport: Salem, Massachusetts
Normal cruising waters:
Massachusetts Bay, Buzzards Bay
Sparred length: 171'
LOA: 116'
LOD: 104'
LWL: 99'
Draft: 11' 3"
Beam: 30'
Rig height: 112'
Freeboard: 10'
Sail area: 9,409 square feet
Tons: 99 GRT
Power: twin 300 HP diesels
Hull: wood

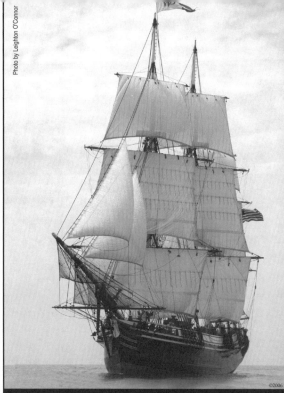

Photo by Leighton O'Connor

©2006 Leig

FRIENDSHIP OF SALEM

Friendship, a full size replica of a Salem East Indiaman, built for the National Park Service and berthed at Salem Maritime National Historic Site in Salem, Massachusetts, was launched in August 1998. Although she represents a specific vessel built in Salem in 1797, she is typical of a class of commercial carriers commonly employed in both the East India and transatlantic trades during the early years of the new American republic. Her historic predecessor is credited with 15 voyages to the Far East, South America, Mediterranean, and northern Europe. She had the misfortune of being taken as a prize of war by the British Royal Navy on a return voyage from Archangel, Russia, in 1812. Sold by the British government in 1813, her ultimate fate remains a mystery. Today's *Friendship* is built from wood laminates and solid timbers and was designed as a passenger carrying and sail training vessel while exhibiting the look and function of an historic vessel. *Friendship* is accessible to the public for dockside tours.

Who sails: When fully certified, *Friendship* will welcome all age groups through school programs as well as general public on day sails and weekly programmed trips. Elderhostel programs will be part of the formal offerings.
Program type: Dockside programs and hands on interpretation as an historic site exhibit; informal sea education in maritime history. Special events at other ports and dockside leasing for special events at Salem.
Season: Open for tours all year
Designer: Bay Marine, Inc., Barrington, RI **Built:** 1998: Scarano Boats, Albany, NY; 1999-2002: Salem, MA., Dion Yacht Yard, NPS & USS Constitution Naval Detachment
Coast Guard certification: Sailing School Vessel (Subchapter R), Passenger Vessel (Subchapter T) pending
Crew: 5 **Trainees-passengers:** 20 daysails
Contact: Colleen Bruce, Project Manager, Salem Maritime National Historic Site, 174 Derby Street, Salem, MA 01915 USA
Tel: 978-740-1694 **Fax:** 978-740-1685
E-mail: colleen_bruce@nps.gov
Website: www.nps.gov/SAMA and www.salemweb.com/frndship

FRYDERYK CHOPIN

SPECIFICATIONS

Flag: Poland
Rig: Brig
Homeport: Szczecin, Poland
Normal cruising waters: Worldwide
Sparred length: 181'
Draft: 13'
Beam: 28'
Rig height: 111'
Sail area: 12,912 square feet
Tons: 306 GRT
Power: 520 HP SCANIA diesel
Hull: steel

The American Foundation for Education Under Sail Inc. (AFEUS) is an American based sister company to West Island College International. AFEUS seeks to create an independent school network, as well as a university network, that will allow students to spend a semester on board a tall ship as a study aboard and experiential learning extension of their existing curriculum. AFEUS provides the perfect combination of travel study, exploration, academic enrichment and independence that nurtures each participant's academic experience and hones leadership potential while in university or secondary school. Challenging academics come alive through the interactive learning opportunities afforded in the many exotic ports that we visit. Classes are balanced by the adventure and excitement of sailing a tall ship to four different continents. Students will also engage in a rewarding humanitarian project, in Senegal, West Africa.
The AFEUS program will take place onboard the *Fryderyk Chopin*, a brig built in 1992 with the specific purpose of taking young people to sea for extended academic voyages.

Who sails: University and secondary school students
Program type: Full-curriculum academics
Designer: Zygmund Choren **Built:** 1992: Gdansk Shipyard
Contact: American Foundation for Education Under Sail Inc., Terry D. Davies, President, 391 Normandy Road, Morrsville, North Carolina 28117 USA
Tel: 704-664-7429
E-mail: discovery@classafloat.com

Flag: USA
Rig: Barquentine, three-masted
Homeport:
Philadelphia, Pennsylvania
Normal cruising waters:
Delaware River and the
Atlantic Coast
Sparred length: 177'
LOA: 150'
LOD: 140'
LWL: 133'
Draft: 17'
Beam: 26"
Rig height: 100'
Sail area: 8,910 square feet
Tons: 299 GRT
Power: diesel
Hull: wood, copper clad

GAZELA

The wooden barkentine, *Gazela Primeiro*, was originally built to fish for cod in the Grand Banks. Now owned and operated by the Philadelphia Ship Preservation Guild, a nonprofit volunteer organization, the *Gazela* sails as a goodwill ambassador for the Commonwealth of Pennsylvania and the Ports of Philadelphia, Pennsylvania and Camden, New Jersey. Our mission extends beyond historic preservation to community outreach through such activities as maritime education of disadvantaged youth. *Gazela* has been featured in several major motion pictures including "Interview with the Vampire" and "The Widow of St. Pierre", as well as several documentaries including "The Irish in America".

Who sails: Volunteers who support the Philadelphia Ship Preservation Guild
Program type: Sail training for crew and apprentices; sea education based on informal in-house programming; dockside interpretation both in homeport and on out-port visits
Built: 1883: Cacihas, Portugal, major rebuild 1901: Setubal, Portugal
Crew: 35 (volunteer)
Contact: Philadelphia Ship Preservation Guild, 301 S.Columbus Blvd., Philadelphia, PA 19106 USA
Tel: 215-238-0280
Fax: 215-238-0281
E-mail: office@gazela.org or pspgoffice@gazela.org
Website: www.gazela.org

GERONIMO

SPECIFICATIONS

Flag: USA
Rig: Sloop
Homeport:
Newport, Rhode Island
Normal cruising waters:
North Atlantic and Caribbean
Sparred length: 69' 8"
LOA: 69' 8"
LOD: 68'
LWL: 53' 11"
Draft: 6' 8" – 13' 5"
Beam: 18' 7"
Rig height: 85' 6"
Sail area: 2,091 square feet
Freeboard: 5'
Tons: 53 GRT
Power: diesel
Hull: fiberglass

The sailing vessel *Geronimo* sails year round between the Canadian maritime and the greater Carribean. Trainees are taught Nautical Science and Oceanography/Marine Biology while on board. During the academic year, *Geronimo* carries students from St. George's School on six-week long voyages. During these trips, the students stand watch, learn the intricacies of handling a modern sailing vessel and conduct research on sea turtles working in conjunction with the Archie Carr Center for Sea Turtle Research University of Florida, Gainsville. In the summer months, the vessel makes three shorter trips along the east coast. Summer trainees range in age from high school to adult.

Who sails: High school students through adults
Program type: Marine/nautical science
Season: Year-round
Designer: Ted Hood Design Group
Built: 1998: Portsmouth, RI, New England Boatworks
Coast Guard certification: Sailing School Vessel (Subchapter R)
Crew: 2 **Trainees-passengers:** 8
Contact: Captain Deborah Hayes, Program Director, St. George's School, 372 Purgatory Road, PO Box 1910, Newport, RI 02840 USA
Tel: 401-842-6702
Fax: 401-842-6696
E-mail: Deborah_Hayes@stgeorges.edu
Website: www.sailgeronimo.org

SPECIFICATIONS

Flag: Sweden
Rig: Schooner
Homeport: Karlskrona, Sweden
Sparred length: 129'
Draft: 13' 9"
Beam: 23'
Hull: steel

Photo by Thad Koza

GLADAN

Gladan and her sister ship *Falken* are twin schooners built in 1947, in the same yard and according to the same plans. Differentiated only by their sail numbers, these two vessels train future officers of the Swedish Royal Navy as they have since their commissioning.

Program type: Sail training vessel of the Swedish Royal Navy
Built: 1947
Contact: Embassy of Sweden, 1501 M Street, NW, Suite 900, Washington, DC 20005-1702
Tel: 202-467-2600
Fax: 202-467-2699

GLENN L. SWETMAN

SPECIFICATIONS

Flag: USA
Rig: Gaff topsail schooner, two-masted
Homeport: Biloxi, Mississippi
Normal cruising waters: Coastwise Gulf of Mexico
Sparred length: 76'
LOA: 65'
LOD: 50'
LWL: 47'
Draft: 4' 10"
Beam: 17'
Sail area: 2,400 square feet
Freeboard: 4' 6"
Tons: 21 GRT
Power: 4-71 Detroit diesel
Hull: wood, Juniper

The *Glenn L. Swetman* is the first of two replica Biloxi oyster schooners built by the Biloxi Schooner Project under the auspices of the Maritime and Seafood Industry Museum. She is available for charter trips in the Mississippi Sound and to the barrier islands, Cat Island, Horn Island, and Ship Island. Walk-up day sailing trips are made when she is not under charter. Groups can learn about the maritime and seafood heritage of the Gulf Coast, and about the vessels that began Biloxi's seafood industry. The *Glenn L. Swetman* is an integral part of the museum's Sea and Sail Summer Camp, and sailing classes are also offered through local colleges. *Glenn L. Swetman* also accommodates weddings, parties, and Elderhostel and school groups.

Who sails: Groups and individuals of all ages
Program type: Sail training for volunteer and paying trainees; sea education in maritime history, marine science, and ecology for college students and adults in cooperation with accredited institutions, organized groups, and as informal in-house programming; children's summer camp; private charters
Season: Year-round
Designer: William Holland
Built: 1989: Biloxi, Mississippi, William T. Holland
Coast Guard certification: Passenger Vessel (Subchapter T)
Crew: 3 **Trainees-passengers:** 49 daysails
Contact: Maritime and Seafood Industry Museum of Biloxi, PO Box 1907, Biloxi, MS 39533 USA
Tel: 228-435-6320
Fax: 228-435-6309
E-mail: schooner@maritimemuseum.org
Website: www.maritimemuseum.org

SPECIFICATIONS

Flag: Colombia
Rig: Barque, 3-masted
Homeport: Cartegena, Colombia
Normal cruising waters: Worldwide
Sparred length: 249' 4"
LOA: 212'
LOD: 189'
LWL: 184'
Draft: 14' 9"
Beam: 34' 9"
Rig height: 126' 4"
Sail area: 15,075 square feet
Freeboard: 21' 7"
Tons: 934 GRT
Power: twin 256 HP KV
Hull: steel

GLORIA

Built in Bilbao, Spain for the Colombian Navy in 1966, the three masted barque *Gloria* is used as a school ship for the cadets of the Colombian Naval Academy. She carries a compliment of 150 men and women, ranging from enlisted to midshipmen and officers. The cruises are aimed at training officers in their third year at the Naval Academy, to implement their academic knowledge in the areas of star navigation, seamanship, leadership and teambuilding. *Gloria* is a proud goodwill ambassador of the Colombian Navy. During her service has made 46 cruises, navigating over 500,000 nautical miles, visiting 143 different ports around the world.

Who sails: Midshipmen, enlisted and officers of the Colombian Navy
Program type: Sail training vessel of the Colombian Navy
Season: Year-round
Designer: Sener
Built: 1969: Bilbao, Spain, A. T. Celaya
Certification: Colombian Naval Vessel
Crew: 69 **Trainees-passengers:** 80 students
Contact: Naval Operations Director, Navy of Colombia, Avenida El Dorado Carrera 52 CAN., Bogotá, D.C., Cundinamarca, 01-110 Colombia
Tel: 751-266-0189 or 751-266-0288
Fax: 751-266-0448
E-mail: jemnm3@armada.mil.co
Website: www.armada.mil.co

GODSPEED

SPECIFICATIONS

Flag: USA
Rig: Bark, three-masted (lateen mizzen)
Homeport: Jamestown Settlement, Virginia
Normal cruising waters: Chesapeake Bay, US East Coast
Sparred length: 88'
LOA: 74'
LOD: 65'
LWL: 56'
Draft: 7'
Beam: 17'
Rig height: 72'
Sail area: 2,420 square feet
Freeboard: 7' 6"
Power: twin 115 HP diesel
Hull: wood

Godspeed is a full-scale re-creation of one of the three ships that brought America's first permanent English colonists to Virginia in 1607. Together with the *Susan Constant* and *Discovery*, *Godspeed* is on exhibit at Jamestown Settlement, a living-history museum of 17th-century Virginia, and hosts about a half-million visitors every year. Jamestown Settlement is administered by the Jamestown-Yorktown Foundation, a Virginia state agency. Built at Rockport Marine in Maine and commissioned at Jamestown Settlement in 2006, *Godspeed* is a third-generation re-creation. The first was built for the 1957 350th-anniversary commemoration of the founding of Jamestown. *Godspeed, Susan Constant* and *Discovery* are based on the historically documented tonnages of the original ships and 17th-century principles of tonnage measurement. With a crew of staff and volunteers, *Godspeed* and *Susan Constant* periodically sail to other ports in the Chesapeake Bay region to participate in commemorative and community events and host educational programs. A volunteer sail-training program is offered to individuals 18 and older.

Who sails: Crew consisting of Jamestown Settlement staff and volunteers. Age 18 years and older
Program type: Sail training and dockside interpretation
Season: Year-round
Designer: Tri-Coastal Marine
Built: 2006: Rockport Marine, Inc., Rockport, Maine
Coast Guard certification: Moored Attraction Vessel
Crew: 12 **Trainees-passengers:** 20
Contact: Capt. Eric Speth, Maritime Program Manager, Jamestown Settlement, PO Box 1607, Williamsburg, VA 23187 USA
Tel: 757-253-4838
Fax: 757-253-7350
Website: www.historyisfun.org

SPECIFICATIONS

Flag: Germany
Rig: Barque
Homeport: Kiel, Germany
Normal cruising waters:
Worldwide
Sparred length: 293'
Draft: 15' 6"
Beam: 39'
Sail Area: 21,140 square feet
Hull: steel

Photo by Lewis Notarianni

GORCH FOCK II

Built from the same plans and in the same shipyard (Blohm & Voss in Hamburg, Germany) as the original, *Gorch Fock II* boasts contemporary safety features and the latest navigational equipment. She is an eminent replacement for her namesake (now the training vessel *Tovarishch* from Ukraine). Since her launch in 1958, *Gorch Fock II* has logged thousands of nautical miles in her twice-yearly voyages and has hosted more than ten thousand cadets for training cruises. The barque is named for a popular German writer of sea stories, Hans Kinau (1880 – 1916), who used the pseudonym Gorch Fock (fock means "foresail" in German). Kinau became part of the romantic mythology of the sea when he perished aboard the cruiser *Weisbaden*, which was sunk during the Battle of Jutland on 31 May 1916. The training vessel of the German Navy, *Gorch Fock II* is a proud symbol of Germany's distinguished sailing and shipbuilding traditions.

Program type: Sail training vessel of the German Navy.
Built: 1958: Hamburg, Germany, Blohm & Voss
Crew: 73 **Trainees-passengers:** 200
Contact: Embassy of the Federal Republic of Germany, 4645 Reservoir Road, NW, Washington, DC 20007 USA
Tel: 202-298-8140
Fax: 202-298-4249

Photo by Fred LeBlanc

GRACE BAILEY

SPECIFICATIONS

Flag: USA
Rig: Gaff schooner
Homeport: Camden, Maine
Normal cruising waters: Penobscot Bay – off the coast of mid-coast Maine
Sparred length: 123'
LOD: 81'
LWL: 72'
Draft: 6' board up, 16' board down
Beam: 24'
Rig height: 70'
Sail area: 4,985 square feet
Freeboard: 4'
Tons: 58 GRT
Power: carries neither inboard engines nor powered deck machinery, propulsion when needed by 14' yawl boat w/diesel motor.
Hull: wood

The *Grace Bailey* was built in 1882 by Oliver Perry Smith in Patchoque, New York. Her work included carrying lumber from South Carolina and Georgia and in the mid 1800s was registered for foreign trade and made voyages to the West Indies. In 1906 she was renamed the *Mattie* and sailed as a bay coaster in Maine waters carrying general cargo. She also carried granite to New York City, for the Post Office Building and for Grand Central Station. Capt. Frank Swift chartered her in 1939 to be used as a cruise schooner and soon was purchased and chosen as the flagship of his growing Windjammer Cruise fleet. The *Grace Bailey* was totally restored in 1990, by present owners Capt. Ray & Ann Williamson, and rechristened with her original name and designated a National Historic Landmark. She carries 29 passengers and does five-day and weekend cruises off the coast of Maine and is one of five surviving two-masted coasting schooners in the USA. She is a pure sailing vessel with cotton sails and all natural fiber running rigging. The full time crew of four includes captain, cook, first mate and deckhand. The fifth crew position is an apprentice, which rotates every month.

Who sails: 16 and up (any age with full boat charter)
Program type: cruising
Season: End of May thru early October
Designer: Smith
Built: 1882: Oliver Perry Smith, Patchoque, New York
Coast Guard certification: Passenger Vessel (Subchapter T)
Crew: 5 **Passengers-trainees:** 49 daysails, 29 overnight
Contact: Captain Ray and Ann Williamson, owners, Maine Windjammer Cruises®, PO Box 617, Camden, Maine 04843 USA
Tel: 207-236-2938 – Reservations 800-736-7981
E-mail: sail@MaineWindjammerCruises.com
Website: www.MaineWindjammerCruises.com

Flag: Ecuador
Rig: Barque
Homeport: Guayquil, Ecuador
Normal cruising waters:
Worldwide
Sparred length: 257'
LOA: 221'
LOD: 218'
LWL: 184'
Draft: 15' 4"
Beam: 34' 9"
Sail area: 15,784 square feet
Power: diesel
Hull: steel

GUAYAS

Guayas was built in the Celaya Shipyard in Bilbao, Spain. She is named after the Chief of Huancavilcas, a native culture in the Ecuadorian coastal region. Commissioned in 1977, the *Guayas* is proud to serve as a goodwill ambassador for the Ecuadorian Navy. The ship carries a complement of 16 officers, 43 midshipmen, and 94 enlisted men, including the ship's band. During a cruise, considered one semester at the Ecuadorian Naval Academy, midshipmen apply, in a very challenging environment, theoretical principals of navigation, seamanship and other subjects learned in the classroom.

Who sails: Ecuadorian Naval Academy cadets
Program type: Sail training for Ecuadorian Naval Academy cadets
Season: Year-round
Designer: Celaya
Built: 1976: Bilbao, Spain, Celaya Shipyard
Certification: Ecuadorian Naval Vessel
Crew: 76
Contact: Naval Attaché, Embassy of Ecuador, 2535 15th Street NW, Washington, DC 20009 USA
Tel: 202-265-7674
Fax: 202-667-3482

Photo by Bruce Blackstone

SPECIFICATIONS

Flag: USA
Rig: Viking faering boat
Homeport: Oakley, Maryland
Normal cruising waters:
East Coast and Chesapeake Bay
LOA: 21'
Draft: 1'
Beam: 5'
Rig height: 10'
Sail area: 80 square feet
Freeboard: 1'
Tons: 200 lbs
Hull: wood

GYRFALCON

Gyrfalcon is a copy of one of the faering (four-oared) boats buried with the *Gokstad* ship in Norway in the 9th century. She was built by the boat-building program at the Hampton Mariner's Museum, now the North Carolina Maritime Museum in Beaufort, North Carolina, under the direction of Geoffrey Scofield. *Gyrfalcon* is often seen at cultural, waterfront, community and boat festivals, historic reenactment events, and school demonstrations. She also participates in living history events in concert with the Markland Medieval Mercenary Militia's Viking reenactment camps, where the public enjoys the spectacle of crews, dressed in medieval style clothing and armor, offering historic interpretation. As an enticement to school children and adults to discover more about the Viking Age, *Gyrfalcon* has often spent off-season time on display at area libraries and schools. The *Gyrfalcon*, and her consort, *Sae Hrafn*, are both owned and operated by the Longship Company, Ltd., a member-supported, nonprofit educational association.

Who sails: School groups from elementary through college; individuals of all ages
Program type: Sail training for volunteer crew and apprentices; sea education in maritime history based on informal-in-house programming; dockside interpretation
Season: March to November
Designer: Traditional Norse design
Built: 1981: Beaufort, NC, Hampton Mariners Museum (now the North Carolina Maritime Museum - http://www.ah.dcr.state.nc.us/sections/maritime/)
Coast Guard certification: Uninspected vessel
Crew: 1-4 **Trainees-passengers:** 1-3
Contact: Longship Company, Ltd., 38825 Burch Road, Avenue, MD 20609 USA
Tel: 301-390-4089
E-mail: longshipco@hotmail.com
Website: www.longshipco.org

H. M. KRENTZ

SPECIFICATIONS

Flag: USA
Rig: Skipjack/sloop
Homeport: Potomac River, Maryland
Normal cruising waters: Chesapeake Bay
Sparred length: 70'
LOA: 54'
LOD: 48'
LWL: 45'
Draft: 4'8"
Beam: 16'
Rig height: 65'
Sail area: 1,850 square feet
Tons: 8 GRT
Power: 150 HP diesel; yawl boat
Hull: wood

One of the last skipjacks to be built, and still commercially dredging oysters during the winter months (November – March), the *H. M. Krentz* offers day sails on the Chesapeake's Eastern Shore waters near St. Michaels, Maryland, from April through October. Get the feel of a true working vessel and learn about the history of the working fleet of sailing vessels on the Chesapeake Bay. Experience dragging for oysters and then explore the ecology and economic development of the Chesapeake region through discussing the past and present status of this once abundant natural resource. What we can learn about ourselves and about our surrounding world through sailing is what makes the present the greatest age of sail. By working with the technologies and traditions of the past, perhaps we can have a better vision for the future. Since 1972, Captain Ed Farley has been a commercial oysterman and has worked to preserve several of the working skipjacks. Since 1985, he has been sharing his life experience with school children, business leaders, politicians and family groups.

Who sails: School groups from elementary through college, as well as families and individuals of all ages
Program type: Sail training for professional and volunteer crew/trainees; sea education in marine science, maritime history and ecology as informal in-house programming; dockside interpretation while in port
Season: Mid-April to late October
Designer: Krentz/Skipjack
Coast Guard certification: Passenger Vessel (Subchapter T)
Crew: 1 **Trainees-passengers:** 32
Contact: Captain Ed Farley, Chesapeake Skipjack Sailing Tours, LLC, PO Box 582, St. Michaels, MD 21663 USA
Tel: 410-745-6080
E-mail: hmkrentz@bluecrab.org
Website: www.oystercatcher.com

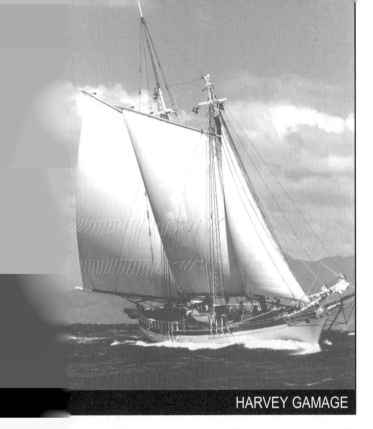

SPECIFICATIONS

Flag: USA
Rig: Gaff topsail schooner, two-masted
Homeport: Boothbay Harbor, Maine
Normal cruising waters: North Atlantic Ocean and Caribbean Sea, Canada to South America
Sparred length: 131'
LOA: 95'
LOD: 90'
LWL: 85'
Draft: 9' 7"
Beam: 24'
Freeboard: 7'
Rig height: 91'
Sail area: 4,200 square feet
Tons: 94 GRT
Power: 220 HP diesel
Hull: wood

HARVEY GAMAGE

Owned by the Ocean Classroom Foundation, the schooner *Harvey Gamage* sails on programs of education under sail for the youth of America. Programs range from a four month semester-at-sea to week-long programs with schools and youth groups. Trainees sail the ship and learn traditional seamanship skills under the captain and crew, while they explore maritime subjects with the onboard academic staff. The Ocean Classroom program is a semester-at-sea for qualified high school students, fully accredited by Proctor Academy. The voyage covers more than 4,000 nautical miles, connecting South American shores to the Canadian Maritimes. Students live and work as sailors on a true voyage of discovery, while they study maritime history, maritime literature, marine science, applied mathematics, and navigation. Ocean Classroom is offered Fall, Spring, and summer terms. Other programs include SEAmester (a complete semester-at-sea for college credit), OceanBound (for high school and college students), and Summer Seafaring Camp (for teens age 13 – 16). The Ocean Classroom Foundation also owns and operates the schooners *Spirit of Massachusetts and Westward.*

Who sails: Individuals and school groups from middle school through college; affiliated institutions include Proctor Academy, University of Massachusetts/Dartmouth, Center for Coastal Studies, Hurricane Outward Bound School, and other schools
Program type: Traditional seamanship training combined with accredited academic studies in maritime subjects
Season: Year-round
Designer: McCurdy & Rhodes
Built: 1973: South Bristol, ME, Harvey Gamage Shipyard
Coast Guard certification: Sailing School Vessel (Subchapter R), Passenger Vessel (Subchapter T)
Crew: 8-11 including faculty **Students:** 27 overnight
Contact: Executive Director, Ocean Classroom Foundation, 29 McKown Street, Boothbay Harbor, Maine 04538 USA
Tel: 800-724-7245 **Fax:** 401-596-4583
E-mail: mail@oceanclassroom.org
Website: www.oceanclassroom.org

Flag: USA
Rig: Square topsail ketch
Homeport: Grays Harbor, Aberdeen,Washington
Normal cruising waters: West Coast of North America
Sparred length: 103'
LOD: 65'
LWL: 62'
Draft: 6'
Beam: 22'
Rig height: 75'
Sail area: 4,200 square feet
Freeboard: 3'
Tons: 64 GRT
Power: twin diesels
Hull: wood

HAWAIIAN CHIEFTAIN

Hawaiian Chieftain is a 103-foot square-rigged topsail ketch owned and operated by Grays Harbor Historical Seaport Authority. Built in Lahaina, Hawaii in 1988, she is a contemporary interpretation of a traditional design based on the European trading vessels that called in Hawaii during the 18th-century. Each year *Hawaiian Chieftain* sails the West Coast from British Columbia to San Diego in company with the *Lady Washington* providing "Voyages of Discovery" sailing and dockside educational programs. This hands-on-history program teaches 4th & 5th grade students about the exploration of the west coast during the 1790's. On weekends, the ships offer dockside tours and sea battle reenactment sails for the public. *Hawaiian Chieftain* and *Lady Washington* also offer "Two Weeks Before the Mast," a crew training program, on a year round basis. Summer programs include "Family Camp" and "Youth Camp" for ages 12 to 16. *Hawaiian Chieftain* programs are designed to educate, excite, inspire and empower students and the general public. *Hawaiian Chieftain* also offers sail training and team building for adults, private charters and natural history cruises.

Who sails: Individuals and groups
Program type: Sail training for apprentices and paying trainees; maritime heritage programs for schools, homeschools and youth organizations; public programs include summer camps, three-hour sails, dockside tours and passages
Season: Year-round
Designer: Raymond R. Richards
Built: 1988: Lahaina, Maui, Hawaii, Lahaina Welding Co.
Coast Guard certification: Passenger Vessel (Subchapter T)
Crew: 8 **Trainees-passengers:** 45 overnight
Contact: Capt. Les Bolton, Executive Director, Grays Harbor Historical Seaport Authority, PO Box 2019, Aberdeen, WA 98520 USA
Tel: 800-200-5239 **Fax:** 360-533-9384
E-mail: les@historicalseaport.org
Website: www.historicalseaport.org

SPECIFICATIONS

Flag: USA
Rig: Square topsail schooner, two-masted
Homeport: Miami, Florida
Sparred length: 85'
LOA: 68'
LOD: 65'
LWL: 62'
Draft: 6'
Beam: 17' 9"
Rig height: 64'
Sail area: 2,200 square feet
Freeboard: 8'
Tons: 47 GRT
Power: 140 HP diesel
Hull: steel

HERITAGE OF MIAMI II

The *Heritage of Miami II* is an 83-foot square topsail schooner that is modern in materials and construction but traditional in style. Built specifically for crossing wide expanses of open water, she has a wide, spacious deck that provides ample room for working the sails, lounging in the sun, and sleeping in the evening. Her shoal draft makes even small islands accessible while her long bowsprit, topmasts, and yards allow extra sails for speed between them.

Heritage of Miami II's travels take her from her Miami home base down through the coral reefs of the Florida Keys to Garden Key and the famous Fort Jefferson in the Dry Tortugas. Sea Explorer cruises last for six days and five nights. Co-winner of the 1999 ASTA Sail Training Program of the Year, her professional captain and crew help the Explorers experience the life of the sea: setting and furling sails, manning the helm, and even catching, cleaning, and cooking fish. The program offers a unique opportunity to explore a part of the Florida Keys while enjoying a hands-on sailing experience.

Who sails: School groups from elementary through college as well as individuals
Program type: Sail training for crew, apprentices, and paying trainees; sea education in maritime history and ecology in cooperation with accredited schools and colleges and other organized groups; passenger day sails and overnight passages; dockside interpretation
Season: Year-round
Designer: Merritt Walters
Built: 1988: Norfolk, VA, Howdy Bailey
Coast Guard certification: Passenger Vessel (Subchapter T)
Contact: Captain Joseph A. Maggio, The Schooner Heritage of Miami, Inc., 3145 Virginia Street, Coconut Grove, FL 33133 USA
Tel: 305-442-9697
Fax: 305-442-0119
E-mail: heritage2@mindspring.com
Website: www.heritageschooner.com

SPECIFICATIONS

Flag: USA
Rig: Dipping lug
Homeport: Grays Harbor,
Aberdeen, Washington
Normal cruising waters:
Grays Harbor, Puget Sound,
Western Washington
Sparred length: 26'
LOA: 25'
LOD: 25'
LWL: 25'
Draft: 20'
Beam: 7'
Rig height: 16'
Sail area: 316 square feet
Freeboard: 20"
Tons: 3,800 LBS
Hull: wood

HEWITT R. JACKSON

On May 12, 1792 Captain Robert Gray sailed his ship, *Columbia Rediviva*, over the bar of the "Great River of the West" and named it Columbia's River in honor of his ship. Captain Gray never would have entered that river had it not been for the information he received from the first American vessel to enter the river, *Columbia's* longboat. Unnamed and unheralded, ship's longboats were the workhorses of the 16th- to 19th-century. Powered by either oars or sails, these versatile seaworthy craft carried all manner of cargo from ship to shore and back again. Grays Harbor Historical Seaport Authority built two 18th-century ship's longboat reproductions in 1993. Noted maritime historian and artist Hewitt R. Jackson, who worked closely with naval architect Stewart Hoagland and Seaport Director Les Bolton to ensure both historical accuracy and the meeting of specific program needs, painstakingly researched the design for the Seaport longboats. Powered by ten oars, or up to a three-masted dipping lugsail rig, these versatile vessels are ideal for exploring the protected inland waterways of Washington. Programs are customized to the needs and interests of specific groups.

Who sails: Students in grades elementary through college and groups and individuals of all ages
Program type: Sail training for volunteer and paying crew and trainees in cooperation with accredited institutions and other organized groups; sea education in maritime history, marine science, and ecology; passenger day sails; dockside interpretation
Designer: Stewart Hoagland, Hewitt Jackson Built: 1993: Aberdeen, WA, Grays Harbor Historical Seaport Authority
Coast Guard certification: Sailing School Vessel (Subchapter R)
Crew: 2 **Trainees-passengers:** 8 – 13 day sails
Contact: Capt. Les Bolton, Executive Director, Grays Harbor Historical Seaport Authority, PO Box 2019, Aberdeen, WA 98520 USA
Tel: 800-200-5239 **Fax:** 360-533-9384
E-mail: les@historicalseaport.org
Website: www.historicalseaport.org

SPECIFICATIONS

Flag: USA
Rig: Gaff topsail schooner
Homeport: Port Huron, Michigan
Normal cruising waters:
Great Lakes and
Eastern Seaboard
Sparred length: 154'
LOA: 126'
LOD: 119'
LWL: 100'
Draft:14'
Beam: 25' 6"
Rig height: 125'
Sail area: 9,728 square feet
Freeboard: 4' 8"
Tons: 135 GRT
Power: twin Detroit diesel,
8V-92, 350 HP each
Hull: white oak

HIGHLANDER SEA

Dedicated to showcasing the marine lore of Port Huron, Michigan and the Great Lakes region, Acheson Ventures, LLC purchased *Highlander Sea* for her new role as Port Huron's flagship ambassador. The ship was repatriated to the US in April 2002. Originally christened *Pilot*, she served 47 years as a Boston Harbor pilot ship. In the 1970s, she was purchased to circumnavigate the globe, got as far as Fiji and was sold. Her next owner renamed her *Star Pilot* and obtained US Coast Guard Certification as a school-ship. In 1998 Secunda Marine Services acquired the ship in San Diego, sailed her to Nova Scotia, Canada, renamed her *Highlander Sea* and refit her extensively to train young seafarers. Today, *Highlander Sea* offers opportunities for character development, teamwork, and community citizenship for the people of Port Huron, in particular its youth, through leadership and training. The ship rests in Port Huron, sails the Great Lakes and Eastern Seaboard, and is available for public tours, educational programs, and special events.

Who sails: Enthusiastic individuals age 16 and up
Program type: Sail training opportunities for volunteer crew or trainees; sea education in maritime history and ecology in cooperation with accredited institutions and other organized groups; overnight passages and passenger day sails; dockside interpretation
Season: April to November
Designer: W. Starling Burgess
Built: 1924: Essex, MA, J. F. James and Son
Coast Guard certification: Passenger Vessel ((OUPV)
Crew: 12 **Trainees-passengers:** 12 daysails, 12 overnight
Contact: Liz Mathews, Highlander Sea, 2336 Military Street, Port Huron, MI 48060 USA
Tel: 810-966-3488
Fax: 810-982-1900
E-mail: caphighlandersea@achesonventures.com
Website: www.highlandersea.com

SPECIFICATIONS

Flag: USA
Rig: Gaff schooner
Homeport: Provincetown, Massachusetts
Normal cruising waters: Cape Cod Bay
Sparred length: 73'
LOA: 64'
LOD: 61' 3"
LWL: 47'
Draft: 9'
Beam: 15'
Rig height: 60'
Sail area: 2,500 square feet
Freeboard: 4'
Tons: 29 GRT
Power: 90 HP diesel
Hull: wood

HINDU

Hindu was designed by William Hand, Jr. and built as a private yacht in 1925 in East Boothbay, Maine, by the Hodgdon Brothers. She is a 79-foot wooden vessel designed as a half-scale model of a 19th-century Grand Banks fishing schooner. In her long career, she has been a private yacht, a cargo ship transporting spice from India, and a US Navy U-boat tracker in World War II on the Eastern Seaboard. For over sixty years, tourist and locals alike have enjoyed the exhilaration and delights of a sail on the Schooner *Hindu* of Provincetown. She has entertained generations of families including family reunions, weddings, sunset tours and even the occasional burial at sea.

Who sails: Enthusiastic individuals of all ages
Program type: family reunions, weddings, sunset tours and even the occasional burial at sea
Designer: William Hand, Jr.
Built: 1925: Boothbay Harbor, Maine, Hodgdon Brothers
Contact: Captain Kevin Foley, P.O. Box 389, Provincetown, MA 02657 USA
Tel: 1-888-666-HINDU
E-mail: info@theschoonerhindu.com
Website: www.theschoonerhindu.com

HURRICANE (1 through 22)

SPECIFICATIONS

Flag: USA
Rig: Sharpie schooner
Homeport: Wheeler's Bay, Maine
Normal cruising waters:
Maine Coast, Florida Keys
Sparred length: 30'
LWL: 27' 6"
Draft: 12" board up, 5' board down
Beam: 8' 6"
Rig height: 30'
Sail area: 340 square feet
Freeboard: 2'
Hull: fiberglass

Built exclusively for Outward Bound's second school in the United States, and modeled after traditional whaling vessels and Coast Guard rescue boats, the Hurricane Island ketch-rigged pulling boat has served since 1965. The fleet is being replaced by a new design based on the New Haven Sharpie. Outward Bound has built its reputation teaching sailing on the East Coast and internationally for 40 years, primarily using its small open boats, as well as historic schooners such as *Westward, Harvey Gamage*, and *Spirit of Massachusetts*. Students experience open ocean adventure and island living, sailing the coast of Maine, the Canadian Maritimes, or the Caribbean. Living as student-crew, participants rotate responsibilities, learning to sail and navigate, as well as developing teamwork and leadership skills. Outward Bound is a nonprofit educational organization that offers more than 750 Wilderness courses throughout the US as well as internationally. To learn about our range of activities, locations and course types, visit www.outwardbound.org or call 1-888-88BOUND.

Who sails: Individuals and groups 14 and older, coed; corporations and organizations
Program type: Sail training and seamanship, taught to encourage growth, discovery and life enhancement
Designer: Rodger Martin Design, Newport, R.I.
Built: 2007: Union River Boat/Southport Island Marine, Maine
Crew: 2 **Trainees-passengers:** 6
Contact: Outward Bound Wilderness, 910 Jackson St., Golden, CO 80401 USA
Tel: 800-477-2627
Fax: 720-497-2441
E-mail: contactus@outwardbound.org
Website: www.outwardbound.org

SPECIFICATIONS

Flag: USA
Rig: Gaff schooner
Homeport: New York, New York
Normal cruising waters:
New York Harbor
Sparred length: 80'
LOA: 65'
LOD: 64' 6"
LWL: 58'
Draft: 8'
Beam: 16'
Rig height: 62'
Freeboard: 3' 4"
Sail area: 1,850 square feet
Tons: 41 GRT
Power: twin 55 HP diesels
Hull: wood

IMAGINE

The schooner *Imagine* was launched in 1997. She is the fifth of a series of series of schooners designed and built by Scarano Boat in the 1990s. Although dimensionally very similar to the other four vessels, she has an interior layout more suitable for sail training and can accommodate up to 14 trainees and crew for extended sailing adventures.

Who sails: School groups from elementary through college, private and corporate charters, families, and individuals of all ages
Program type: Sail training with paying trainees, passenger day sails
Built: 1997; Albany, NY, Scarano Boat
Coast Guard certification: Passenger Vessel (Subchapter T)
Crew: 3 Trainees-passengers: 49 daysails, 14 overnight
Contact: Sarah Greer, Manager, Classic Harbor Line, Chelsea Piers Suite 5912, 23rd St. at Hudson River, NY, NY 10011 USA
Tel: 212-827-1825
Fax: 646-349-5963
E-mail: CaptSarah@Sail-NYC.com
Website: www.Sail-NYC.com

SPECIFICATIONS

Flag: USA
Rig: Gaff schooner, two-masted
Homeport: Suttons Bay, Michigan
Normal cruising waters: Grand Traverse Bay, Lake Michigan
Sparred length: 77'
LOA: 61' 6"
LOD: 61' 6"
LWL: 53'
Draft: 7'
Beam: 17'
Rig height: 66'
Sail area: 1,800 square feet
Freeboard: 4'
Tons: 41 GRT
Power: 130 HP diesel
Hull: steel

INLAND SEAS

The *Inland Seas* Education Association (ISEA) was created in 1989 to teach culturally diverse students from throughout the state of Michigan, the Midwest and beyond about the science and heritage of the Great Lakes. ISEA's award-winning experiential educational programs are designed for students in grades 5 – 12 and are modified for learners of all ages. More than 75,000 participants have experienced the Great Lakes Schoolship Program, including students from over 140 Michigan communities. Summer shipboard experiences for all ages include astronomy, history, and science programs on Grand Traverse Bay and Lake Michigan. The goal of every ISEA program is to encourage young people to pursue academic interests related to the Great Lakes, particularly the sciences, and to provide enhanced public understanding and stewardship of the Great Lakes for future generations. The heart of the Schoolship Program is the work of 200 dedicated and professionally trained volunteers who donate nearly 8,000 hours annually aboard the School-ship.

Who sails: School groups and individuals of all ages
Program type: Sail training for volunteer and paying trainees; sea education in marine science, maritime history, and ecology for students from elementary through college, adults, and at-youth risk; dockside interpretation during port visits
Season: May through early October
Designer: Charles W. Wittholz, Woodin & Marean
Built: 1994: Palm Coast, FL, Treworgy Yachts
Coast Guard certification: Passenger Vessel (Subchapter T)
Crew: 5 **Trainees-passengers:** 30 daysails, 10 overnight
Contact: Thomas M. Kelly, Executive Director, Inland Seas Education Association, PO Box 218, Suttons Bay, MI 49682 USA
Tel: 231-271-3077
Fax: 231-271-3088
E-mail: isea@greatlakeseducation.org
Website: www.greatlakeseducation.org

Photo by Volker Correll

Flag: USA
Rig: Brigantine
Homeport: Los Angeles, California
Normal cruising waters: Southern California and offshore islands
Sparred length: 110' 8"
LOA: 90'
LOD: 81' 7"
LWL: 72' 6"
Draft: 11'
Beam: 21' 9"
Rig height: 87' 8"
Sail area: 4,540 square feet
Tons: 99 GRT
Power: 315 HP diesel
Hull: wood

IRVING JOHNSON

In April of 2002, the Los Angeles Maritime Institute launched the twin brigantines *Exy Johnson* and *Irving Johnson*. Named in honor of the Johnsons and their lifelong commitment to character-building sailing adventures, the brigantines were constructed on the waterfront in San Pedro, California. Designed for LAMI's TopSail Youth Program, the brigantines were built especially to meet the needs of middle school youth. The TopSail Youth Program uses sail training to provide youth with real-life challenges that develop the knowledge, skills and attitudes needed to live healthy, productive lives. TopSail enriches, validates and challenges conventional school curricula by bringing biology, history, mathematics, physics, geography, literature and the environment to life in the real world classroom of the sea. Irving McClure Johnson began training for a sailor's life as a teenager. In 1929 he sailed around Cape Horn on the barque *Peking*. Captain Johnson met his wife Electa, "Exy", sailing trans-Atlantic aboard *Wanderbird*. The Johnsons sailed around the world seven times with youth crew on two different *Yankees*, then cruised European and African waters in their third *Yankee*, a ketch. In 2006, LAMI hosted a reunion of world-voyagers and Girl Scout Mariners, sailing the twin brigantines with a new generation of youth crew carrying on the Johnsons' tradition through TopSail.

Who sails: Youth/school groups from diverse communities, mostly middle schoolers from 'at-risk' urban areas
Program type: Educational sailing adventures for youth and adult groups
Season: Year-round
Coast Guard certification: Sailing School Vessel (Subchapter R), Passenger Vessel (Subchapter T)
Contact: Captain Jim Gladson, President, Los Angeles Maritime Institute, Berth 84, Foot of Sixth Street, San Pedro, CA 90731 USA
Tel: 310-833-6055
Fax: 310-548-2055
Website: www.LAMITopSail.org

ISKRA

SPECIFICATIONS

Flag: Poland
Rig: Barquentine
Homeport: Gdynia, Poland
Normal cruising waters:
Baltic Sea
Sparred length: 161'
LOA: 140'
LOD: 137'
LWL: 121'
Draft: 13' 9'
Beam: 26'
Freeboard: 5'
Rig height: 115'
Sail area: 377 square feet
Hull: steel

The ship took her name after a 3-masted gaff schooner, *Iskra*, which sailed under the Polish navy ensign for 50 years between 1927 and 1977. ORP *Iskra* was built in 1982 in Gdanska Shipyard. She is a 3-masted barquentine with different rigging on all three masts. The foremast has five square sails; main sail is gaff-rigged; and mizzen is Bermudian. The main purpose of the ship is to train Polish Naval Academy cadets on their summer practices. Every year since 1987, she has participated in the Cutty Sark Tall Ships' Races. During her years of sailing, the ship has won numerous prizes including the United Nations Peace Medal in 1990, the Cutty Sark Trophy in 1989, the Fair Play Prize in the 1999 Cutty Sark Tall Ships Race, and the Polish Navy's Best Ship Prize (five times). The letters ORP in front of her name are the abbreviation for "Ship of the Republic of Poland" and indicate that the ship belongs to the Polish Navy. The name *Iskra* means "spark".

Who sails: Cadets of the Polish Naval Academy
Program type: Training vessel
Designer: Zygmunt Choren
Built: 1982: Gdanska Shipyard
Contact: Commanding Officer, ORP Iskra, JW 1449 ORP ISKRA, Gdynia, Wojewodztwo Pomorskie, 81-103 Gdynia 3 Poland
Tel: 48-58-626-25-54
Fax: 48-58-626-25-54
E-mail: iskra2@poczta.fm

SPECIFICATIONS

Flag: USA
Rig: Schooner
Homeport: Rockland, Maine
Normal cruising waters: New England
Sparred length: 118'
LOD: 89'
Draft: 7.5' (centerboard up) 14' (centerboard down)
Beam: 22' 6"
Rig height: 74'
Freeboard: 2' 6"
Sail area: 4,000 square feet
Tons: 61 GRT
Hull: Oak

Photo by Elizabeth Poisson

J. & E. RIGGIN

This traditional sailing vessel was built as an oyster dredger in 1927, and is now a National Historic Landmark. The Schooner *J. & E. Riggin* is a family run business. The captain, Jon Finger, has almost two decades of professional experience on the water from Maine to the Mediterranean. His wife and the cook on board, Annie Mahle, also holds her captain's license and is a trained chef. Windjamming is the best of both worlds: adventure and relaxation. Sail where the wind and tide take you and experience freedom from everyday noises and distractions. Throw itineraries to the wind, anchor in a different harbor every night, and even enjoying a traditional lobster bake on the beach, Maine-style! The sight of lighthouses, pink-granite islands and colorful sunrises, the smell of fresh bread just out of the wood stove or freshly brewed coffee, all are part of your trip on our windjammer. From May to October twenty-four people join us as our guests for a week of sailing, sightseeing and nature-watching. Our quiet adventures travel from Boothbay, Maine to Bar Harbor, Maine.

Who sails: Groups and individuals of all ages
Program type: Sail training for paying trainees; passenger day sails; group charters
Season: June to October
Designer: Charles Riggin
Built: 1927: Dorchester, NJ
Coast Guard certification: Passenger Vessel (Subchapter T)
Crew: 6 **Trainees-passengers:** 24
Contact: Captains Jon Finger and Anne Mahle, Schooner J. & E. Riggin, 136 Holmes Street, Rockland, ME 04841 USA
Tel: 800-869-0604
Fax: 207-594-4921
Email: info@mainewindjammer.com
Website: www.mainewindjammer.com

JOLLY BREEZE OF ST. ANDREWS

SPECIFICATIONS

Flag: Canada
Rig: Topsail, square-sail cutter
Homeport: St. Andrews,
New Brunswick
Normal cruising waters: Bay of
Fundy
Sparred length: 72'
LOD: 57'
LWL: 49'
Draft: 8'
Beam: 15'
Rig height: 58'
Sail area: 2,200 square feet
Tons: 240 HP 6068 turbo charged
John Deere
Hull: steel

The *Jolly Breeze of St. Andrews* is a 72' topsail, square sail cutter, drawn on the lines of the famous 1900s *Jolie Brise* of LaHavre, France. She was designed by Seibe deJonge, Holland and built for the late Captain Marc Witteveen in New Zealand. After being launched in 1989, the *Jolly Breeze* (formerly S/V *Cory*) sailed 25,000 miles voyaging the world. In 1994, amid 70 entries, she won a prize for Concours D'Elegance in theAntigua Classic Boat Regatta. Since 1995 she has been operating whale watching and nature tours out of beautiful St. Andrews by the Sea, New Brunswick, Canada from June through October. St. Andrews is Canada's oldest seaside resort town, with an historic downtown, friendly people and with close access to whales and Bay of Fundy wildlife, 3 tours per day. Besides catering to tourists, we offer discounts to schools, cadets and charitable organizations. A sail training program is currently under development. Paid crew positions available seasonally.

Who sails: All ages
Program type: Whale watching, sight-seeing
Season: May - October
Designer: Siebe de Jonge (Holland)
Built: 1989: Henk Osterbroek, New Zealand
Certification: Transport Canada inspected Passenger Vessel
Crew: 3 **Passengers:** 40
Contact: Robert and Joanne Carney, Owners, Tall Ship Whale Adventures, 4 King Street, St. Andrews, New Brunswick, E5B 1Y2 Canada
Tel: 506-529-8116
E-mail: jollybreeze@hotmail.com
Website: www.jollybreeze.com

Flag: USA
Rig: Ship, three-masted
Homeport: Mystic, Connecticut
Sparred length: 118' 6"
LOA: 100' 8"
Draft: 12'
Beam: 25' 3"
Rig height: 98' 6"
Tons: 213 GRT
Hull: iron

JOSEPH CONRAD

For over 50 years, young people have come to Mystic Seaport, our nation's leading maritime museum to learn to sail and live on board the tall ship *Joseph Conrad*. Each morning, campers tackle the wind and current of the Mystic River and then set off for an active afternoon investigating the Museum's unique exhibitions. After a late-day sailing session, some "R and R" and dinner, campers spend their evenings with new friends, stargazing in a planetarium, climbing the rigging of the *Conrad* or enjoying a lively sea music sing-a-long. The *Joseph Conrad* program is open to individual boys and girls and organized groups ages 10 – 15. Groups must have one adult leader per ten participants. No prior experience is required for beginner sessions, only a desire to participate and learn. Intermediate sessions are for those who have attended a previous beginner session or have had sailing experience. All must hold current Red Cross swimmers certification or its equivalent.

Who sails: Individuals and organized groups ages 10 – 15
Program type: Sail training; dockside visitation for school groups and individuals
Season: June – August
Designer: Burmeister and Wain
Built: 1882: Copenhagen, Denmark, Burmeister & Wain
Contact: Mystic Seaport Watercraft Department, PO Box 6000, Mystic, CT 06355-0990 USA
Tel: 860-572-5323
Fax: 860-572-5355
Website: www.mysticseaport.org

JUAN SEBASTIAN DE ELCANO

SPECIFICATIONS

Flag: Spain
Rig: Topsail schooner, 4-masted
Homeport: Cadiz, Spain
LOA: 305' 6"
Draft: 23' 7"
Beam: 42' 7"
Rig height: 164'
Power: GM358 Diesel
Hull: iron

The official training vessel for the midshipmen and ensigns of the Spanish Navy, *Juan Sebastian de Elcano* was launched in 1927 and delivered to the Spanish Navy in 1928. Her hull is made of iron, and she has four masts, each named after other training ships which preceded her (*Blanca*, *Almansa*, *Asturias*, and *Nautilus*). She is named in honor of *Juan Sebastion de Elcano*, captain of Ferdinand Magellan's last exploratory fleet. The ship also carries the *de Elcano* coat of arms— a terraqueous globe and the motto "Primus Circumdedisti Me" (first to circumnavigate me) which emperor Charles I conferred on *de Elcano* after he returned to Spain having completed Magellan's global expedition. She has sailed in more than 50 training voyages, including six circumnavigations of the globe.

Who sails: Midshipmen of the Spanish Navy
Program type: Training vessel of the Spanish Naval Academy
Designer: Nicholson, England
Built: 1927: Cadiz, Spain, Shipyard Echevarrieta y Larrinaga
Certification: Spanish Naval Vessel
Crew: 250 – 270 including midshipmen
Contact: Office of the Naval Attache, Embassy of Spain, 4801 Wisconsin Avenue, NW, 3rd Floor, Washington, DC 20016 USA
Tel: 202-244-2166
Fax: 202-362-3993
E-mail: armada@agredwas.org

Flag: Japan
Rig: Brigantine
Homeport: Sausalito, California
LOA: 151'
Draft: 11' 2"
Beam: 25'
Hull: steel

KAISEI

Launched in 1990, *Kaisei* has already traversed the globe and sailed thousands of people to far reaching ports in the spirit of Global Partnership. Kaisei participated in the Columbus Fleet Events in 1992 and had the honor of flying the UN flag due to her international crew and mission. *Kaisei* has visited over 15 countries, crewed by volunteers from over 26 nations. Her voyages have created a powerfully diverse network of supporters; dissolving racial, ethnic, religious, political, and age barriers around the world. *Kaisei* has sailed International Peace Missions with citizens of political "hot spots" such as joint crews of Japanese and Korean citizens. Kaisei is now operated by Ocean Voyages Institute, a non-profit organization (501 C3) founded in 1979 by a group of international sailors, educators, and conservationists with a mission of teaching the maritime arts and sciences, and researching and preserving the world's oceans. Selective partnerships with leading international youth and environmental organizations have paved the way for innovative programs rich with challenge, service, and humble appreciation of the inter-connectedness of humanity and the resources that sustain us.

Contact: Ocean Voyages Institute, 1709 Bridgeway, Sausalito CA 94965 USA
Tel: 415-332-4681
Fax: 415-332-7460
E-mail: sail@oceanvoyages.com
Website: www.oceanvoyages.com

KALIAKRA

Photo by Thad Koza

KALIAKRA

SPECIFICATIONS

Flag: Bulgaria
Rig: Barquentine
Homeport: Varna, Bulgaria
Sparred length: 159'
Draft: 11'
Beam: 27'
Hull: steel

Completed in 1984, *Kaliakra* trains future officers for the Bulgarian Navy and is a sister ship to *Iskra*. Her home port is Varna on the Black Sea, although she has been a frequent participant in European and American tall ship gatherings. As initially rigged, only four yardarms crossed her foremast because of variations in deck thickness that affected the height of the foremast. Since her refitting in 1992, however, she carries five yardarms in her barquentine configuration. Her figurehead is a stylized version of a Bulgarian mythological figure.

Program type: Training vessel of the Bulgarian Navy
Built: 1984
Contact: Embassy of the Republic of Bulgaria, 1621 22nd Street NW, Washington, DC 20008 USA
Tel: 202-387-7969
Fax: 202-234-7973

Flag: USA
Rig: Full-rigged ship
Homeport: Wilmington, Delaware
Normal cruising waters: Mid-Atlantic and Northeast
Sparred length: 141'
LOA: 93'
LOD: 91'
LWL: 89' 2"
Draft: 12' 5"
Beam: 24' 11"
Rig height: 105'
Sail area: 7,600 square feet
Freeboard: 8'
Tons: 168 GRT
Power: 2 Caterpillar 3208 @ 180 HP ea
Hull: wood

Photo by Thad Koza

KALMAR NYCKEL

The *Kalmar Nyckel*, the tall ship of Delaware, is a re-creation of the first Swedish colonial settlement ship to arrive in America in 1638, which established the colony of New Sweden in what is now Wilmington, Delaware. Launched in the fall of 1997, commissioned in May of 1998, and USCG certified in June of 2000, this ornately carved 17th Century Dutch pinnace sails the Northeast and Mid-Atlantic regions seasonally, carrying out her mission of education and goodwill. She transforms Delaware's history into hands-on educational opportunities for children through adults, from teaching fourth and sixth graders history and physics to conducting her bi-annual volunteer crew sail training. She provides economic development opportunities, private charters both underway and dockside, public sails and public tours, and statewide marketing initiatives on a national scale, serving as Delaware's tall ship ambassador. A professional captain, mates and a volunteer crew man the *Kalmar Nyckel*.

Who sails: School groups from elementary through college, as well as individuals and families
Program type: Sail training for volunteers; education programs for school children, dockside interpretation during port visits
Season: May through October
Designer: Tom Gillmer
Built: 1997: Wilmington, Delaware, Allen C. Rawl
Coast Guard certification: Passenger Vessel (Subchapter T)
Crew: 8 **Trainees-passengers:** 49 daysails
Contact: Marcia Ferranto, Executive Director, Kalmar Nyckel Foundation, 1124 East Seventh Street, Wilmington, DE 19801 USA
Tel: 302-429-7447 **Fax:** 302-429-0350
E-mail: officemanager@kalmarnyckel.org
Website: www.kalmarnyckel.org

KOREANA

Flag: Korea
Rig: Schooner, four-masted
Homeport: Yeosu, Korea
Normal cruising waters:
Korea and Japan
Sparred length: 135'
LOA: 108'
LOD: 101'
LWL: 93' 6 "
Draft: 10'
Beam: 23'
Rig height: 85'
Sail area: 4,284 square feet
Tons: 135 GRT
Power: 400 HP inboard motor
Hull: steel

This lovely vessel was designed for world cruising and charter use. She is a rare breed in todays world. There are L-Shaped settees and tables in the salon. The entertainment center has a large television, VCR, dual cassette tape deck, speakers inside and on deck. There are six cabins for sleeping. There are five heads and showers and 10 sinks. Originally three luxurious staterooms, in 1995 she was extended and the interior was converted to a sailtraining configuration. This refit was completed at the Pusan shipyard in Korea.

Who sails: Groups and individuals of all ages
Program type: Sail training
Season: Year-round
Designer: Roonstra
Built: 1983: W. Huisman B.V., Holland
Crew: 7 **Trainees-passengers:** 72 daysails, 55 overnight
Contact: Chae Ho Chung, Owner & Captain, Korea Yacht School, 502-2   Soho-Dong, Yeosu, Jeolla Nam Do 555-060 Korea
Tel: (82) 061-684-2580 or 011-623-1010
Fax: (82) 061-682-9999
E-mail: HL4chc@hanmail.net
Website: www.yachtschool.co.kr

SPECIFICATIONS

Flag: Russia
Rig: Barque, four-masted
Homeport: Kalingrad, Russia
Normal cruising waters:
Western European waters (summer)
Southern European waters (winter)
Sparred length: 376'
LOA: 346'
LOD: 329'
LWL: 311' 6"
Draft: 19'
Beam: 46'
Rig height: 176'
Freeboard: 27' 9"
Sail area: 36,380 square feet
Power: twin 600 HP diesels
Hull: steel

KRUZENSHTERN

Kruzenshtern was built as *Padua* in 1927 in Bremerhaven, Germany. The sister ship to *Peking*, she is the last of the "Flying P" liners still under sail. These vessels were engaged in the grain trade from Australia to Europe. In 1933, *Kruzenshtern* sailed from her homeport of Hamburg to Port Lincoln in Australia in only 67 days. At the end of World War II she was handed to the USSR and converted into a sail training ship. Since 1990, up to 40 trainees of all ages have been welcomed onboard to sail along with the Russian students of the Baltic Academy in Kalingrad, Russia, learning the ropes, manning the helm, or climbing the rigging to set more than 30,000 square feet of sail. No previous experience is necessary. *Kruzenshtern* is supported by Tall Ship Friends, a nonprofit organization in Hamburg, Germany. The goals of Tall Ship Friends are to promote sail training on square-riggers, to contribute to the further existence of these beautiful ships, and to provide an unforgettable experience for the participants. Members of Tall Ship Friends receive the quarterly Tall Ships News (English/German) and a personal sailing log.

Who sails: Groups and individuals of all ages
Program type: Sail training for paying trainees; fully accredited sea education in traditional seamanship
Built: 1927: Bremerhaven, Germany, J.C. Tecklenborg
Certification: Special Purpose (School Vessel), Russia
Crew: 45-70 **Trainees-passengers:** 250 daysails, 60 overnight
Contact: Wulf Marquard, Managing Director, Tall Ship Friends Germany, Schweriner Sir. 17, Hamburg, D22143 Germany
Tel: 49-40-675 635 97
Fax: 49-40-675 635 99
E-mail: tallshipl@aol.com
Website: www.tallship-friends.de

SPECIFICATIONS

Flag: Cook Islands
Rig: Topsail cutter
Homeport: Rarotonga, Cook Islands
Normal cruising waters: Hawaii to Cook Islands
Sparred length: 125'
LOA: 118'
LOD: 116'
LWL: 110'
Draft: 9' to 11'
Beam: 23'
Rig height: 70'
Freeboard: 2' to 4'
Sail area: 2,000 square feet
Tons: 179 GRT
Power: 365 HP Detroit diesel
Hull: steel

KWAI

Kwai is a traditional sailing cargo ship, trading between Hawaii, the Line Islands of Kiribati, and the Cook Islands on voyages lasting five to ten weeks. She works today as a motor sailer carrying general cargo and will soon be rigged as a topsail ketch. The trainees sail as crew, standing watches, handling sail, working cargo, and maintain the ship with time ashore to share cultures on remote Pacific Islands. The ship is under a continuing refit into a full sailing vessel with additional accommodation for sail trainees and adventure travelers. Training in ironwork, ships carpentry and rigging are emphasized aboard and in our workshop ashore. *Kwai* is a working ship with an active relationship with our island clients. Trainees participate in all operations from sailing the ship across the trade winds to selling rice and T-shirts ashore islands like Puka-puka.

Who sails: Trainees ages 18 to 80
Program type: Sail training and cargo
Season: Year-round
Built: 1950: Brmer Vulkan, Bremen, Germany
Crew: 6 Trainees-passengers: 2-4
Contact: Brad Ives, Senior Captain, KWAI,13-3988 Honua'ula St., Pahoa, Hawaii 96778 USA
Tel: 808-965-0221
Fax: 808-965-0224
E-mail: info@svkwai.com
Website: www.svkwai.com

Flag: France
Rig: Topsail schooner
Homeport: Brest, France
Sparred length: 124'
Draft: 12'
Beam: 24'
Hull: wood

Photo by Thad Koza

LA BELLE POULE

Along with her sister ship *Etoile*, the schooner *La Belle Poule* serves the French Navy in the training of future officers. Designed with the hull shape and the rigging of fishing vessels from Breton, *La Belle Poule* and *Etoile* were built in 1932 in the fishing port of Fecamp in northern Normandy, France. During World War II, both vessels relocated to Portsmouth, England, where they served the Free France Forces. They are permitted to fly the French ensign with the imposed Cross of Lorraine in recognition of their service during the war.

Program type: Sail training vessel of the French Navy
Built: 1932: Fecamp, Normandy, France
Contact: Embassy of France, 4101 Resevoir Road, NW, Washington, DC 20007 USA
Tel: 202-944-6000
Fax: 202-944-6166

LA REVENANTE

SPECIFICATIONS

Flag: Canada
Rig: Gaff-rigged schooner
Homeport: Gaspé, Québec
Normal cruising waters: Great Lakes, St. Lawrence and Nova Scotia
Sparred length: 64'
LOA: 58'
LOD: 44'
LWL: 40'
Draft: 6' 9"
Beam: 13'
Rig height: 60'
Freeboard: 3'
Sail area: 850 square feet
Tons: 18.8 GRT
Power: 90 HP Ford Lehman
Hull: wood

The schooner *La Revenante* is a replica of an 18th century New England "pinky" schooner. Her purpose is to serve as an historical display and voyaging vessel in support of historical pageantry, re-enactments, community commemorations of aspects of North American colonial marine history, voyaging expeditions in support of scholarly research into colonial history, and work in film and television productions.

Who sails: Volunteer crew (adult)
Program type: Contract appearances
Season: May-October
Designer: Leonard Nelson
Built: 1965: Boston, Massachusetts, Leonard Nelson
Crew: 4 **Trainees-passengers:** 10
Contact: John Wootton & Vernon Fairhead, Co-owners, The Schooner La Revenante Association, Box 700 Shawville, Québec J0X 2Y0 Canada
Tel: 819-647-2574
Fax: 819-647-2409
E-mail: woottonjc@mac.com
Website: www.revenante.com

SPECIFICATIONS

Flag: USA
Rig: Pungy schooner
(gaff rigged), two-masted
Homeport: Baltimore, Maryland
Normal cruising waters:
Chesapeake and Delaware Bays,
East Coast between Maryland
and Maine
Sparred length: 104'
LOD: 72'
LWL: 64' 3"
Draft: 7'
Beam: 22'
Rig height: 85'
Freeboard: 3'
Sail area: 2,994 square feet
Tons: 60 GRT
Power: twin 80 HP diesels

LADY MARYLAND

Lady Maryland is an authentic pungy schooner, an elegant boat designed to haul cargo, fish, dredge for oysters, and to carry luxury items quickly from port to port on Chesapeake Bay and along the Atlantic Coast. Instead of carrying watermelons and oysters, her mission today is to provide students with the opportunity to experience sailing a historic vessel while studying history, sailing, seamanship, marine science, and ecology on her traditional waters from Maryland to Maine. The Living Classrooms Foundation has developed a flexible educational program that can fit the needs of a variety of school and community groups. More than 50,000 students participate in LCF programs each year. The *Lady Maryland* operates educational day experiences for 32 trainees and extended live-aboard sail training and marine science programs for up to 14 people.

Who sails: Student and other organized groups, individuals, and families
Program type: Sail training with paying trainees; sea education in marine science, maritime history, and ecology for school groups from elementary school through college as well as adults
Season: March through November
Designer: Thomas Gilmer
Built: 1986: Baltimore, Maryland, G. Peter Boudreau
Coast Guard certification: Passenger Vessel (Subchapter T)
Crew: 6 day sails, 8 overnight **Trainees-passengers:** 32 daysails, 12-14 overnight
Contact: Living Classrooms Foundation, 802 South Caroline Street, Baltimore, MD 21231-3311 USA
Tel: 410-685-0295
Fax: 410-752-8433
Website: www.livingclassrooms.org

LADY WASHINGTON

SPECIFICATIONS

Flag: USA
Rig: Brig
Homeport: Grays Harbor, Aberdeen, Washington
Normal cruising waters: Washington, West Coast of North America
Sparred length: 112'
LOA: 87'
LOD: 66' 9"
LWL: 58'
Draft: 11'
Beam: 24'
Rig height: 89'
Freeboard: 6'
Sail area: 4,400 square feet
Tons: 99 GRT
Power: diesel
Hull: wood

As a privateer during the American Revolution, the original *Lady Washington* fought to help the colonies gain their independence from England. In 1788, she became the first American vessel to visit the West Coast of North America, opening trade between the colonies and the native peoples of the Northwest Coast. Built at Grays Harbor Historical Seaport in Aberdeen, Washington, and launched in 1989 as a Washington State Centennial project, the reproduction *Lady Washington* sails the waters of Washington State and the West Coast of North America as the tall ship ambassador for the state of Washington. With a busy year-round sailing schedule, *Lady Washington* regularly tours the West Coast, providing shipboard education programs for schools in 89 port communities in Washington, Oregon, California, British Columbia, and Alaska. More than 15,000 school children visit *Lady Washington* each year to learn about the rich and colorful maritime heritage of our nation. Crew are paid professionals and volunteer trainees.

Who sails: School groups from elementary school through college, individuals, and families
Program type: Sail training for crew, apprentices, and paying trainees; sea education in maritime history in cooperation with accredited institutions based on informal, in-house programming; passenger day sails, overnight passages, and family camps; dockside interpretation
Season: Year-round
Designer: Ray Wallace
Built: 1989: Aberdeen, Washington, Grays Harbor Historical Seaport Authority
Coast Guard certification: Passenger Vessel (Subchapter T)
Crew: 12 **Trainees-passengers:** 48 daysails, 8 overnight
Contact: Capt. Les Bolton, Executive Director, Grays Harbor Historical Seaport Authority, PO Box 2019, Aberdeen, WA 98520 USA
Tel: 800-200-5239 **Fax:** 360-533-9384
E-mail: les@historicalseaport.org
Website: www.historicalseaport.org

SPECIFICATIONS

Flag: USA
Rig: Gaff topsail schooner, two-masted
Homeport:
New York City, New York
Normal cruising waters:
Northeast United States
Sparred length: 125'
LOD: 83'
LWL: 71'
Draft: 11'
Beam: 21'
Rig height: 91'
Sail area: 5,017 square feet
Freeboard: 4'
Tons: 54 GRT
Power: twin 85 HP diesels
Hull: wood

LETTIE G. HOWARD

The *Lettie G. Howard* is the sole surviving example of a Georges Bank fishing schooner. A Fredonia model-fishing schooner built in Essex, Massachusetts, she exemplifies the type of craft used widely up and down the Eastern seaboard of the United States from Maine to the Gulf Coast. Operating out of Gloucester for her first eight years, the fishing would have been done with hand lines set from the vessels deck as the waters of Georges Bank were too treacherous for dory fishing. The *Lettie* was similar to the schooners that carried their Long Island and New Jersey catches to New York City's Fulton Fish Market. In 1901, the *Lettie* was purchased by the E.E. Saunders company of Pensacola, Florida, for use off Mexico's Yucatan Peninsula. Completely rebuilt in 1923, she was fitted with her first auxiliary engine a year later. She remained in the Gulf of Mexico until 1968, when she was sold to the South Street Seaport Museum in New York City. The *Lettie G. Howard* was designated a National Historic Landmark in 1989. Between 1991 and 1993, the Museum completely restored her to her original 1893 appearance, while outfitting her to accommodate trainees on educational cruises.

Who sails: School groups, colleges and universities, corporate teambuilding programs, Elderhostel, individual adults, and families
Program type: Sea education and sail training programs focusing on nautical science, fishery and maritime history, natural and social sciences
Built: 1893: Essex, MA, A. D. Story (restored at South Street Seaport Museum in 1993)
Coast Guard certification: Sailing School Vessel (Subchapter R)
Crew: 7-9 **Trainees-passengers:** 33 daysails, 13 overnight
Contact: Lettie G. Howard, South Street Seaport Museum, 12 Fulton Street, New York, NY 10038 USA
Tel: 212-748-8596
Fax: 212-748-8610
E-mail: lettieghoward@southstseaport.org
Website: www.southstseaport.org or www.southstreetseaportmuseum.org

Photo by Thad Koza

LIBERTAD

SPECIFICATIONS

Flag: Argentina
Rig: Full-rigged ship
Homeport: Buenos Aires, Argentina
Sparred length: 356'
LOD: 317'
LWL: 263'
Draft: 21' 9"
Beam: 45' 3"
Freeboard: 15'
Rig height: 147' 6"
Sail area: 28,545 square feet
Power: two 1,200 HP diesel engines
Hull: steel

The frigate, A.R.A. *Libertad,* was initiated as a training ship in 1963 for the Argentine Navy. As a training ship, her mission is to enhance the maritime knowledge and cultural background of her midshipmen while integrating them to life at sea and instructing them on the fundamentals of the art of sailing. *Libertad* also serves as a floating ambassador representing the Argentine Republic establishing professional and friendly ties with navies around the world while preparing her cadets academically, physically and spiritually. In 1966, *Libertad* established the world record for speed crossing the North Atlantic sailing from Cape Race (Canada) to Dursey Island (Ireland) in six days and 21 hours. The International Sail Training Association (ISTA) officially recognized her record, and *Libertad* flies a pennant commemorating this achievement. Her figurehead was made by a Spanish sculptor and depicts Liberty, for which the ship is named. *Libertad* has sailed the seven seas and participates in regattas and port visits around the world.

Who sails: Cadets from the Military Naval School (20 – 23)
Program type: Naval training vessel
Season: May through December
Designer: Astilleros y Fabricas Navales del Estado (AFNE)
Built: 1960 (launched 1956): Rio Santiago (BA), Argentina, Astilleros y Fabricas Navales del Estado (AFNE)
Crew: 150 **Trainees-passengers:** 150
Contact: Argentine Naval Attache Office, Embassy of Argentina, 630 Indiana Avenue, NW, Washington, DC 20004 USA
Tel: 202-626-2164
Fax: 202-626-2180
E-mail: MICassain@argnavattache-usa.org
Website: www.argnavattache-usa.org or www.ara.mil.ar

SPECIFICATIONS

Flag: USA
Rig: Gaff topsail schooner
Homeport: Boston, Massachusetts (summer), Key West, Florida (winter)
Normal cruising waters: East Coast US
Sparred length: 80'
LOA: 64'
LOD: 61'
LWL: 53'
Draft: 7'
Beam: 17'
Rig height: 65'
Freeboard: 5'
Sail area: 1,744 square feet
Tons: 50 GRT
Power: diesel
Hull: steel

LIBERTY

Liberty is modeled on early 1800s coastal schooners used by New England fisherman and as cargo vessels along the East Coast to the Florida Keys. She is based in Key West, where she offers three, two-hour sails each day. *Liberty* is kept "shipshape and Bristol fashion" and is available for charter day and evening for every occasion.

Who sails: School groups from elementary through high school, individuals, and families
Program type: Passenger day sails and overnight passages; corporate and private charters
Designer: Charles Wittholz
Built: 1993: Palm Coast, FL, Treworgy Yachts
Coast Guard certification: Passenger Vessel (Subchapter T)
Crew: 3 daysails, 4 overnight **Trainees-passengers:** 49 daysails, 8 overnight
Contact: Gregory E. Muzzy, President, The Liberty Fleet of Tall Ships, Hilton Resort & Marina, Key West, FL 33040 USA
Tel: 305-295-0095
Fax: 305-292-6411
E-mail: info@libertyfleet.com
Website: www.libertyfleet.com

LIBERTY CLIPPER

SPECIFICATIONS

Flag: USA
Rig: Gaff topsail schooner
Homeport: Boston, MA (summer),
Key West, FL (winter)
Normal cruising waters: East
Coast US
Sparred length: 125'
LOD: 86'
LWL: 76'
Draft: 8'(min.), 13'(max.)
Beam: 25'
Rig height: 78'
Freeboard: 5'
Sail area: 4,300 square feet
Tons: 99 GRT
Power: diesel
Hull: steel

The *Liberty Clipper* is a replica of the mid-19th century Baltimore Clippers famous for their fast passages around Cape Horn on their way to California and other Pacific ports. The *Liberty Clipper* operates in Boston Harbor during the summer and, with the schooner *Liberty*, in Key West, Florida during the winter. *Liberty Clipper* is available for charter on day and evening cruises for up to 110 passengers. Her spacious decks and on-board hospitality create an ambiance under sail that will meet the expectations of the most discriminating clients. In addition to a variety of high quality charter opportunities, during the summer months, the *Liberty Clipper* offers the Liberty Classroom program for Boston area youth groups. *Liberty* Classroom is a sail training and harbor education program designed to give trainees an introduction to essential topics in seamanship, safety, and Boston's maritime history. Much of the *Liberty* Classroom curriculum is based on active participation in the operation of the vessel, allowing one to master the first two skill levels in the ASTA Training Logbook. For those interested in extended trips, *Liberty Clipper* offers a limited number of berths for the passage between Boston and Key West in the spring and fall.

Who sails: School groups from elementary through high school, individuals, and families
Program type: Passenger day sails and overnight passages; corporate and private charters
Designer: Charles Wiftholz
Built: 1983: Warren, RI, Blount Marine Corporation
Coast Guard certification: Passenger Vessel (Subchapter T)
Crew: 5 daysails, 10 overnight **Trainees-passengers:** 115 daysails, 24 overnight
Contact: Gregory E. Muzzy, President, The Liberty Fleet of Tall Ships, 67 Long Wharf, Boston, MA 02210 USA
Tel: 617-742-0333
Fax: 617-742-1322
E-mail: info@libertyfleet.com
Website: www.libertyfleet.com

Flag: USA
Rig: Barque, three-masted
Homeport: Georgetown, Maryland
Normal cruising waters:
Chesapeake Bay
Sparred length: 90'
LOA: 90'
LOD: 60'
LWL: 55'
Draft: 9'
Beam: 19'
Rig height: 70'
Freeboard: 7'
Sail area: 6,000 square feet
Tons: 88 GRT
Power: 160 HP Volvo diesel
Hull: steel

LIONESS

The goal of all services of Youth Services Agency is to maintain "at risk" youth in their family and community systems and to prevent these youth from long term institutional placements. We strive to keep families intact by utilizing an array of integrated supportive services that meet individual and family needs, and by teaching skills which develop self-sufficiency and a strong community service ethic. Youth Services' programs provide healthy, structured, challenging and supportive environments to youths who are resistant to traditional treatment experiences. Our mission is to help these youths become responsible and functional members of the community. We provide comprehensive and complementary services to achieve this goal through out Pennsylvania and the Mid-Atlantic region. Our tall ship, the *Lioness*, is used by all of our programs to provide an additional facet to our adventure programming. YSA clients are given the opportunity to experience all aspects of sailing such a large vessel, under the watchful eye of our trained staff.

Who sails: Youth Services Agency clients age 13 to 18
Program type: Youth Adventure/Challenge Activities
Season: March to December
Built: 1988: Canada
Coast Guard certification: Sailing School Vessel (Subchapter R)
Crew: 3 (plus Counselors) **Trainees-passengers:** 15 daysails, 8 overnight
Contact: Captain Stephen Weisbrod, Ship Captain / Maritime Operations Manager, Youth Services Agency, Inc.
1398 State Route 903, Suite 1, Jim Thorpe, PA 18229 USA
Tel: 410-215-3875
Fax: 570-325-8068
E-mail: barquelioness@yahoo.com
Website: www.youthservicesagency.org

LORD NELSON

Flag: United Kingdom
Rig: Barque, three-masted
Homeport: Southampton, United Kingdom
Normal cruising waters: United Kingdom (summer), Canary Islands (winter)
Sparred length: 180'
LOA: 140' 5"
LOD: 133'
LWL: 121' 5"
Draft: 13' 6"
Beam: 29' 6"
Rig height: 108'
Freeboard: 6' 8"
Sail area: 11,030 square feet
Tons: 368 GRT
Power: twin 260 HP
Hull: steel

The 180-foot, three-masted barque *Lord Nelson* was built in 1986 for the Jubilee Sailing Trust to encourage integration between able-bodied and physically disabled people by offering them the opportunity to experience the excitement of tall ship sailing together. Voyages last from four to eleven days, departing from a wide variety of ports and sailing in the English Channel, and the North and Irish Seas. A winter season of voyages based in the Canary Islands is also available. Above deck, the ship's equipment enables physically disabled crew to work alongside their able-bodied crewmates. Features include power steering, wide decks to accommodate wheelchairs, a speaking compass, powered lifts between decks, and Braille marking. Below are specially designed wheelchair-accessible cabins, showers, and heads. Voyages are open to anyone between the ages of 16 to 70+ with or without sailing experience. Twenty people with physical disabilities, including eight wheelchair users, serve alongside an equal number of able-bodied people. There is a permanent crew of ten including a medically trained person and a cook. *Lord Nelson* participates annually in the Sail Training International Tall Ships Races.

Who sails: Physically disabled and able-bodied people, aged 16 to 70+
Program type: Sail training for paying trainees; integration of physically disabled and able-bodied people through the medium of tall ship sailing
Designer: Colin Mudie
Built: 1986: Wivenhoe, UK, James W. Cook & Co., Ltd.
Certfication: Lloyds 10Oal A1
Crew: 10 **Trainees-passengers:** 40
Contact: Ms Amanda Butcher, Jubilee Sailing Trust, Jubilee Yard, Hazel Road, Woolston, Southampton, Hampshire S019 7GB, United Kingdom
Tel: 44-23-8044-9108
Fax: 44-23-8044-9145
E-mail: jst@jst.org.uk
Website: www.jst.org.uk

Flag: USA
Rig: Square topsail schooner
Homeport:
Newport Beach,CA
Sparred Length: 122'
LOA: 78'
LOD: 76'
LWL: 72'
Draft: 9'
Beam: 23'
Freeboard: 5'
Rig height: 94'
Sail Area: 4,669 square feet
Tons: 94 GRT
Power: Cat 3306B - 290 HP
hundested variable pitch propeller
Hull: wood

LYNX

The square topsail schooner *Lynx* has been designed and built to interpret the general configuration and operation of a privateer schooner or naval schooner from the War of 1812, the original *Lynx* being a "letter of marque" Baltimore Clipper commissioned during the opening days of the war. Serving effectively as a blockade-runner and offensive weapon of war, she was among the first ships to defend American freedom. Dedicated to all those who cherish the blessings of America, *Lynx* sails as a living history museum, providing inspiration and resolve at this time in our nation's history. She is fitted with period ordnance and flies flags and pennants from the 1812 era. To complement her historic character, the *Lynx* crew members wear period uniforms and operate the ship in keeping with the maritime traditions of early 19th century America. *Lynx* also operates as a sail training vessel to serve as a classroom for the study of historical, environmental, and ecological issues. In addition, she undertakes "cruises of opportunity" that lead to personal growth and awareness through the experience of life at sea aboard a traditional sailing vessel. *Lynx* is operated by the Lynx Educational Foundation a non-profit 501-(c) (3) organization.

Who sails: Schools groups from elementary age thru college. Troops, individuals, families, and company charters
Program type: Sail training; maritime history; Life, Earth, and Physical Science; charters; team building; public sails and dockside programs
Season: Year-round
Designer: Melbourne Smith - International Historical Watercraft Society
Built: Rockport, ME, Rockport Marine; launched July 28, 2001 in Rockport, ME
Coast Guard certification: Passenger Vessel (Subchapter T)
Crew: 8 **Trainees-passengers:** 40 daysails, 6 overnight
Contact: Jeffrey Woods, Director of Operations, Lynx Educational Foundation, 509 29th Street, Newport Beach, CA. 92663 USA
Tel: 866-446-5969 **Fax:** 949-723-1958
E-mail: lynxdirector@adelphia.net
Website: www.privateerlynx.org

MADELINE

MADELINE

SPECIFICATIONS

Flag: USA
Rig: Gaff topsail schooner, two-masted
Homeport: Traverse City, Michigan
Normal cruising waters: Upper Great Lakes
Sparred length: 92'
LOA: 55' 6"
LWL: 52'
Draft: 7' 7"
Beam: 16' 2"
Rig height: 71'
Freeboard: 2' 2"
Sail area: 2,270 square feet
Tons: 42 GRT

The *Madeline* is a reconstruction of a mid-19th-century schooner, typical of the trading schooners that once sailed the upper Great Lakes. The original *Madeline* was once the first EuroAmerican School in the Grand Traverse region and for a short time served as a lightship in the Straits of Mackinac. Launched in 1990, the modern *Madeline* was built over period of five years by volunteers of the Maritime Heritage Alliance (MHA), using traditional methods and materials. From her homeport, Traverse City, Michigan, she has sailed with her volunteer crew on all five Great Lakes, visiting over 60 ports with dockside tours and historical interpretation. *Madeline* is the State of Michigan's official tall ship and is designated as the City of Traverse City's goodwill ambassador. *Madeline's* dockside programs bring visitorson board to learn about schooners and Great Lakes history first-hand. Crewmembers, trained as historical interpreters, share their knowledge of history, marlinespike skills, and wooden boat building. School programs with special hands-on activities are also available. The Maritime Heritage Alliance, a nonprofit organzation, fosters the study and practice of upper Great Lakes' maritime history. MHA programs, focusing on building and operating indigenous crafts, include crew training, traditional boat carpentry, and other wooden boat maintenance skills.

Who sails: Trained crew members of the Maritime Heritage Alliance; *Madeline* is associated with the Association for Great Lakes History
Program type: Adult sail training and maritime history
Designer: Kenneth (Bob) Core
Built: 1990: Traverse City, MI, Maritime Heritage Alliance
Coast Guard certification: Uninspected Vessel
Crew: 9
Contact: Ms. Kelly Curtis, Office Manager, Maritime Heritage Alliance, 322 Sixth Street, Traverse City, MI 49684 USA
Tel: 231-946-2647
Fax: 231-946-6750
E-mail: mhatc@earthlink.net
Website: www.mhatc.net

Flag: USA
Rig: Staysail schooner, three masted
Homeport: Kaneohe Bay, Hawaii
Normal cruising waters: Hawaiian Islands
Sparred length: 96'
LOA: 85'
LOD: 75'
LWL: 63'
Draft: 8'
Beam: 20'
Rig height: 65'
Freeboard: 5'
Sail area: 2,000 square feet
Tons: 68 GRT
Power: 210 HP
Hull: steel

MAKANI OLU (Gracious Wind)

The *Makani Olu* (Gracious Wind) is owned and operated by Marimed Foundation, a non-profit organization involved with sail training since 1988. The 96-foot, three-masted staysail schooner, retrofitted for sail training in Hawaiian waters, is the central component of a model experiential education and treatment program for at-risk adolescents built around ocean voyaging. Voyaging challenges and experiences are designed to be powerful and transformational. From *Makani Olu's* home port in Kaneohe Bay on Oahu, cadets make a series of six-day voyages throughout the Hawaiian Island chain. While learning to operate the sailing ship, the cadets learn marine, navigation and team-building skills. Elderhostel International provides sail training experiences aboard *Makani Olu*, as well. These programs feature a six-day voyage that includes hands-on opportunities to sail and operate the ship, additional learning opportunities at ports-of-call, and a chance to see and experience the islands of Maui, Molokai, Lanai and Oahu as few people, even Hawaii residents, have. The *Makani Olu* is also available to youth, families and community organizations for day, weekend and six-day sail training and team building trips.

Who sails: Groups and individuals of all ages
Program type: Sail training for paying trainees; fully accredited sea education in marine science, maritime history, and ecology, as well as service learning, in cooperation with accredited institutions and other organized groups, and as informal in-house programming
Season: Year-round
Designer: Thomas Kolvin
Built: 1998: St. Augustine, FL, Schrieber
Coast Guard certification: Sailing School Vessel (Subchapter R)
Crew: 5 **Trainees-passengers:** 30 daysails, 20 overnight
Contact: Matthew Claybaugh, Ph.D., President and CEO, Marimed Foundation, 45-021 Likeke Place, Kaneohe, HI 96744 USA
Tel: 808-236-2288 **Fax:** 808-235-1074
E-mail: info@marimed.org
Website: www.marimed.org

MAKULU II

SPECIFICATIONS

Flag: USA
Rig: Ketch
Homeport: Dover, DE
Normal Cruising Waters:
Worldwide
LOA: 43'
Draft: 6'
Beam: 13'
Rig height: 55'
Freeboard: 5'
Tons: 27 GRT
Power: 75 HP Yanmar
Hull: fiberglass

Reach the World is an organization that uses technology and travel to bring the world into underprivileged classrooms. RTW's mission is to connect students and teachers in high-needs schools with online journeys that have the power to bring the world into the classroom, making learning come alive. Since 1998, RTW has operated three online journeys: the world circumnavigations of *Makulu*, a 43-foot ketch. On board, five crewmembers serve as eyes and ears in foreign ports for RTW's students, most of whom are elementary and middle school-age students in New York City's poorest public schools. RTW's crewmembers fill the following positions on board: captain, first mate, curriculum director, field curriculum coordinator, and science coordinator. Crewmembers work full-time.

Who sails: Full-time crewmembers, generally with a background in education. Age range tends to be early 20s through early 30s.
Program type: Digital Education
Season: Year-round
Designer: Sparkman & Stephens
Built: 1979: Nautorís Swan, Finland
Coast Guard certification: Sailing School Vessel (Subchapter R), Passenger Vessel (Subchapter T) Oceanographic Research Vessel (Subchapter U), Moored Attraction Vessel, Un-inspected Small Passenger Vessel (Subchapter C, no more than 6 passengers)
Crew: 5 **Trainees-passengers:** Total capacity is 6 persons.
Contact: Heather Halstead, Executive Director, Reach the World, 329 E 82nd Street, New York, NY 10028 USA
Tel: 212-288-6987 **Fax:** 866-411-5090
E-mail: rtwinfo@reachtheworld.org
Website: www.reachtheworld.org

SPECIFICATIONS

Flag: USA
Rig: Staysail schooner
Homeport: Seattle, Washington
Normal cruising waters: Pacific Northwest, Canada, and Alaska
Rig: Staysail schooner
Sparred length: 65'
LOA: 60'
LOD: 60'
LWL: 50'
Draft: 5' (min.) 8' (max.)
Beam: 16'
Rig Height: 65'
Freeboard: 5'
Sail area: 1,545 square feet
Tons: 38 GRT
Power: diesel
Hull: composite

MALLORY TODD

Named for Captain Mallory Todd, who served as master on American vessels during the Revolutionary War, the *Mallory Todd* is a modern 65-foot schooner built in the classic style with fireplaces and exceptionally intricate woodwork. Designed for long distance voyages, she has sailed the West Coast from Mexico to Alaska for 18 years. Sail training trips to the San Juan Islands, Canada, and Alaska via the Inside Passage, are blessed with the full bounty of nature. These trips are open to anyone between 18 and 80 with or without sailing experience. When at homeport in Seattle, she relieves the tedium of long-term cancer treatment with recreational outings for hospital patients and their caregivers under the auspices of the nonprofit Sailing Heritage Society. Together, part time volunteers, trainees, and professionals get the job done. Hands on tending the sails, steering, scrubbing, navigating, fishing, or clamming, each contributes where a need fits their abilities. Schooner *Mallory Todd* also offers corporate and private charters that provide a unique and delightful venue for business or recreational activities-be it an exclusive executive meeting or a picnic outing.

Who sails: All ages for volunteers, paying trainees, and apprentices
Program type: Sail training for crew, volunteers, trainees, and apprentices; sea education based on programmed and day to day events; passenger day sails for corporate team building or recreational events
Season: All year, but primarily May through September. MT is sometimes gone for April and May on charters to Alaska
Designer: Perry & Todd
Built: 1981: Seattle, WA
Coast Guard certification: Passenger Vessel (Subchapter T)
Crew: 2 **Trainees-passengers:** 25 daysails, 6 overnight
Contact: Captain George Todd, Sailing Heritage Society, 10042 NE 13th Street Bellevue, WA 98004 USA
Tel: 206-381-6919 **Fax:** 206-381-9556
E-mail: helpers@sailingheritage.org
Website: www.sailingheritage.org

SPECIFICATIONS

Flag: USA
Rig: Gaff topsail schooner, two-masted
Homeport: Traverse City, Michigan
Normal cruising waters: Great Lakes
Sparred length: 114'
LOD: 77'
LWL: 65'
Draft: 7' (min.) 11' (max.)
Beam: 21'
Rig height: 77'
Freeboard: 6'
Sail area: 3,000 square feet
Tons: 82 GRT
Power: 150 HP diesel
Hull: steel

MANITOU

Owned and operated by Traverse Tall Ship Co., LLC, the schooner *Manitou* is one of the largest sailing vessels on the Great Lakes. This replica of a 19th century "coaster" can accommodate 24 overnight guests and 62 passengers for day excursions. *Manitou* is fully certified by the US Coast Guard and offers day sails on Grand Traverse Bay, Lake Michigan. In addition, join us for an adventurous overnight as part of our "Floating Bed & Breakfast." Wake up in the morning to hot coffee and fresh baked muffins from the galley before sitting down to a full breakfast prepared from scratch on the wood stove. For a more in depth experience, *Manitou* offers three and four day sailing adventures to the islands, bays and coastal villages of northern Lake Michigan. In conjunction with Inland Seas Education Association *Manitou* operates the Schoolship Program, which provides an environmental, historical, and sail training education for students during the spring. The schooner offers partial as well as private charter service to family, company, and motor coach groups.

Who sails: School groups; individual, family, and corporate groups for day sails and bed & breakfast
Program type: Sail training for crew; sea education in marine science, maritime history and ecology; individual and group day sails; "Floating Bed & Breakfast"
Season: May to October
Designer: Woodin & Marean
Built: 1982: Portsmouth, NH, Roger Gagnon Steel Ship Company
Coast Guard certification: Passenger Vessel (Subchapter T)
Crew: 5 **Trainees-passengers:** 62 daysails, 24 overnight
Contact: Captain Dave McGinnis, Traverse Tall Ship Co., LLC, 13390 SW Bay Shore Drive, Traverse City, MI 49684 USA
Tel: 231-941-2000
Fax: 231-941-0520
E-mail: info@tallshipsailing.com
Website: www.talishipsailing.com

Flag: Canada
Rig: Gaff schooner
Homeport: Victoria, British Columbia
Normal cruising waters: British Columbia & Alaska coasts
Sparred Length: 92'
LOA: 77'
LOD: 75'
LWL: 59'
Draft: 11'
Beam: 15'
Rig height: 96'
Freeboard: 5'
Sail area: 3,300 square feet
Tons: 40.75 GRT
Power: 260 HP diesel
Hull: wood

MAPLE LEAF

The *Maple Leaf* is a 92-foot classic wooden schooner with a rich history of operation along the North Pacific Coast. Launched in 1904 as a private yacht for a lumber baron who spared no expense on her construction. Her second life began in the middle of the century; as a halibut schooner on the North Pacific *Maple Leaf* out-fished every other boat in the fleet. Vessel and crew became legendary, with the result being a loving rebuild of their prized *Maple Leaf*. Again no expense was spared. *Maple Leaf* fished for decades and then underwent an award-winning, six-year restoration and was re-launched in 1986. Her third incarnation now has her proudly offering sail training and eco-tourism adventures. Since 1988 *Maple Leaf* has been part of the Royal Canadian Sea Cadets sail training program. While experiencing the opportunity to sail the beautiful British Columbia coast, cadets gain an appreciation for the age-old traditions of sailing a tall ship and the inherent life and leadership skills that come from meeting new challenges. In addition to youth sailtraining, *Maple Leaf* offers 5 to 11-day eco-tourism adventures on the B.C. and Alaska coasts. These explorations of the coast's natural and cultural history are accompanied by expert naturalists and a gourmet chef. *Maple Leaf* is also available for private charter.

Who sails: Sea cadets (sail training) and charter guests
Program type: Youth sail training / Eco-tourism
Season: Sail Training: April, July, August Eco-tourism: April, May, June, September, October
Designer: William Watts
Built: 1904: Vancouver, British Columbia, Canada
Certification: Inspected passenger carrying vessel, Home Trade 3
Crew: 5 **Trainees-passengers:** 30 daysails, 18 overnight **Adult eco-tourism guests:** 9
Contact: Maple Leaf Adventures, Box 8845, 28 Bastion Square, Victoria, BC V8W 3Z1 Canada
Tel: 250-386-7245 (FUN SAIL) (outside North America), 1-888-599-5323 (inside North America)
E-mail: mapleleaf@mapleleafadventures.com
Website: www.mapleleafadventures.com

MARY E

MARY E

SPECIFICATIONS

Flag: USA
Rig: Gaff-rigged schooner with a forward square topsail
Homeport: Greenport, New York
Normal cruising waters: Long Island and Florida
Sparred Length: 75'
LOD: 53'
LWL: 49'
Draft: 6'
Beam: 14' 4"
Rig height: 42'
Freeboard: 2'
Sail area: 1,500 square feet
Tons: 16 GRT
Power: GM 471 diesel
Hull: Oak

Built in Bath, Maine in 1906, the 75' clipper schooner *Mary E* is the lone survivor of more than 4,000 commercial wooden sailing ships constructed in that celebrated "City of Ships." Originally put into service as a commercial vessel traveling from Block Island to Providence, she operated as an official United States mail carrier, also transporting cargo and passengers. The *Mary E* was later engaged in the prosperous sword fishing industry. These days she enjoys leisure day sails primarily out of Greenport, NY. She will be operating at several Maritime Festivals in and around Long Island. She will be offering custom charters at the festivals for groups and individuals. School groups are encouraged to come aboard her salt stained deck and take the helm. As she sails up and down the east coast she is available for scheduled charters.

Who sails: Students and adult passengers from 0-100 years old
Program type: Educational and Public Day Sail Charter
Season: May until October in NY- November until April in the Southeastern US
Designer: Thomas Hagan
Built: 1906:Thomas Hagan, Bath, Maine
Coast Guard certification: Passenger Vessel (Subchapter T)
Crew: 4 to 6 **Trainees-passengers:** 25 daysails 6 overnight
Contact: Captain Eric G. Van Dormolen, Hudson Marine, 210 Bellerose Ave., East Northport, NY 11731 USA
Tel: 631-332-0699
E-mail: captericvandy@aol.com
Website: www.Schoonermarye.com

SPECIFICATIONS

Flag: USA
Rig: Brigantine
Homeport: Beaufort, North Carolina
Normal cruising waters: North Carolina (summer) Caribbean (winter)
Sparred length: 52'
LOA: 36'
LWL: 32'
Draft: 7'
Beam: 12' 5"
Rig height: 55'
Freeboard: 3'
Sail area: 900 square feet
Tons: 18 GRT

MEKA II

The *Meka II* has an overall length of 54-feet and is a half-scale replica of an 18th century, two masted pirate brigantine. Captain Horatio Sinbad built the *Meka II* in Detroit, Michigan and launched her in 1967, first cruising the Great Lakes. In 1970 she found her way to the high seas through the St. Lawrence Seaway and has since earned the respect of many high seas adventurers for her sail training and historical educational voyages, following in the wake of great pirates and privateers. The *Meka II*, Captain Sinbad, and his crew are active participants in reenactments of historical context and tall ship events throughout the east coast, Bahamas, Jamaica, and Cayman Islands. The *Meka II's* homeport is Beaufort, NC where locals and tourists take pride and part in her ongoing efforts to preserve historical heritage.

Who sails: Groups and individuals of all ages
Program type: Sail training for paying trainess; sea education and maritime history, as informal in-house programming; overnight passages; dockside interpretation
Designer: Captain Sinbad & Gerald White, Westlawn
Built: 1967: Detroit, MI, Captain Sinbad
Coast Guard certification: Uninspected Vessel
Contact: Captain Horatio Sinbad, Pirate Privateer, PO Box 705, Beaufort, NC 28516 USA
Tel: 252-728-7978
E-mail: Sinbad@mail.clis.com
Website: www.pirate-privateer.com

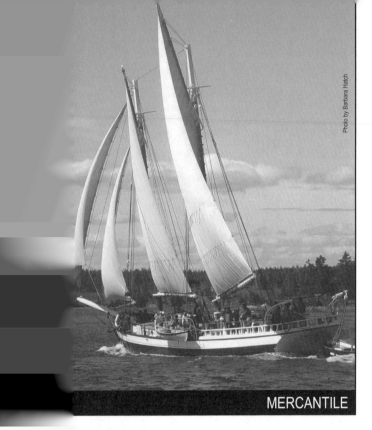
Photo by Barbara Hatch

MERCANTILE

SPECIFICATIONS

Flag: USA
Rig: Gaff schooner
Homeport: Camden, Maine
Normal cruising waters:
Penobscot Bay – off the coast of
mid-coast Maine
Sparred length: 115'
LOD: 80'
LWL: 72'
Draft: 6' board up 16' board down
Beam: 22'
Rig height: 62'
Sail area: 3,800 square feet
Freeboard: 4'
Tons: 47 GRT
Power: 14' yawl boat w/diesel motor
Hull: wood

The *Mercantile* was launched in 1916. In the early 40s, sailing out of Camden with her first passengers under the ownership of Capt. Frank Swift, she became part of the original Maine Windjammer Cruises® fleet. The Schooner *Mercantile* was totally restored in 1989, by present owners Capt. Ray and Ann Williamson, and designated a National Historic Landmark. The *Mercantile* carries 29 passengers and does three-day and four-day cruises off the coast of Maine and is one of five surviving two-masted coasting schooners in the USA. She is a pure sailing vessel with cotton sails and all natural fiber running rigging. Her traditional yawl boat provides motor assist. The full time crew of four includes Captain, Cook, First Mate and Deckhand. The fifth crew position is an Apprentice, which rotates every month.

Who sails: 16 and up (any age with full boat charter)
Program type: Cruising
Season: End of May thru early October
Designer: Billings
Built: 1916: Billings Family, Little Deer Isle, Maine
Coast Guard certification: Passenger Vessel (Subchapter T)
Crew: 5   **Trainees-passengers:** 49 daysails 29 overnight
Contact: Captain Ray and Ann Williamson, owners, Maine Windjammer Cruises®, PO Box 617, Camden, Maine 04843 USA
Tel:207-236-2938 – Reservations 800-736-7981
E-mail: sail@MaineWindjammerCruises.com
Website: www.MaineWindjammerCruises.com

Flag: USA
Rig: Gaff topsail schooner, two-masted
Homeport: Biloxi, Mississippi
Normal cruising waters: Coastwise Gulf of Mexico
Sparred length: 78'
LOA: 78'
LOD: 50'
LWL: 43'
Draft: 5' 10"
Beam: 17'
Sail area: 2,499 square feet
Tons: 24 GRT
Power: 4-71 Detroit diesel
Hull: wood

MIKE SEKUL

The *Mike Sekul* is one of the two Biloxi oyster schooner replicas built as part of the Biloxi Schooner Project under the auspices of the Maritime and Seafood Industry Museum. She was launched in April of 1994 as part of the effort to preserve the maritime and seafood industry of the Mississippi Gulf Coast. Money for construction and fitting out of the *Mike Sekul* and her sister ship, *Glenn L. Swetman*, has come from donations and fundraising events. The *Mike Sekul* is available for charter for two-and-a-half hours, half-day, and full-day trips in the Mississippi Sound and to the barrier islands, Cat Island, Horn Island, and Ship Island. Walkup day sailing trips are made when she is not under charter. Groups of up to 45 passengers learn about the maritime and seafood heritage of the Gulf Coast and about the vessels working in Biloxi's seafood industry. Sailing classes are offered through local colleges and the museum's Sea and Sail Adventure summer camp. Wedding parties, Elderhostel, and school groups are also accommodated.

Who sails: Elementary students through college age, adults, and families; affiliated institutions include William Carey College, Seashore Methodist Assembly, J.L. Scoff Marine Education Center, and Mississippi State University
Program type: Sail training for paying and volunteer trainees; sea education in marine science, maritime history, and ecology in cooperation with accredited institutions and organized groups and as informal, in-house programming
Season: Year-round
Designer: Neil Covacevich **Built:** 1994: Biloxi, Mississippi, Neil Covacevich
Coast Guard certification: Passenger Vessel (Subchapter T)
Crew: 3 **Trainees-passengers:** 45 daysails - Age: 15+
Contact: Robin Krohn, Executive Director, Maritime and Seafood Industry Museum of Biloxi, PO Box 1907, Biloxi, MS 39533 USA
Tel: 228-435-6320 **Fax:** 228-435-6309
E-mail: schooner@maritimemuseum.org
Website: www.maritimemuseum.org

MINNIE V

SPECIFICATIONS

Flag: USA
Rig: Sloop
Homeport: Baltimore, Maryland
Normal cruising waters:
Baltimore Harbor
Sparred length: 69'
LOD: 45' 3"
Draft: 3'
Beam: 15' 7"
Rig height: 58'
Freeboard: 2'
Sail area: 1,450 square feet
Tons: 10 GRT
Hull: wood

The skipjack *Minnie V*, built in Wenona, Maryland, was used to dredge oysters on the Chesapeake Bay for many years. The vessel was rebuilt by the City of Baltimore in 1981 and is now owned and operated by the Living Classrooms Foundation. The Foundation uses the vessel for educational programs and as a tourist attraction offering interpretive tours of the historic port of Baltimore. While on board the *Minnie V*, students learn about the oyster trade, its importance to the economy of Maryland, and the hard life of a waterman as they relive history by raising the sails on one the Chesapeake's few remaining skipjacks.

Who sails: School groups from middle school through college; individuals and families
Program type: Sea education in marine science, maritime history, and ecology in cooperation with accredited schools, colleges, and other organized groups; passenger day sails; dockside interpretation
Season: April through October
Built: 1906: Wenona, MD, Vetra
Coast Guard certification: Passenger Vessel (Subchapter T)
Crew: 2 **Trainees-passengers:** 24
Contact: Christine Truett, Director of Education Living Classrooms Foundation, 802 South Caroline Street, Baltimore, MD 21231-3311 USA
Tel: 410-685-0295
Fax: 410-752-8433
Website: www.livingclassrooms.org

Flag: Russia
Rig: Full-rigged ship
Homeport: St. Petersburg, Russia
Normal cruising waters:
West and southwest European
Sparred length: 345' 9"
LOA: 328'
LOD: 300' 9"
LWL: 254'
Draft: 18'
Beam: 44' 9"
Rig height: 149'
Freeboard: 34' 6"
Sail area: 29,997 square feet
Tons: 2,856 GRT
Power: Twin 570 HP diesels
Hull: steel

Photo by Thad Koza

MIR

Mir is regarded by many as the fastest Class A sail training ship in the world. She was the overall winner of the 1992 Columbus Race and the winner of the Cutty Sark Tall Ship Races in 1996, 1997, and 1998 under the command of Captain Victor Antonov. *Mir* was launched in 1989 at the Lenin shipyard in Gdansk, Poland, the builders of five more of the M 108 type ships: *Dar Mlodziezy, Pallada, Khersones, Druzhba*, and Nadezhda. *Mir* is the school ship of the Makaroz Maritime Academy in St. Petersburg, Russia, training future navigators and engineers for the Russian merchant fleet. Since 1990 up to 60 trainees of all ages are welcomed on board to sail along with the Russian students, learning the ropes, manning the helm, or climbing the rigging to set the sails. No previous experience is necessary. *Mir* is supported by Tall Ship Friends, a nonprofit organization in Hamburg, Germany. The goals of Tall Ship Friends are to promote sail training on square-riggers, to contribute to the further existence of these beautiful ships, and to provide an unforgettable experience for the participants. Members of Tall Ship Friends receive the quarterly Tall Ships News (English/German) and a personal sailing log.

Who sails: Students and individuals of all ages. Affiliated with Tall Ship Friends clubs in France, UK, Switzerland, Austria, Ireland, and Italy
Program type: Sail training for paying trainees; fully accredited sea education in traditional seamanship; dockside interpretation during port visits
Designer: Z. Choren
Built: 1987: Gdansk, Poland, Stocznia Gdanska
Certification: Russian registered Sailing School Vessel
Crew: 45-70 **Trainees-passengers:** up to 250 daysails, 60 overnight
Contact: Wulf Marquard, Managing Director, Tall Ship Friends Germany Schweriner Str. 17, Hamburg, D22 143 Germany
Tel: 49-40-675 635 97 **Fax:** 49-40-675 635 99
E-mail: tallshipl@aol.com
Website: www.tallship-friends.de

MIRCEA

MIRCEA

SPECIFICATIONS

Flag: Romania
Rig: Barque
Homeport: Constanta, Romania
Sparred length: 328'
LOA: 266'
LOD: 241' 6
LWL: 203'
Draft: 18'
Beam: 39' 6"
Rig height: 144'
Freeboard: 8'
Sail area: 18,837 square feet
Tons: 1320 GRT
Power: 1,100 hp Diesel
Hull: steel

Mircea is the flagship and the training vessel of the Romanian Naval Forces. The last of a quartet of sailing school ships built in Blohm & Voss Shipyard, Hamburg, Germany, in the 1930s, *Mircea* and her sister ships became the models for sailing vessels built during the last three decades. During overhaul concluded in 2002 *Mircea* has been equipped with modern navigation and communication devices that made her up-to-date despite the 65 years of age.

Who sails: Students and cadets of the Romanian Naval Academy and Romanian Petty Officer School
Program type: Schoolship for the Romanian Naval Forces' cadets
Built: 1938: Hamburg, Germany, Blohm & Voss Shipyard
Crew: 65 **Trainees-passengers:** 120
Contact: Public Affairs Officer, Romanian Naval Academy, Fulgerului Street, Constanta, Romania 900218
Tel: +40 241 643040
Fax: +40 241 643096
E-mail: relpub@navedo.anmb.ro
Website: www.anmb.ro

Flag: USA
Rig: Gaff schooner
Homeport: Camden, Maine
Normal cruising waters:
Penobscot Bay – off the coast of
mid-coast Maine
Sparred length: 60'
LOD: 46'
LWL: 40'
Draft: 6'
Beam: 13'
Rig height: 45'
Sail area: 1,200 square feet
Freeboard: 4'
Tons: 13 GRT
Power: Propulsion engine: 60 HP
diesel
Hull: wood

MISTRESS

The *Mistress* was built 1967, Deer Island, Maine for private use. Before she ever hit the water, Capt. Jim Nesbit, owner of Maine Windjammer Cruises® at the time, admired and purchased her to add to his fleet as a more private 6-passenger windjammer. She was fitted out as a with 3 private cabins with its own head and sink. This vessel has filled a nitch in the industry for people who want to go windjamming but require more privacy than the larger boats offer. She is rigged in the traditional manner, block and tackle, deadeyes and lanyard etc. In 1992 this vessel was significantly rebuilt. At that time seven feet was added to her length, the beam was increased, and a lead keel was fixed externally. She also had new masts, riggings, and sails during this refit. Owned by Capt. Ray & Ann Williamson, Camden, Maine, she does weekend, 3-day, 4-day and 5-day cruises.

Who sails: 16 and up (any age with full boat charter)
Program type: Cruising
Season: End of May thru early October
Built: 1967: Deer Isle, Maine
Crew: 2
Contact: Captain Ray and Ann Williamson, owners, Maine Windjammer Cruises®, PO Box 617, Camden, Maine 04843 USA
Tel:207-236-2938 – Reservations 800-736-7981
E-mail: sail@MaineWindjammerCruises.com
Website: www.MaineWindjammerCruises.com

MYSTIC

SPECIFICATIONS

Flag: USA
Rig: Square topsail schooner, three-masted
Homeport: Mystic, Connecticut
Normal cruising waters:
New England, Chesapeake Bay, Bahamas
Sparred length: 170'
LOD: 127'
LWL: 100'
Draft: 9' 6" (min.) 18' (max.)
Beam: 34'
Rig height: 107'
Freeboard: 5'
Sail Area: 8,500 square feet
Tons: 99 tons
Power: 500 HP Lugger diesel
Hull: steel

Voyager Cruises operates the tall ship *Mystic* out of Mystic, Connecticut, June through September. *Mystic* also operates in the Bahamas December through March and the in the Chesapeake Bay area during the spring and fall. She carries 36 overnight passengers in 18 double-occupancy staterooms. Overnight passengers travel on two to six day cruises into one of our many ports-of-call. As well as being available for overnight public or chartered cruises, *Mystic* can be chartered for three-hour evening cruises and can accommodate up to 150 passengers. The deck of the *Mystic* is comfortably and tastefully appointed with a main salon/ dining area, a lounge, and the ship's store. While at our ports-of-call, passengers may swim, relax, be brought to shore to spend time, or can utilize the kayaks and other sporting equipment kept on board. Some cruises offer guest lecturers covering topics that may include photography, marine life, local history, watercolor painting, and much more.

Who sails: All ages
Season: Year-round
Designer: Marine Design
Built: 2007: TFreeport, Florida
Coast Guard certification: Passenger Vessel (Subchapter T); Moored Attraction Vessel
Crew: 14 Trainees-passengers: 150 day, 36 overnight
Contact: Captain Amy Blumberg, Voyager Cruises, 15 Holmes St., Mystic, CT 06355 USA
Tel: 800-536-0416
Fax: 860-536-0000
E-mail: amyblumberg@voyagermystic.com
Website: www.voyagermystic.com

Flag: USA
Rig: Gaff-rigged schooner
Homeport: New London, Connecticut
Normal cruising waters: Hudson River in Spring, Southeast New England in Summer, Chesapeake Bay in Fall
Sparred length: 110'
LOA: 83'
LOD: 83'
LWL: 78'
Draft: 7' 6" (min.) 13' (max.)
Beam: 25'
Rig height: 90'
Freeboard: 7'
Sail Area: 3,000 square feet
Tons: 100 GRT
Power: 175 HP diesel
Hull: steel

MYSTIC WHALER

Built in 1967 and rebuilt in 1993, the *Mystic Whaler* carries passengers and trainees on a variety of cruises, ranging from 3 hours to 5 days. In April, May, and early June, the schooner joins Clearwater on the Hudson River, for environmental education programs. Sailing from New London, CT throughout the summer months, the *Mystic Whaler* offers great sailing opportunities for both novice and experienced passengers. Three-hour Lobster Dinner Cruises are popular as are the 5-hour Day sails, or try an overnight of 2, 3 or 5 days. In September and October, the *Mystic Whaler* travels to Baltimore Maryland for three weeks of 3-day overnight sails and to participate in the Great Chesapeake Bay Schooner Race. Some of the overnight cruises have special interest extras such as lighthouse tours, sea music and full moon cruises. Two-week apprenticeship programs run throughout the season (June-September).

Who sails: School groups from elementary school through college, as well as individuals and families ages 5 and up
Program type: Sail training for crew and apprentices; sea education in maritime history and ecology based on informal programming with organized groups such as Scouts; passenger day sails and overnight passages
Season: March through November
Designer: "Chub" Crockett
Built: 1967: Tarpon Springs, Florida, George Sutton
Coast Guard certification: Passenger Vessel (Subchapter T)
Crew: 5   **Trainees-passengers:** 65 daysails, 34 overnight
Contact: Captain John Eginton, Mystic Whaler Cruises Inc., PO Box 189, Mystic, CT 06355-0189 USA
Tel: 800-697-8420
Fax: 860-535-1577
E-mail: info@mysticwhaler.com
Website: www.mysticwhaler.com

Photo by Thad Koza

NADEZHDA

SPECIFICATIONS

Flag: Russia
Rig: Ship
Homeport: Vladivostok, Russia
LOA: 359'
Draft: 21.5'
Hull: steel

The *Nadezhda*, the name is Russian word for "hope", is the last of 6 "DAR –class" full-rigged ships that were built in the Gdansk shipyard in the 1980s. *NADEZHDA* was completed in 1990, and delivered and commissioned to the Far Eastern State Maritime Academy in Vladivostok, Russia in 1991.

Contact: FESMA (Far Eastern State Maritime Academy), 50a Verkhneportovaya St., Vladivostok, 690059 Russia
E-mail: fesma@ints.vtc.ru

SPECIFICATIONS

Flag: USA
Rig: Ketch
Homeport: San Francisco, California
Normal cruising waters: San Francisco Bay
Sparred length: 57'
LOD: 47'
LWL: 39'
Draft: 6' 6"
Beam: 14'
Freeboard: 5'
Rig height: 58'
Tons: 23 GRT
Power: 85 HP Perkins
Hull: wood

NEHEMIAH

Nehemiah has circumnavigated the world twice and also, the Pacific Rim. The hull is Port Orford cedar over oak frames. The deck is planked with Kapur. *Nehemiah* is used for tallship-style sail-training during day sails at this time. Programing is being developed on the theme of the "Barque of St. Peter" as a metaphor of the Catholic Church.

Who sails: Any age with emphasis on youth
Program type: Basic sail-training and character-building through role models
Season: April - December
Designer: William Garden
Built: 1971: Joseph Meyr, Carpenteria, CA
Crew: 2 Trainees-Passengers: 33 daysails
Coast Guard certification: Passenger Vessel (Subchapter T)
Contact: Rod Phillips, Captain, Sailing Vessel Nehemiah, 92 Seabreeze Drive, Richmond, CA 94804 USA
Tel: 510-234-5054
E-mail: captain@sailingacross.com
Website: www.sailingacross.com

NIAGARA

SPECIFICATIONS

Flag: USA
Rig: Brig
Homeport: Erie, Pennsylvania
Normal cruising waters:
Great Lakes and connecting waters
Sparred length: 198'
LOA: 123'
LOD: 116'
LWL: 110'
Draft: 11'
Beam: 32' 6"
Rig height: 120'
Sail area: 11,600 square feet
Tons: 162 GRT
Power: twin 200 HP diesels
Hull: wood

The US Brig *Niagara* was built in 1988 as a reconstruction of the warship aboard which Oliver Hazard Perry won the Battle of Lake Erie in 1813 during the War of 1812. Her mission is to interpret War of 1812 history, promote the Commonwealth of Pennsylvania and the Erie Region, and to preserve the skills of square-rig seafaring. Each summer U.S. Brig *Niagara* sails out of Erie, PA and makes passages to other ports throughout the Great Lakes. On summer day sails, overnight training sails, and longer voyages, the 18 professional crewmembers teach up to 20 live-aboard trainees the way of a ship at sea, square-rig seafaring skills, and how to assist in conducting public tours at port festival events. All hands onboard experience a one-of-a-kind adventure within the confines of a large wooden square-rigger. Deckhands and trainees sleep in hammocks on a single berth deck, which is converted three times a day into a mess hall for meals. They are divided into watches and divisions and taught to climb aloft, stand watch, handle sails, and many other skills of the seaman. Together, the crew and trainees learn the value of maintaining effective communication, camaraderie, discipline, and respect for one another while serving the broader needs of the ship.

Who sails: Trainees must be at least 16 years-old, ambulatory, and of average physical fitness. No previous experience is required.
Program type: Experiential-education with focus on seamanship skills, the technology of a sailing warship, and War of 1812 history. During any three week course the vessel conducts daysails, overnight training sails, and/or voyages from Erie to other Great Lakes ports for public visitation. College history programs (3-credit) are also available through partner universities.
Designer: Melbourne Smith **Built:** 1988: Erie, PA
Coast Guard certification: Sailing School Vessel (Subchapter R) and Attraction Vessel
Crew: 18 professionals, 22 trainees (3-week, live-aboard) and up to 50 daysail students
Contact: Captain Wesley W. Heerssen, Jr., Pennsylvania Historical and Museum Commission, Erie Maritime Museum, 150 East Front Street, Suite 100, Erie, PA 16507 USA
Tel: 814-452-2744 **Fax:** 814-455-6760
E-mail: sail@brigniagara.org **Website:** www.brigniagara.org

SPECIFICATIONS

Flag: Brazil/USA
Rig: 15th century caravel redondo
Homeport: Nuevo Vallarta, Mexico
Sparred length: 92'
LOA: 68'
LOD: 65'
LWL: 58'
Draft: 7'
Beam: 18'
Rig height: 54'
Sail area: 1,919 square feet
Freeboard: 5'
Tons: 37 GRT
Power: 128 HP diesel
Hull: wood

NINA

The *Nina* is a historically accurate replica of a 15th century caravel. John Sarsfield, the leading authority on caravels, was designer and builder until his death halfway through the project. Jonathon Nance, a noted British designer and archaeologist, finished the vessel and designed the sail plan and rig. She was built in Valenca, Bahia, Brazil, using only traditional tools and techniques of the 15th century. Her mission today is to educate the public on the "space shuttle" of the 15th century, and over one million students and teachers have visited the *Nina* since her completion in 1992. Starting in November 2004 the *Nina* will be in Nuevo Vallarta, Mexico taking passengers on 2-hour day sails. The ship is available for filming and charters. Look for our new caravel coming to the Cayman Islands in winter 2005.

Who sails: families and individuals of all ages
Program type: Day sailing
Designer: John Sarsfield/Jonathon Nance
Built: 1988-1991: Valenca, Brazil, John Sarsfield/Jonathon Nance/Ralph Eric Nicholson
Coast Guard certification: Attraction Vessel
Crew: 6 **Trainees-passengers:** 50 daysails
Contact: Morgan P. Sanger, Captain/Director, Columbus Foundation, Box 305179, St. Thomas, VI 00803
Tel: 284-495-4618
Fax: 284-495-4616
E-mail: columfnd@surfbvi.com
Website: www.thenina.com

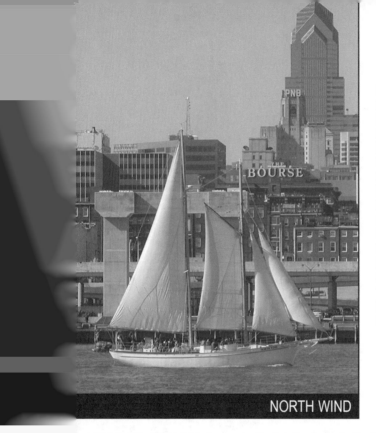

NORTH WIND

SPECIFICATIONS

Flag: USA
Rig: Staysail schooner
Homeport: Philadelphia, Pennsylvania
Normal cruising waters: Delaware and Chesapeake Bays
LOA: 75'
LOD: 57'
LWL: 47'
Draft: 8'
Beam: 16'
Rig height: 70'
Freeboard: 5'
Sail area: 1,457 square feet
Tons: 40 GRT
Power: Volvo diesel
Hull: steel

Philadelphia City Sail, Inc. is a nonprofit educational organization that inspires Philadelphia area youth to value themselves and their education, with a focus on reaching underserved populations. Through sailing and maritime topics, students gain hands-on experiences while learning about the environment, science, mathematics, and maritime arts. Philadelphia City Sail empowers youth to think critically and act responsibly as they expand their worldview.

Who sails: Middle through high school students and individuals of all ages
Program type: Sail training for Philadelphia youth in the maritime arts and sciences
Designer: Woodin and Marin
Built: 1995: Treworgy Yachts, FL
Crew: 3 - 5 **Trainees - passengers:** 30 day sails, 12 overnight
Coast Guard certification: Passenger Vessel (Subchapter T)
Contact: Michele Raymond, Executive Director or Brett Hart, Captain, Philadelphia City Sail, 475 N. 5th Street, Philadelphia, PA 19123 USA
Tel: 215-413-0451
Fax: 215-422-0737
E-mail: brett@citysail.org
Website: www.citysail.org

Flag: UK
Rig: Schooner, two-masted
Homeport: Road Town,
Tortola, BVI
Normal cruising waters:
Eastern Caribbean
Sparred length: 115'
LOA: 88'
LOD: 73'
LWL: 65'
Draft: 9'
Beam: 20'
Rig height: 92'
Sail area: 4,600 square feet
Freeboard: 5'
Tons: 70 GRT
Power: 210 HP diesel
Hull: Steel

OCEAN STAR

Launched in 1991 as the school ship for Ocean Navigator Magazine, *Ocean Star* now sails under the banner of Sea-mester programs as a college level semester voyage. Sea-mester programs offer 20, 40 and 80-day semesters aboard that are based on principles of experiential and adventure education. Learning through interaction and practical activities, the primary academic foci of oceanography, marine science, communication, and leadership skills development are brought from the textbook into real-life application. Under the guidance of professional staff, our students earn college credits for both academic and vocational activities, while piloting *Ocean Star* throughout the islands of Lesser Antilles. Along the way the crew visit up to 20 individual Caribbean islands, undertaking research and service projects with local government and private organizations while simultaneously working toward certificates in sailing and scuba diving. No experience is necessary. Programs are available to high school seniors, high school graduates, and college-aged students.

Who sails: 12th grade high school students (fall semester), high school graduates and college age students (fall, spring, and summer)
Program type: Experiential education semesters for high school graduates and college students; accredited academics with sail and scuba training; service projects and adventure travel
Season: Year-round
Designer: Bill Peterson
Built: 1991: Norfolk, VA, Marine Metals
Crew: Crew: 4 **Trainees-passengers:** 14
Certification: MCA (UK) inspected Small Commercial Vessel up to 24 meters Load Line, Category 1 service
Contact: Sea-mester Programs, PO Box 5477, Sarasota, FL 34277 USA
Tel: 941-924-6789 or 800-317-6789 **Fax:** 941-924-6075
E-mail: info@seamester.com
Website: www.seamester.com

sss ODYSSEY

SPECIFICATIONS

Flag: USA
Rig: Yawl
Homeport: Tacoma, Washington
Normal cruising waters: Puget Sound/ San Juan Islands and Canadian Gulf Islands
LOA: 88' 6"
LWL: 62'
Draft: 11'
Beam: 18'
Rig height: 105'
Sail area: 3,453 square feet
Power: 671 Grey Marine diesel
Hull: white cedar and mahogany over white oak

The *Odyssey* is a co-ed Sea Scout Ship offering a highly successful, year round sail training program for youth 14-20 as well as adult volunteers. She is also Tacoma's official tall ship. The *Odyssey* was designed by Olin Stephens as a birthday gift from Mrs. Barklie Henry to her husband. The Odyssey was built at the Nevins' yard, City Island, New York and launched in 1938. The ship sails every Thursday night, September to June, from the Foss Waterway in Tacoma, Washington. She is available for crewed 3 and 4 hour public and private charters on many weekends or longer time periods by special arrangements. She sails in the San Juan Islands for 8-10 weeks during the summer for a week long, High Adventure/ Learn to Sail opportunity with priority given to scouting programs from around the world. Our website will give you a glance at historical and contemporary photos as well as further program and chartering information.

Who sails: Boys and girls ages 14 -20
Program type: Boy Scouts of America Sea Scout Ship
Season: Tacoma - September to June, San Juan Islands - June thru August
Designer: Sparkman-Stephens
Built: 1938: Henry B. Nevins, City Island, NY
Crew: 10-20 **Trainees-passengers:** 45 daysails 17 overnight
Coast Guard certification: Passenger Vessel (Subchapter T)
Contact: Chris Dorsey, Sea Scout Ship *Odyssey* Ship 190, PO Box 1433, Tacoma, WA 98401 USA
Tel: 253-925-0956
E-mail: cdorsey@harbornet.com
Website: www.sssodyssey.org

Flag: USA
Rig: Ketch
Homeport: Key West, Florida
Normal cruising waters:
Worldwide
LOA: 93'
LOD: 80'
Draft: 11' 6"
Beam: 18' 3"
Rig height: 88'
Tons: 40 GRT
Power: 2 diesel Kohler 13.5 KW
generators
Hull: steel

ODYSSEY

Ocean Alliance, Inc., a 501(c)3 organization, was founded in 1971 by renowned biologist Dr. Roger Payne. Led by Dr. Payne and Chief Executive Officer Iain Kerr, Ocean Alliance maintains a rich history of research and discovery and works toward whale and ocean conservation through global research programs and public education initiatives. In response to growing concern about the impact of chemical pollution in the marine environment, Ocean Alliance launched the Voyage of the *Odyssey* in March of 2000 to establish the first ever global baseline dataset on the concentration, distribution and potential effects of synthetic contaminants in the world's oceans. To achieve this goal, Ocean Alliance's research vessel *Odyssey*, a 93-foot ketch, circumnavigated the globe collecting biopsy samples from marine mammals, as well as squid and predatory fish in the equatorial zone. Ocean Alliance has now turned our attention to the treasure trove of data, the tens of thousands of images, hundreds of hours of video and sound recordings generated by the expedition.

Designer: Bill Peterson
Built: 1976: Whangarei, New Zealand
Crew: 4 - 9
Coast Guard certification: Sailing School Vessel (Subchapter R)
Contact: Iain Kerr, CEO, Ocean Alliance, 191 Weston Road, Lincoln, MA 01773 USA
Tel: 781-259-0423 **Fax:** 781 259 0288
E-mail: question@oceanalliance.org
Website: www.oceanalliance.org

HMCS ORIOLE

SPECIFICATIONS

Flag: Canada
Rig: Marconi rigged ketch
Homeport: Esquimalt, British Columbia, Canada
LOA: 102'
LOD: 91'
LWL: 19'
Draft: 10'
Beam: 19'
Rig height: 67' 8"
Sail area: 15,700 square feet
Freeboard: 6' 8" (forward) 4' 9" (aft)
Power: 261 HP Detroit Diesel

The oldest commissioned ship in the Canadian Navy has a pedigree that goes back to 1880 when George Gooderham sailed the first *Oriole* as the flagship of the Royal Canadian Yacht Club of Toronto. Gooderham, who was for several years Commodore of the Toronto club, built *Oriole II* in 1886 and *Oriole III* in 1909. In 1921, the last of the *Orioles* - then called *Oriole IV*, was thought to be the most majestic of all R.C.Y.C. flagships. She was started by the Toronto Dominon Shipbuilding company but due to labor problems, was completed by George Lawley & Sons, a Boston shipyard. She was launched at Neponset, Mass, June 4, 1921, commissioned *HMCS Oriole* June 19, 1952 and two years later the navy moved her to the West Coast to become a training vessel to VENTURE the Naval Officer Training Center. She was purchased by the Royal Canadian Navy in 1957. HMCS *Oriole* is both the oldest vessel and the longest serving commissioned ship in the Canadian Navy. Her distinctive red, white, and blue spinnaker displays an orange oriole.

Program type: Training vessel of the Canadian Navy
Built: 1921
Crew: 5 **Trainees-passengers:** 16
Contact: Embassy of Canada, 501 Pennsylvania Avenue, NW, Washington, DC 20001 USA
Tel: 202-682-1740
Fax: 202-682-7726

Flag: Canada
Rig: Gaff topsail schooner
Homeport: Victoria, British Columbia, Canada
Normal cruising waters: Coastal waters of British Columbia
Sparred length: 138' 7"
LOA: 115'
LOD: 108' 7"
LWL: 89' 6"
Draft: 11' 6"
Beam: 22' 2"
Rig height: 115'
Sail area: 7,564 square feet
Freeboard: 3' 7"
Tons: 175 GRT
Power: twin diesels
Hull: wood

PACIFIC GRACE

Built over seven winters, *Pacific Grace* was launched in her homeport of Victoria, British Columbia on October 9, 1999. She replaces the *Robertson II*, one of Canada's last original Grand Banks fishing schooners, and is built along the lines of the old ship using traditional methods. After three years sailing, *Pacific Grace* embarked on a nine-month offshore voyage in 2003 which saw her travel down the west coast of North and Central America and on to exotic ports of call in the South Pacific. During the summer months of July and August 10-day trips are available to anyone aged 13 - 25. In the spring and fall shorter school programs are offered. Each year over one thousand young people participate aboard *Pacific Grace* in an experience which combines all aspects of shipboard life from galley chores to helmsmanship, with formal instruction in navigation, pilotage, seamanship and small boat handling. S.A.L.TS. is a registered charitable organization that seeks to develop through shipboard life in a Christian context, the spiritual, mental and physical potential of young people.

Who sails: Students and young adults ages 13 – 25
Program type: Sail training for paying trainees
Season: March through October
Built: 1999: Victoria, British Columbia, Canada, SALTS
Certification: Passenger Vessel, Sailing School Vessel
Crew: 5 **Trainees-passengers:** 40 daysails, 30 overnight
Contact: Lauren Hagerty, Executive Director, Sail and Life Training Society (SALTS), PO Box 5014, Station B, Victoria, British Columbia V8R 6N3 Canada
Tel: 250-383-6811
Fax: 250-383-7781
E-mail: info@salts.ca
Website: www.salts.ca

PACIFIC SWIFT

PACIFIC SWIFT

SPECIFICATIONS

Flag: Canada
Rig: Square topsail schooner, two-masted
Homeport: Victoria, British Columbia, Canada
Normal cruising waters: Coastal waters of British Columbia
Sparred length: 111'
LOA: 81'
LOD: 77' 3"
LWL: 73'
Draft: 10' 8"
Beam: 20' 6"
Rig height: 88'
Sail area: 5,205 square feet
Freeboard: 3' 6"
Tons: 98 GRT
Power: 220 HP diesel
Hull: wood

Built as a working exhibit at Expo '86 in Vancouver, British Columbia, the *Pacific Swift* has sailed over 100,000 deep-sea miles on training voyages for young crewmembers. Her offshore travels have taken her to Australia and Europe, to remote communities on Easter and Pitcairn Islands, and to many other unusual and far-flung ports of call. When not offshore, the *Swift* provides coastal sail training programs among the cruising grounds of the Pacific Northwest, which include shorter school programs in the spring and fall, and 10-day summer trips open to anyone aged 13 to 25. Each year over one thousand young people participate in an experience, which combines all aspects of shipboard life, from galley chores to helmsmanship, with formal instruction in navigation, pilotage, seamanship, and small boat handling. Rooted in Christian values, SALTS believes that training under sail provides the human spirit a real chance to develop and mature. SALTS received the 1998 Sail Training Program of the Year Award from the American Sail Training Association.

Who sails: Individuals and groups
Program type: Offshore and coastal sail training
Season: March through October
Built: 1986: Vancouver, British Columbia, Canada, SALTS
Certification: Passenger vessel, Sailing School Vessel
Crew: 5 **Trainees-passengers:** 35 Age: 13 – 25
Contact: Lauren Hagerty, Executive Director, Sail and Life Training Society (SALTS), PO Box 5014, Station B, Victoria, British Columbia V8R 6N3 Canada
Tel: 250-383-6811
Fax: 250-383-7781
E-mail: info@salts.ca
Website: www.salts.ca

SPECIFICATIONS

Flag: Russia
Rig: Full-rigged ship
Homeport:
Vladivostok, Russia
Normal cruising waters:
Worldwide
Sparred length: 356' 4"
Draft: 22' 4"
Beam: 45' 9"
Hull: steel

PALLADA

Pallada is the fifth ship of the *Dar Mlodziezy*-class built in Poland during the 1980s. Unlike her white- hulled sisters, *Pallada* has a black hull with false gunports and resembles the great Russian Barque *Kruzenshtern*. She is named for the Greek goddess Pallas Athena. She is owned by Dalryba, a conglomerate of fishing companies, and offers sail training to foreign marine-college cadets. Though her homeport is in Vladivostok, which is on the far eastern coast of Russia, *Pallada* voyages widely. She visited the West Coast of the United States in 1989 and Europe in 1991; participated in the European Columbus Regatta in 1992; completed a circumnavigation to celebrate the 500th anniversary of the Russian navy in 1996; and sailed in the 1997 Hong Kong to Osaka race. *Pallada* sails with a compliment of 143 cadets and a permanent crew of 56 officers, teachers, and professionals. With twenty-six sails and masts soaring 162 feet above the deck, *Pallada* combines traditional sail training with a modern maritime college curriculum.

Who sails: Marine-college cadets
Program type: Sail training and sea education for marine-college cadets
Season: Year-round
Designer: Zygmunt Choren
Built: 1989: Gdansk, Poland
Crew: Crew: 56 **Trainees-passengers:** 143
Contact: Evgeny N. Malyavin, Far Eastern State Technical Fisheries University, 52-B, Lugovaya Street, Vladivostok 690950 Russia
Tel: +0117 42 32 44-03-06
Fax: +011 7 42 32 44-24-32

SPECIFICATIONS

Flag: Canada
Rig: Brigantine
Homeport: Toronto, Ontario, Canada
Normal cruising waters:
Great Lakes
Sparred length: 72'
LOA: 60'
LOD: 58'
LWL: 45'
Draft: 8'
Beam: 15' 3"
Rig height: 54'
Freeboard: 4'
Sail area: 2,600 square feet
Tons: 31.63 GRT
Power: 150 HP diesel
Hull: steel

PATHFINDER

Tall Ship Adventures conducts sail training on board *Pathfinder*, a square--rigged ship designed specifically for youth sail training on the Great Lakes. Since 1964 over 15,000 young people have lived and worked aboard *Pathfinder* and her sister ship, *Playfair*. Youth between the ages of 13 and 18 become the working crew on one or two week adventures, making 24-hour passages from ports all over the Great Lakes. The program is delivered by youth officers between the ages of 15 and 18, trained and qualified during Tall Ship Adventures' Winter Training Programs. The captain is the only adult on board. Every year each ship sails over 4,000 miles, spends over 40 nights at sea, and introduces 300 trainees to the tall ship experience. *Pathfinder* is owned and operated by Toronto Brigantine, Inc., a registered charity.

Who sails: In July and August, youth programs for ages 13-18; in May, June, and September, school groups from middle school through college, and interested adult group**s**
Program type: Sail training for paying trainees, including seamanship and leadership training based on informal, in-house programming; shoreside winter program; dockside interpretation. Affiliated institutions include the Canadian Sail Training Association and the Ontario Camping Association. A Bursary fund is available for qualified applicants
Designer: Francis A. Maclachian
Built: 1963: Kingston, Ontario, Canada, Kingston Shipyards
Crew: 10 **Trainees:** 25 daysails, 18 overnight
Contact: Toronto Brigantine, Inc., 249 Queen's Quay West, Ste. 111, Toronto, Ontario, M5V 2N5 Canada
Tel: 416-596-7117
Fax: 416-596- 7117
E-mail: mail@tallshipadventures.on.ca
Website: www.tallshipadventures.on.ca

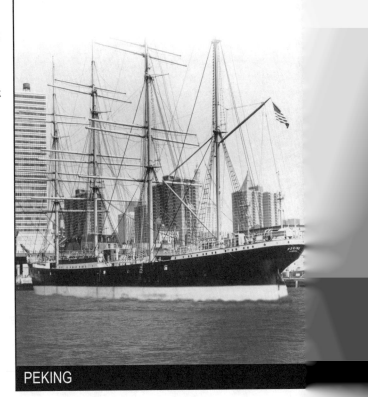

PEKING

Peking was launched in 1911 at Hamburg, Germany by the Blohm & Voss shipyard. She was owned by the F. Laeisz Company of that port, who used her to carry fuel and manufactured goods to the West Coast of South America, around Cape Horn, and return to European ports with nitrate mined in northern Chile. With her four-masted barque rig, steel hull and masts, and mid-ship bridge deck, *Peking* represents the final generation of sailing ships built for world trade. Though a product of the 20th century, she still sailed in the traditional way, with few labor saving devices or safety features. Her crew followed the standard sailing vessel routine of four hours on duty and four hours off duty, around the clock, seven days a week. *Peking* was retired in 1933, when steamers using the Panama Canal took over what was left of the nitrate trade. She served as a nautical school for boys, moored on a British River, until she was acquired by the South Street Seaport Museum in 1974. She now serves as a floating dockside exhibit. Educational programs for children and young adults take place on board, with a wet lab on the ship interpreting the biology of New York harbor.

Program type: Sea education in marine science, maritime history, and ecology based on informal, in-house programming
Built: 1911: Hamburg, Germany, Blohm & Voss
Contact: South Street Seaport Museum, 207 Front Street, New York, NY, 10038 USA
Tel: 212-748-8681
Fax: 212-748-8610
Website: www.southstseaport.org

PICKLE

SPECIFICATIONS

Flag: UK
Rig: Topsail schooner
Homeport: Gloucester
Normal cruising waters:
UK & Northern Europe
Sparred length: 96' 6"
LOA: 65'"
LOD: 61' 4"
LWL: 58' 4"
Draft: 7' 4"
Beam: 15' 4"
Rig height: 75' 0"
Sail area: 2,287 square feet
Freeboard: 6'
Tons: 67 GRT
Power: Volva Penta TAMD 145
Hull: wood

The *Pickle* has been built as a sail training vessel to an 18th century design for fast, armed top sail schooners used at that time by the British Royal Navy. They were used for carrying messages and small cargo to service the Fleet. The original HMS *Pickle* brought the sad news of Lord Nelson's death and Vice Admiral Collingwood's dispatches of the battle back to England in 1805. The 1000 mile gale ridden voyage from Cadiz to Falmouth took 9 days. The *Pickle* is used for sail training program activities.

Who Sails: 16 to 25 years
Program type: Sail Training
Season: April to October
Designer: Grumant
Built: 1995: Petrosawodsk, St Petersburg, Askold
Crew: 14 **Trainees-Passengers:** 10
Certification: Finland 2004, Re-registered United Kingdom 2004/5
Contact: Barry Johnson, Director, OCEAN YOUTH TRUST (OYT), 102 Ewe Lamb Lane, Bramcote, Nottingham, Nottinghamshire NG9 3JW United Kingdom
Tel: 0044 115 939 9825 & 0044 133 266 8253
Fax: 0044 133 266 8253
E-mail: office@oyteast.org.uk
Website: www.oyteast.org.uk

SPECIFICATIONS

Flag: Cook Islands
Rig: Barque, 3-masted
Homeport: Lunenburg,
Nova Scotia, Canada
Normal cruising waters:
Worldwide service with refits in
Lunenburg, Nova Scotia, Canada
Sparred length: 179'
LOA: 148'
LOD: 135'
LWL: 130'
Draft: 14' 6"
Beam: 24'
Rig height: 100'
Sail area: 12,450 square feet
Freeboard: 6'
Tons: 284 GRT
Power: 690 HP diesel
Hull: steel

PICTON CASTLE

The 284-ton Barque *Picton Castle* is a traditionally rigged and operated sail training ship based in Lunenburg, Nova Scotia, Canada, but best known for her voyages around the world. Over the past decade, the ship has made four global circumnavigations, as well as two trips to the Great Lakes and other jaunts up and down the coasts of the United States and Canada. Along the way we've introduced more than 600 people to the rewards of square-rigged sailing. In 2006, ASTA named us its Sail Training Program of the Year. In the spring of 2008, the *Picton Castle* will cast off on an all-new epic adventure, a 12-month voyage around the Atlantic Ocean. Join us as we cross the famed North Atlantic, explore North and Central Europe, sail south to Africa, then back across the Atlantic – and the equator – to Brazil before heading north through the islands of the West Indies. As a training ship all on board work, stand watch, and learn the ways of a square-rigged sailing ship. Workshops are conducted in wire and rope rigging, sail making, boat handling, navigation, and practical seamanship. The ship also delivers much-needed educational materials and other supplies to the remote islands she visits. In the summers between major voyages, the *Picton Castle* makes shorter voyages along the U.S. and Canadian coast. The *Picton Castle* is outfitted to the highest standard with safety gear and equipment. She is a strong, seaworthy home afloat for young adventurers devoted to learning the art of deep-water seafaring.

Who sails: Men and women ages 18 and older on major voyages, 16 years and up on shorter training cruises
Program type: Deep water sail training; maritime education in cooperation with various institutes and organized groups; comprehensive instruction in the arts of seafaring under sail; dockside school visits and receptions; charitable educational/medical supply to isolated islands
Season: Year-round
Designer: Masting and rigging, decks and layout: Daniel Moreland, MM - Stability, calculations and ballasting: Daniel Blachley, NA/ME Webb Institute
Certification: Registered and certified as a Sail Training Vessel for worldwide service by the Cook Islands Ministry of Transportation
Crew: 10 **Trainees-passengers:** 40 coed
Contact: Barque PICTON CASTLE, PO Box 1076, Lunenburg, Nova Scotia B0J 2C0 Canada
Tel: 902-634-9984 **Fax:** 902-634-9985
E-mail: info@picton-castle.com
Website: www.picton-castle.com

SPECIFICATIONS

Flag: USA
Rig: Snow brig
Homeport: Dana Point, California
Normal cruising waters: Point Conception to Ensenada, Mexico
Sparred length: 130'
LOD: 98'
Draft: 9'
Beam: 24' 6"
Rig height: 104'
Sail area: 7,600 square feet
Freeboard: 8'
Tons: 99 GRT
Power: diesel
Hull: wood

PILGRIM

The *Pilgrim* is a full-scale replica of the ship immortalized by Richard Henry Dana in his classic book *Two Years Before the Mast*. Owned and operated by the Ocean Institute, *Pilgrim* is dedicated to multidisciplinary education. During the school year, the Ocean Institute offers an 18-hour, award-winning living history program that offers a hands-on exploration of literature, California history, and group problem solving in which crewmembers recreate the challenge of shipboard life. Students live like sailors of the 1830s as they hoist barrels, row in the harbor, stand night watches, swab the decks, and learn to cope with a stern captain. On summer evenings, audiences are treated to the sights and sounds of the sea as the *Pilgrim's* decks come alive with theatrical and musical performances. In late summer the *Pilgrim* sails on her annual cruise with an all volunteer crew to ports along the California coast as a goodwill ambassador for the City of Dana Point. She returns in September to lead the annual tall ship parade and festival.

Who sails: Student groups and individual volunteers
Program type: Maritime living history and volunteer sail training
Season: Year-round
Designer: Ray Wallace
Built: 1945: Holbaek, Denmark, A. Nielsen
Coast Guard certification: Uninspected Vessel
Crew: 35 **Dockside visitors:** 50
Contact: Daniel Stetson, Director of Maritime Affairs Ocean Institute, 24200 Dana Point, Dana Point, CA 92629 USA
Tel: 949-496-2274
Fax: 949-496-4296
E-mail: dstetson@ocean-institute.org
Website: www.ocean-institute.org

Flag: USA
Rig: Skipjack
Homeport: Greenport, New York
Normal cruising waters: Long Island Sound, Peconic Bay Estuary, Block Island Sound, Key West (winters)
Sparred length: 57'
LOA: 54'
LOD: 34'
LWL: 31'
Draft: 3 feet (board up)
Beam: 11'
Rig height: 40'
Sail area: 900 square feet
Freeboard: 3'
Tons: 8 GRT
Power: diesel, electric OB
Hull: wood

PILGRIM

Join adventure eco-cruises on the beautiful Peconic Bay's estuary. Join Capt. Ted Charles, of *Mary E* fame, aboard this historic skipjack *Pilgrim*. Originally designed to work the shallow oyster grounds of the Chesapeake Bay under sail, her 2½ foot draft allows access to the most beautiful secluded beaches and creeks of the Peconic Bay estuary. In some areas, shipmates may be able to wade ashore to observe marine life in the shallows. In addition, *Pilgrim* will carry one or two kayaks and tow a 20' sailing "sharpie" with an even shallower 6" draft for extended explorations of the myriad small bays, creeks, and flats. Shipmates may observe seldom seen water fowl, marine life, and aquatic plants. A birder's delight! Optional itineraries will be even more adventurous. More extended itineraries might offer overnight voyages to the Connecticut River, Port Jefferson sand dunes, Stonington, CT and others even more ambitious. These will include large nature preserves and wild habitat. There will also be informal instruction in sailing and seamanship, if you wish to participate.

Who sails: Ratsey, Doyle, others ('92-'98)
Program type: Instructional eco-tours, recreational, explorational**Season:** Year-round
Season: April-October, southern waters optional
Designer: Chappelle/Richardson
Built: 1978: Jim Richardson, Solomon Island, Chesapeake
Coast Guard certification: Uninspected Small Passenger Vessel (Subchapter C, no more than 6 passengers)
Crew: 1 - 4 **Trainees-passengers:** 6 - 10
Contact: Captain Ted Charles, Volante Cruises, Ltd., 1062 Northville Turnpike, Riverhead, NY 11901 USA
Tel: 631-369-0468
E-mail: captted77@optonline.net
Website: www.teddy-charles.com

PIONEER

PIONEER

SPECIFICATIONS

Flag: USA
Rig: Gaff topsail schooner, two-masted
Homeport: New York, New York
Normal cruising waters: New York Harbor, Hudson River, and Atlantic Coast
Sparred length: 102'
LOA: 65'
LOD: 65'
LWL: 58' 11"
Draft: 4' 8" (min.) 12' (max.)
Beam: 21' 6"
Rig height: 79'
Sail area: 2,700 square feet
Tons: 43 GRT
Power: diesel
Hull: steel

The first iron sloop built in the United States *Pioneer* is the only surviving American iron-hulled sailing vessel. Built in 1885 by the *Pioneer* Iron Foundary in Chester, Pennsylvania, she sailed the Delaware River, hauling sand for use in the iron molding process. Ten years later *Pioneer* was converted to a schooner rig for ease of sail handling. In 1966, the then abandoned vessel was acquired and rebuilt by Russell Grinnell, Jr. of Gloucester, Massachusetts. In 1970 the fully restored schooner was donated to the South Street Seaport Museum. Today historic *Pioneer* serves as a vital education platform. Students of all ages can come on history and other curricular subjects during the hands-on program. *Pioneer* also offers corporate and private charters, Elderhostel day programs, and public sails.

Who sails: School groups from elementary school through college, charter groups, museum members, and the general public
Program type: Sail training for crew and volunteers; hands-on education sails designed to augment school curriculums in history, ecology, marine science, physics, and math; corporate and private charters, Elderhostel programs, and public sails
Season: April through October
Built: 1885: Marcus Hook, PA, Pioneer Iron Works (rebuilt 1968; Somerset, MA)
Coast Guard certification: Passenger Vessel (Subchapter T)
Crew: 3
Contact: South Street Seaport Museum, 207 Front Street, New York, NY 10038 USA
Tel: 212-748-8684
Fax: 212-748-8610
Website: www.southstseaport.org

SPECIFICATIONS

Flag: Canada
Rig: Brigantine
Homeport: Toronto, Ontario, Canada
Normal cruising waters: Great Lakes
Sparred length: 72'
LOA: 60'
LOD: 58'
LWL: 45'
Draft: 7' 6"
Beam: 16'
Rig height: 54'
Freeboard: 4'
Sail area: 2,600 square feet
Tons: 33 GRT
Power: 110 HP diesel
Hull: steel

PLAYFAIR

Tall Ship Adventures conducts sail training on board *Playfair*, a square rigged ship designed specifically for youth sail training on the Great Lakes. Since 1964 over 15,000 young people have lived and worked aboard *Playfair* and her sister ship, *Pathfinder*. Youth between the ages of 13 and 18 become the working crew on one or two week adventures, making 24-hour passages from ports all over the Great Lakes. The program is delivered by youth officers between the ages of 15 and 18. Our youth officers are trained and qualified during Tall Ship Adventures' Winter Training Programs. The captain is the only adult on board. Every year each ship sails over 4,000 miles, spends over 40 nights at sea, and introduces 300 trainees to the tall ship experience. *Playfair* is owned and operated by Toronto Brigantine, Inc., a registered charity.

Who sails: In July and August, youth programs for ages 13-18; in May, June, and September, school groups from middle school through college, and interested adult groups
Program type: Sail training for paying trainees, including seamanship and leadership training based on in-house programming; shoreside winter program; dockside interpretation. Affiliated institutions include the Canadian Sail Training Association and the Ontario Camping Association. A Bursary fund is available for qualified applicants.
Designer: Francis A. Maclachian
Built: 1973: Kingston, Ontario, Canada, Canada Dredge and Dock Co.
Crew: 10 **Trainees:** 25 daysails, 18 overnight
Contact: Toronto Brigantine, Inc., 249 Queen's Quay West, Ste. 111, Toronto, Ontario M5V 2N5 Canada
Tel: 416-596-7117 **Fax:** 416-596-7117
E-mail: mail@tallshipadventures.on.ca
Website: www.tallshipadventures.on.ca

Photo by Thad Koza

SPECIFICATIONS

Flag: Poland
Rig: Barkentine
Homeport: Gdynia, Poland
Sparred Length: 154'
Draft: 11' 6"
Beam: 26'
Hull: steel

POGORIA

Pogoria holds the distinction of being the first completed square-rigger by Polish naval architect Zygmunt Choren. Built for the Steel Workers Union in 1980, *Pogoria* has served as the background for a movie and as a floating classroom for West Island College of Quebec, Canada. She is now the flagship of the Polish Sail Training Association in Gdansk. Pogoria's hull design served as the model for three other vessels: *Iskra* for the Polish navy, *Kaliakra* for the Bulgarian navy, and *Oceania,* a specially rigged oceanographic vessel from Gdynia, Poland. Trainees live in the 4, 8,10 and 12 persons cabins, each of them has his/her own bunk. They are divided into four watches of 8-10 each. Three of those do four hours on watch and eight off while the fourth one is the galley watch, helping the cook and keeping the ship tidy. Most of the watch time is spent on look-out, taking the helm, keeping the log and trimming sails. One doesn't have to go aloft, but most trainees do for the experience and thrill of handling square sails. The permanent crew consists of Chief Mate, Boatswain, Engineer, Motorman and Cook with voluntary Master and four mates. The usual trainee age is between 15 and 25.

Who sails: Youth ages 15 - 25
Program type: Sail training
Crew: 8 **Trainees-passengers:** 40
Contact: Sail Training Association POLAND, PO BOX 113, 81-964 Gdynia 1, Poland
Tel: ++48 58 614770 **Fax:** ++48 58 206225
Website: www.pogoria.pl

Flag: USA
Rig: Brig
Homeport: Gloucester, Massachusetts
Sparred Length: 72'
Draft: 7'
Beam: 18'
Rig Height: 55'
Sail Area: 3,000 square feet
Hull: steel

POINCARE

Poincare (pwan-car-ay) can carry up to six passengers on day trips. They offer an extensive day charter schedule, sailing from East Boston, Massachusetts, often in the company of their sister ship *Formidable*. *Poincare* is rigged as a brig and sets three square sails on each mast.

Contact: Captain Keating Wilcox, Longmeadow Way, Box 403, Hamilton, MA 01936-0403 USA
Tel: 866-921-9674
Fax: 978-468-1954
E-mail: kwillcox@shore.net
Website: www.tallshipformidable.com

PRIDE OF BALTIMORE II

SPECIFICATIONS

Flag: USA
Rig: topsail schooner
Homeport: Baltimore, Maryland
Normal cruising waters: East Coast, Nova Scotia, Great Lakes and Europe
Sparred length: 157'
LOA: 105'
LOD: 100'
LWL: 91'
Draft: 12' 6"
Beam: 26' 4"
Rig height: 107'
Freeboard: 4' 4"
Sail area: 9,018 square feet
Tons: 97 GRT
Power: 2-165 hp Caterpillar diesel engines
Hull: wood

Pride of Baltimore II is a topsail schooner built to the lines of an 1812-era Baltimore Clipper. Owned by the State of Maryland and operated by Pride of Baltimore, Inc., a 501(c)(3) non profit, her mission is threefold: to promote Maryland trade and tourism; to represent the goodwill of all Maryland's citizens; and to provide a unique education platform through onboard activities and the Internet for American history and marine sciences. *Pride of Baltimore II* is available for charter and for dockside and sailing receptions in each of her destinations as well as public day sails. She can accommodate up to six paying passengers as "working guest crew" between ports of call. *Pride of Baltimore II* maintains an international sailing schedule. She sails with two rotating professional captains and a crew of eleven. Crew positions are open to qualified men and women sailors.

Who sails: Minimum professional crewmember age is 18; overnight guest crew minimum age is 16. Day sail minors must be accompanied by an adult and supervised one-on-one. There is no maximum age limit on crew or passengers
Program type: Economic development venue and goodwill ambassador for the State of Maryland and Maryland businesses.
Season: Spring, Summer, Fall
Designer: Thomas C. Gillmer **Built:** 1987-88: Baltimore, MD, G. Peter Boudreau
Coast Guard certification: Passenger Vessel (Subchapter T)
Crew: 12 **Trainees-passengers:** 6 paying guest crew (passengers) for overnight sails; 35 paying passengers for daysails, no trainees/no volunteers
Contact: Linda E. Christenson, Esq., Executive Director, Pride of Baltimore, Inc., 401 East Pratt Street, Suite 222, Baltimore, MD 21202 USA
Tel: 410-539-1151; toll-free 888-55-PRIDE **Fax:** 410-539-1190
E-mail: pride2@pride2.org
Website: www.marylandspride.org

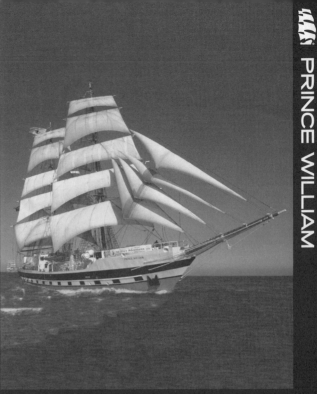

SPECIFICATIONS

Flag: United Kingdom
Rig: Brig
Homeport: Portsmouth, England
Normal cruising waters: UK,
Europe, Mediterranean, Canaries,
Azores and Caribbean
Sparred length: 195'
LOA: 159'
LOD: 159'
LWL: 133'
Draft: 15'
Beam: 33'
Rig height: 148'
Sail area: 12,503 square feet
Tons: 493 GRT
Power: 2x MTU 33OKW
Hull: steel

PRINCE WILLIAM

Prince William is one of the two purposely built sail training vessels owned by the Tall Ships Youth Trust. She is a 60 meter, steel hulled, square-rigged brig built in Appledore, Devon, and was launched in 2001. She is the first and only ship to proudly carry the name of the young prince. The Tall Ships Youth Trust, incorporating the Sail Training Association, is a registered charity founded in 1956 and is dedicated to the personal development of young people aged 16-25 through the crewing of tall ships. Every year over 2,000 people aged 16 to 75 from all over the world sail on either *Prince William* or her identical sister ship *Stavros S Niarchos*. *Prince William* operates all year round. In the summer months she frequents European and Mediterranean waters and during the winter she may head south for the Canaries, Azores and Caribbean. Youth voyages for 16-25 year olds last from 7-14 nights whereas 18+ voyages range from day sails to a 24 night Trans-Atlantic.

Who sails: Groups and individuals of all ages
Program type: Sail training for paying trainees
Season: Year-round
Designer: Burness, Corlett & Partners & Captain Mike Willoughby
Built: 2001: North Devon, United Kingdom, Appledore Shipbuilders
Crew: 6 Permanent and 13 Volunteer Crew **Trainees-passengers:** 44 daysails, 48 overnight
Contact: Tall Ships Youth Trust, 2A The Hard, Portsmouth, Hampshire P01 3PT England
Tel: +44 (0) 23 9283 2055
Fax: +44 (0) 23 9281 5769
E-mail: tallships@tallships.org
Website: www.tallships.org

SPECIFICATIONS

Flag: USA
Rig: Square topsail sloop
Homeport: Providence, Rhode Island
Normal cruising waters: East Coast US
Sparred length: 110'
LOA: 65"
LOD: 61'
LWL: 59'
Draft: 10'
Beam: 20'
Rig height: 94'
Freeboard: 8'
Sail area: 3,470 square feet
Tons: 59 GRT
Power: 170 HP diesel
Hull: fiberglass and wood

PROVIDENCE

The *Providence* is a replica of one of the first ships of the American Navy. Built as a merchant ship in the 1760s. the *Providence* (ex-Katy) went on to become the first command of John Paul Jones and one of the most successful American ships to fight in the Revolutionary War. After a successful career in which she sank or captured 40 British ships, she earned the nickname "Lucky Sloop." John Paul Jones said of her "She was the first and she was the best." The Continental Sloop *Providence* is a statewide resource administered by the *Providence* Maritime Heritage Foundation and the City of *Providence*, Rhode Island. The primary mission of the *Providence* is to inspire and educate the thousands of Rhode Islanders served each year and to keep Rhode Island's rich maritime heritage alive. As Rhode Island's Flagship, the Sloop *Providence* serves youth and adults through the "Classroom Under Sail" programs, which illuminate Rhode Island's maritime history and the importance of the city of *Providence* in our nation's early development. The Sloop *Providence* also serves as the Ocean State's sailing ambassador, representing Rhode Island at waterfront festivals along the East Coast.

Who sails: School groups from elementary school through college, individuals and families
Program type: Sail training for crew and volunteers; passenger day sails; dockside interpretation at homeport and during port visits; sea education in marine science, maritime history, cadet program and more for school groups of all ages
Season: April through November
Designer: Charles W. Wittholz
Built: 1976: Melville, RI
Coast Guard certification: Passenger Vessel (Subchapter T)
Crew: 5-8 **Trainees-passengers:** 40 daysails, 4-6 overnight
Contact: Richard McAuliffe, Jr., Board President, Providence Maritime Heritage Foundation, 408 Broadway, Providence, RI 02909 USA
Tel: 401-274-7447 **Fax:** 401-331-1301
E-mail: info_sloopprovidenceri@cox.net
Website: http://sloopprovidenceonline.com/

Flag: USA
Rig: Gaff schooner, two-masted
Homeport: New Haven, Connecticut
Normal cruising waters: Long Island Sound
Sparred length: 91'
LOA: 65'
LOD: 62'
LWL: 58'
Draft: 4' 5" - 11'
Beam: 20'
Rig height: 77'
Freeboard: 5' 2"
Sail area: 2,400 square feet
Tons: 41 GRT
Power: 135 HP diesel
Hull: wood

QUINNIPIACK

Built in 1984 for the passenger service, *Quinnipiack* now serves as the primary vessel for Schooner Inc., an organization dedicated to teaching environmental education programs focused on Long Island Sound. Since 1975, Schooner Inc. has taught in classrooms, on the shore, and aboard a variety of vessels. Participants of all ages study under sail and explore the ecology of the estuary while getting an introduction to maritime heritage and seamanship. Students work alongside the crew, learning skills in teamwork, self-reliance, responsibility and interdependence that only sailing vessels can teach. *Quinnipiack* programs complement traditional classroom studies in sciences, mathematics, geography, history, literature, folklore, and social studies. Hands on learning activities include collection, identification, and interpretation of estuarine organisms, land use, plankton study, piloting, sail handling, seamanship, sediment analysis, water chemistry, and weather. During the summer Schooner offers weeklong programs for grades K-12. The Seafaring Scientists program is conducted aboard the *Quinnipiack* for grades 6-8 and teaches basic seamanship and marine ecology. Internships are available for high school and college students to learn the operation and care of a traditional sailing vessel while sailing as crew. The *Quinnipiack* is also conducts public sails and is available for corporate charters and special events.

Who sails: School groups from middle school through college, individuals, and families
Program type: Sail training for crew, apprentices, and trainees; sea education in marine science, maritime history, and ecology in cooperation with accredited schools and colleges and as informal, in-house programming; dockside interpretation during port visits; passenger day sails
Season: April – November
Designer: Philip Shelton
Built: 1984: Milbridge, ME, Philip Shelton
Coast Guard certification: Passenger Vessel (subchapter T)
Crew: 5 **Trainees-passengers:** 40 daysails, 4-6 overnight
Contact: Beth McCabe, Executive Director/ Captain Tanya Banks-Christensen, Schooner Inc., 60 South Water Street, New Haven, CT 06519 USA
Tel: 203-865-1737 **Fax:** 203-624-8816
E-mail: director@schoonerinc.org or captain@schoonerinc.org
Website: www.schoonerinc.org

SPECIFICATIONS

Flag: USA
Rig: Gaff schooner
Homeport: Chicago , IL
Normal cruising waters:
Great Lakes
Sparred length: 77'
LOA: 57'
LOD: 54'
LWL: 49'
Draft: 6' 6"
Beam: 17' 6"
Rig height: 73'
Freeboard: 4' 6"
Sail area: 2,100 square feet
Tons: 41 GRT
Power: 125 HP diesel
Hull: wood

RED WITCH

Red Witch is typical of the schooners that once plied Lake Erie and the Great Lakes. She was built in the tradition of the schooners which were the workhorses of America 's 19th century transportation system. Designed by John G. Alden, the *Red Witch* has a hull of cyprus on oak, wooden blocks, and a gaff rig. Although traditional in appearance, the schooner was purpose-built for charter and day cruise service. She has full amenities for up to 49 passengers. *Red Witch's* home port is Chicago, since 2004. She has sailed as far as Hawaii and worked in San Diego before coming to the Great Lakes. As Ohio 's Bicentennial flagship, she represented the state on goodwill cruises to Michigan, Indiana, Wisconsin, and Illinois as well as Ontario, Canada during 2003. In 2006, she represented the city of Chicago in their Tall Ships® Festival. In addition to private charters, and daysails, the *Red Witch* offers sea chanty concert cruises, Chicago Special Event cruises, and freshwater whale watching (none seen yet, but still trying!) Sail training programs for school groups, disadvantaged and at-risk youth are conducted.

Who sails: School groups from elementary school through college; individuals and families, professional groups
Program type: Sail training for volunteer or paying trainees; sea education in marine science and maritime history in cooperation with accredited institutions and organized groups; passenger day sails, evening sails, and private parties
Season: May through October
Designer: John Alden **Built:** 1986: Bayou La Batre, Alabama, Nathaniel Zirlott
Coast Guard certification: Passenger Vessel (Subchapter T)
Crew: 4 **Trainees-passengers:** 49
Contact: Captain Bruce L. Randall, Lakeshore Sail Charters, 30 N. Michigan Ave., Ste. 1316, Chicago, IL 60602 USA
Tel: 312-404-5800 **Fax:** 312-782-1205
E-mail: info@redwitch.com
Website: www.redwitch.com

SPECIFICATIONS

Flag: USA
Rig: Yawl
Homeport: Olympia, WA
Normal cruising waters:
Puget Sound, Canada Inland
Sparred length: 44'
LWL: 30'
Draft: 6'
Beam: 11'
Freeboard: 3'
Rig height: 57' 6"
Sail area: 1,120 square feet
Tons: 15 GRT
Power: Perkins 40
Hull: Mahogany

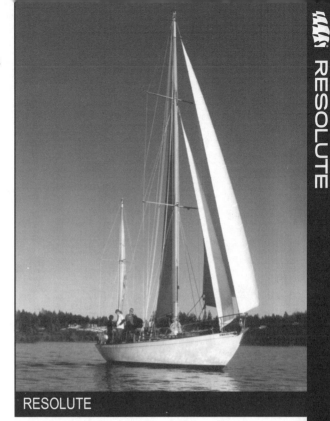

RESOLUTE

Resolute was the third of twelve identical wooden yawls built for the U.S. Naval Academy at Annapolis, Maryland. Over the course of 25 years, some 70,000 American midshipmen trained aboard these vessels. Now the Resolute Sailing Foundation, a 501(c)(3) organization continues that rich heritage, operating *Resolute* to teach traditional nautical skills, maritime history and an appreciation of the marine environment to youth groups, youths at risk and students at educational institutions. Young people, who sail on her learn to overcome their fears, acquire traditional sailing skills and develop self-confidence and personal responsibility. *Resolute* provides that special challenge of sea and sail which encourages teamwork and develops leadership qualities in these youngsters just as she trained great leaders of the past for so many years at Annapolis. *Resolute* participated in the TALL SHIPS CHALLENGE® Race Series in 2005 in Victoria, B.C. and Tacoma, Washington. She is available year round for day and overnight charters out of Olympia, Washington, her hailing port.

Who sails: High school and college age students, adults and families
Program type: Sail training for volunteer crew and paying trainees; sea education in cooperation with accredited institutions
Season: Year round
Designer: Bill Luders
Built: 1939: Stamford, CT, Luders Shipyard
Crew: 2 **Trainees-passengers:** 10 daysails 5 overnight
Contact: Resolute Sailing Foundation, PO Box 88834, Steilacoom, WA 98388 USA
Tel: 253-588 3066
E-mail: Resolute@telisphere.com
Website: www.resolutesailing.org

R. H. LEDBETTER

SPECIFICATIONS

Flag: USA
Rig: Full rigged ship
Homeport: Culver, Indiana
Normal cruising waters: Lake Maxinkuckee in Culver, Indiana
Sparred length: 65'
LOA: 54'
LOD: 50'
Draft: 5'
Beam: 13'
Rig height: 49'
Freeboard: 5'
Tons: 25 GRT
Power: diesel

The *R.H. Ledbetter* is the flagship of the Culver Summer Naval School, located on Lake Maxinkuckee in Culver, Indiana. The three-masted square-rigger, named in honor of Georgia philanthropist and Culver alumnus Robert H. Ledbetter, was built in 1983 - 84 by the T. D. Vinette Co. of Escanaba, Michigan. Dedicated July 7, 1984, the *Ledbetter* replaced the wooden-hulled *O.W Fowler*, which had served as the flagship from 1941- 83. The masts, spars, and sails from the Fowler were used on the *Ledbetter.* During spring 2002, the 100th anniversary of Culver Summer Camps, which began with the founding of the Naval School in 1902, was celebrated with the *R.H. Ledbetter* navigating the Intracoastal Waterway from Palm Beach, Florida to Washington, D.C. The six-week voyage included eight ports-of-call, at which Culver alumni and friends had the opportunity to celebrate the centennial before the boat was trucked back to its homeport. Culver Summer Camps offer two simultaneous coed six-week camps from mid-June to early August (Woodcraft for ages 9-13, and Upper Camp for 13-17) and 10 two-week specialty camps from early to mid-August. Administered by The Culver Educational Foundation, which also operates the Culver Academy, the camps use the facilities of the 1,800-acre wooded campus along the north shore of Indiana's second-largest lake.

Who sails: Students and Alumni of Culver Academy
Program type: Sail training for students of Culver Academy; sea education in cooperation with organized groups such as the American Camping Association; dockside interpretation while in home port
Designer: Marine Power
Built: 1984: Escanoba, MI, T. D. Vinette
Contact: Anthony Mayfield, Director, Culver Summer Camps, 1300 Academy Road, RD# 138, Culver, IN 46511 USA
Tel: 800-221-2020
Fax: 574-842-8462
E-mail: mayfiea@culver.org
Website: www.cuiver.org

Flag: USA
Rig: Brigantine
Homeport: Woods Hole, Massachusetts
Normal cruising waters: Worldwide
Sparred length: 134' 6"
LOA: 119'
LWL: 87' 6"
Draft: 13'
Beam: 26' 6"
Sail area: 8,200 square feet
Power: Caterpillar 3408, 455 HP
Hull: Steel

ROBERT C. SEAMANS

SEA'S newest vessel, launched in the spring of 2001, was built at JM Martinac Shipbuilding in Tacoma, Washington. Designed by Laurent Giles of Hampshire, England, the 134-foot steel brigantine is the most sophisticated sailing research vessel ever built in the United States. Improvements in design and equipment, including a wet/dry laboratory and a large library, classroom, and computer laboratory, will enhance the SEA academic program. The new vessel is conducting SEA Semesters in the Pacific with cruise tracks including Hawaii, Costa Rica, Alaska, and Tahiti.

Who sails: Educators and students who are admitted by competitive selection; Over 150 colleges and universities award credit for SEA programs
Program type: Marine and maritime studies including oceanography, nautical science, history, literature, and contemporary maritime affairs. SEA programs include SEA Semester (college level, 12 weeks long, 17 credits), SEA Summer Session (college level, 8 weeks long, 12 credits), and SEA Seminars for high school students and K-1 2 teachers.
Season: Year-round
Designer: Laurent Giles, Hampshire, England **Built:** Tacoma, WA, JM Martinac Shipbuilding
Coast Guard certification: Sailing School Vessel (Subchapter R)
Crew: 6 professional mariners and 4 scientists **Passengers-Trainees:** Up to 25 in all programs
Contact: Sea Education Association, Inc., PO Box 6, Woods Hole, MA 02543 USA
Tel: 508-540-3954 **Fax:** 508-540-0558
E-mail: admissions@sea.edu
Website: www.sea.edu

ROCKING THE BOAT

ROCKING THE BOAT

SPECIFICATIONS

Homeport: Bronx, New York
Normal cruising waters:
Bronx River
Rig: 10-14' to 21' traditional
Whitehalls and one Cape Cod
Oyster Skiff

Rocking the Boat is a boatbuilding and on-water education program based out of the southwest Bronx, New York City. Through a hands-on alternative approach to education and youth development, Rocking the Boat addresses the need for inner city youth to achieve practical and tangible goals, relevant to both everyday life and future aspirations. This process allows high school students to acquire practical, academic, and social skills. Rocking the Boat runs programming in both boatbuilding and environmental science, coordinating three after school and summer programs in each discipline annually, working directly with over 150 students, all of whom receive high school credit. During the process of building a traditional wooden boat, Rocking the Boat students create something not only beautiful, but practical in their own lives, bridging urban and natural life within their neighborhoods. This approach is mirrored in the on-water education program through direct focus on Bronx River habitat monitoring and restoration and through maritime skills programming. Both programs allow students opportunities to gain a deeper awareness of their own abilities and possibilities in the natural and urban world. Volunteers are always welcome to help out in every aspect of Rocking the Boat.

Who sails: Rocking the Boat students (high school age)
Program type: Traditional wooden boatbuilding and on-water maritime skills and environmental science programming for high school aged students
Season: Year-round
Designer: John Gardner
Built: 1998 to present: The Bronx Builder, Rocking the Boat students
Contact: Adam Green, Executive Director, Rocking the Boat, Inc., 60 East 174th Street, Bronx, NY 10452 USA
Tel: 718- 466-5799
Fax: 718-466-2892
E-mail: shop@rockingtheboat.org
Website: www.rockingtheboat.org

ROSEWAY

SPECIFICATIONS

Flag: USA
Rig: Schooner
Homeport: St. Croix, USVI
Normal cruising waters:
New England (summer)
Caribbean (winter)
Sparred length: 137'
LOA: 112'
LOD: 112'
LWL: 90'
Draft: 14'
Beam: 25'
Rig height: 84'
Freeboard: 51'
Sail area: 5,600 square feet
Tons: 250 GRT
Power: 400 HP diesel
Hull: wood

The World Ocean School is an internationally focused nonprofit, nonsectarian organization dedicated to providing challenging educational programs for youth by fostering an appreciation for, and obligation to, community and relationships; developing a deep commitment to ethical values and cultivating an expanded world view. The World Ocean School provides programs aboard the schooner *Roseway* for an international mix of students ages 15-21. Programs focus on studies in marine ecology, maritime history, stewardship, seamanship, ethical decision- making, and community service. The 137-foot *Roseway* was built in 1925 in Essex, Massachusetts as a private fishing yacht. She was purchased by the Boston Pilots Association in 1941, where she received a bronze plaque in honor of her exemplary wartime service during World War II. The *Roseway* was the last pilot schooner in the United States when she was retired in 1973. In 1974, the *Roseway* was taken to Maine to serve in the Windjammer trade. In 1977, the *Roseway* starred in the television movie, Captains Courageous. In September 2002 she was donated to the World Ocean School. Today, after 78 years of service, she is one of the last Grand Banks schooners built in Essex, and a registered U.S. National Historic Landmark.

Who sails: Middle school through college students; individuals of all ages
Program type: Sea education in ethical decision-making and community service in ports; dockside interpretation during port visits; day sail and charters
Season: Year-round
Designer: John F. James & Sons
Built: 1925: Essex, MA, John F. James & Sons
Coast Guard certification: Passenger Vessel (subchapter T)
Crew: 10
Contact: Abby Kidder, Executive Director, World Ocean School, PO Box 701, Camden, ME 04843 USA
Tel: 617-443-4841 **Fax:** 207-236-4468
E-mail: wos@worldoceanschool.org
Website: www.worldoceanschool.org

SPECIFICATIONS

Flag: USA
Rig: Gaff-rigged square topsail ketch
Homeport: San Francisco, California
Normal cruising waters: Coastal U.S. and Canada
Sparred length: 68'
LOD: 51'
LWL: 36'
Draft: 6'
Beam: 14' 6"
Rig height: 57'
Freeboard: 42 "
Sail area: 1,700 square feet
Power: Perkins diesel
Hull: Mahogany

ROYALISTE

Royaliste is a gaff-rigged, square tops'l ketch built in 1971 in Nova Scotia. In the late 80s she was refit to the specifications of a mid 1700s sailing vessel. Since then care has been taken to maintain both her period look and attitude. *Royaliste* offers sail training with a privateer's flair: a costumed crew, historical re-enactments and mock sea battles with the smell of gunpowder wafting across the bulwarks from her four carronades. Dockside, *Royaliste* displays a large collection of antique edged weaponry and maritime artifacts. *Royaliste* has been featured in several movies, most recently "True Caribbean Pirates" on the History Channel. A unique feature of this ship is her ability to be transported overland. It is a huge undertaking to prepare the ship to travel by trailer, but *Royaliste* has traveled more than 6000 miles via highways! She has crossed the continent twice in order to sail the Atlantic and Pacific oceans and four of the Great Lakes. She is owned and operated by Gary and Kathy Bergman.

Who sails: Groups and individuals of all ages
Program type: "Period" sail training, 1755 rig
Season: Year-round
Designer: James Rosborough
Built: 1969: Nova Scotia, Arthur Theriault
Coast Guard certification: Attraction Vessel
Crew: 5 **Trainees-passengers:** 6 daysails 6 overnight
Contact: Gary Bergman, Privateer, Inc., 1001 Bridgeway #645, Sausalito, CA 94965 USA
Tel: 415-533-7602
E-mail: orcaboat@sbcglobal.net
Website: www.privateerinc.org or www.theroyaliste.com

Flag: New Zealand
Rig: Gaff rigged schooner
Homeport:
Whangarei, New Zealand
Normal cruising waters:
Worldwide
Sparred length: 85'
LOD: 60'
Draft: 6'
Beam: 16'
Sail area: 3,000 square feet
Power: 180 HP Ford diesel
Hull: steel

R. TUCKER THOMPSON

R. Tucker Thompson started building the traditional gaff-rigged schooner *R. Tucker Thompson* in the late 1970s as a project to embody the best features of a traditional design, married to the materials of today. After Tucker's death, the *R. Tucker Thompson* was completed by Tucker's son, Tod Thompson, and Russell Harris. The ship was built in Mangawhai, New Zealand and launched in 1985. Her design is based on the Halibut schooners of the North West American coast which were considered fast, sea kindly, and easily manned. Most of her voyages take place during winter seasons of the years. During summer she operates as a day charter ship and has carried over 60,000 visitors around the Bay of Islands. The ship has taken part in five film productions. The ship's current survey is class seven foreign vessel which means that she can carry passengers around the coast of New Zealand as well as off shore. She has been built and maintained to the highest standards and is professionally manned and equipped to go anywhere in the world at any time. The ship is now operated as a not-for-profit charitable trust, with all income derived from sailing activities used for her maintenance, as well as a providing a contribution for sail training trips Northland youth.

Who sails: Individuals and groups of all ages
Season: Year-round
Built: 1985: Mangawhai, New Zealand, Tod Thompson and Russell Harris
Crew: 15 **Trainees-passengers:** 45 daysails
Contact: Russell Harris, P O Box 42, Opua 0241 Bay of Islands New Zealand
Tel: 64 9 402 8430
Fax: 64 9 402 8431
E-mail: info@tucker.co.nz
Website: www.tucker.co.nz

SAE HRAFN

SAE HRAFN

SPECIFICATIONS

Flag: USA
Rig: Viking longship
Normal cruising waters:
East Coast and
Chesapeake Bay
Sparred Length: 40'
LOA: 38'
LWL: 34'
Freeboard: 1.5'
Draft: 2'
Beam: 9' 6"
Rig height: 25'
Sail area: 320 square feet
Tons: 1 GRT
Power: 12 oars (12' Spruce)
Hull Material: Cedar and Oak

Sae Hrafn (Sea Raven) is designed as a small coastal raiding vessel; an intermediate size between the Ralswiek II ship and the Skuldelev Wreck 5 coastal defense ship. With the *Sae Hrafn* the Longship Company will continue to explore the lost arts of early medieval sailing, navigation and seamanship. The *Sae Hrafn* is sailed once or twice a month on training cruises for our regular crew and guests/trainees, and on occasional overnight voyages to further explore the living conditions of the Viking age. We also participate in various waterfront cultural activities in the Chesapeake Bay region. Like our other vessels, the *Sae Hrafn* will be involved in filming for the History Channel and other educational media, and takes part in various living history demonstrations in concert with the Markland Medieval Mercenary Militia. *Sae Hrafn*, and her consort, the *Gyrfalcon*, are both owned and operated by the Longship Company, Ltd., a member supported nonprofit educational organization. Occasional Viking raids on various fraternal and educational organizations may also, from time to time, be used to supplement our financial resources.

Who sails: Grade school through adult
Program type: History and research
Built: 2004: Kerry Eikenskold, Inyokern, CA
Crew: 8-18 **Trainees-passengers:** 6-12
Contact: Bruce Blackistone, President, Longship Company, LTD., 38825 Burch Road, Avenue, Maryland 20609 USA
Tel: 301-390-4089
E-mail: longshipco@hotmail.com
Website: www.longshipco.org

SPECIFICATIONS

Flag: Portugal
Rig: Barque
Homeport: Lisbon, Portugal
Normal cruising waters:
Worldwide
Sparred length: 293' 6"
Draft: 17'
Beam: 39' 6"
Hull: steel

photo by Max ©

SAGRES

Sagres II sails under the Portuguese flag as a naval training ship. She was built in 1937 at the Blohm & Voss shipyard in Hamburg, Germany, and is virtually a sister ship to *Eagle*, *Mircea*, *Tovarishch*, and *Gorch Fock II*. Originally named *Albert Leo Schlageter*, she served under American and Brazilian flags before being acquired by Portugal in 1962. At that time she replaced the first *Sagres*, which was built in 1896 as the Rickmer Rickmers. The original *Sagres* has now been restored and serves as a museum ship in Hamburg, Germany. The name *Sagres* derives from the historic port that sent forth many famed Portuguese explorers and navigators. It served as the home and base for Prince Henry the Navigator (1394-1460). His court in *Sagres* was responsible for the geographic studies and practical explorations that made Portugal master of the seas in the early 15th century. A bust of Prince Henry serves as the figurehead on the bow of *Sagres II*, and the ship is easily identified by the traditional Portuguese crosses of Christ (Maltese crosses) that mark the square sails on her fore- and mainmasts.

Who sails: Cadets of the Portuguese Navy
Program type: Training vessel for the Portuguese Navy
Season: Year-round
Built: 1937: Hamburg, Germany, Blohm & Voss Shipyard
Contact: Portuguese Defense and Naval Aftaché, Embassy of Portugal, 2310 Tracy Place, Washington, DC 20008 USA
Tel: 202-234-4483
Fax: 202-328-6827
E-mail: ponavnir@mindspring.com

SPECIFICATIONS

Flag: USA
Rig: Ketch
Homeport: Portland, Maine
Sparred length: 63'
LOD: 53'
LWL: 45'
Draft: 7'
Beam: 16'
Rig height: 85'
Freeboard: 4'
Sail area: 1,500 square feet
Tons: 34 GRT
Power: Ford Lehman
Hull: steel

SAMANA

The instructional mission for the School of Ocean Sailing is to teach offshore ocean sailing and ocean navigation in a live- aboard setting. In our sailing school we offer seven and eight day courses. Your classroom and sailing school home is a modern, well founded, romantic, beautiful, fast, and very sea kindly sailing vessel. *Samana*, a 52' steel offshore sailing ketch, was built in 1975 in Holland. *Samana* has circumnavigated the globe and has completed several noteworthy offshore passages. The School of Ocean Sailing operates winters out of Saint Thomas , USVI sailing the Atlantic Ocean and the Caribbean Sea surrounding the USVI and BVI. During the summers the sailing school operates in the North Atlantic Ocean off the coast of Maine during the winter. The curriculum is a rich blend of technical skill, confidence building, and common sense coupled with a spirit of adventure and romance. Instruction centers on the principal objectives underlying the knowledge of ocean sailing, coastal navigation, or celestial navigation. The School of Ocean Sailing is able to accommodate beginners just learning to sail a large ocean vessel, to students interested in advanced ocean navigation or celestial navigation.

Who sails: Individuals of all ages
Program type: Sail training for paying trainees; ocean sailing, celestial navigation, offshore passage making
Designer: Van de Wiele
Built: 1975: The Netherlands
Crew: 3   **Trainees-passengers:** 6
Contact: Captain Larry Wheeler, School of Ocean Sailing, TLC #1, 5600 Royal Dane Mall, Suite 12, St. Thomas, VI 00802
Tel: 868-727-7611
E-mail: svsamana@sailingschool.com
Website: www.sailingschool.com

Flag: United Kingdom
Rig: 15th century caravel rodonda
Homeport: Georgetown, Grand Cayman
Sparred length: 115'
LOA: 95'
LOD: 85'
LWL: 78'
Draft: 8'
Beam: 23'
Rig height: 64'
Freeboard: 6'
Sail area: 3,850 square feet
Tons: 101 GRT
Power: 260 HP
Hull: wood

SANTA CLARA

The *Santa Clara* (aka *Nina*) is a historically correct replica of a Columbus era ship. The exterior of the ship looks and feels like a ship of the 15th century but down below she is 21st century with beautiful examples of Brasilian stone, marble and woodwork from the finest Brasilian shipwrights. The air conditioned main salon can easily accommodate 40 while the upper decks can seat 100 in comfort. Her mission today is daysailing in Grand Cayman year round. Sailtraining is an important part of her role in Grand Cayman, bringing to the local the schools an awareness of a maritime heritage that has been eclipsed by economic growth. Corporate groups, cruise passengers, documentaries and films round out her role as Caymans tall ship.

Who sails: Schools and the general public
Program type: Daysails and evening cruises
Designer: Jonathan Nance, Morgan Sanger
Built: Nicholson Shipyard, Valenca, Brazil
Crew: 6   **Trainees-passengers:** 100
Contact: Captain Morgan Sanger, Director, The Nina Ltd., Box 1776, Georgetown, Grand Cayman, British West Indies
Tel: 345-926-5000 or 787-246-4200
Fax: 345-946-5557
E-mail: thenina2@candw.ky
Website: www.thenina.com

SEAWARD

SPECIFICATIONS

Flag: USA
Rig: Staysail schooner
Homeport: Sausalito, California / San Francisco Bay
Normal cruising waters: Northern California to Mexico
Sparred Length: 82'
LOA: 82'
LOD: 65'
Freeboard: 4'
Draft: 8' 6"
Beam: 17'
Rig Height: 75'
Tons: 59 GRT
Power: 210 HP Cummins 6BT
Hull: steel

Call of the Sea and the schooner *Seaward's* mission is to inspire people of all ages and backgrounds, and especially youth, to connect with the sea, San Francisco Bay, and seafaring. Our hands-on programs focus on the ocean and bay environment, our nautical heritage, seamanship, teamwork, and leadership. *Seaward* is well-suited to both the 'inside' waters of the bay and the 'outside' waters beyond the Golden Gate and our programs range from 3 hour Bay sails for all ages to challenging week-long coastal voyages with teenagers. We offer wintertime voyages along the Mexican coast for adults and youth groups. *Seaward* is also available for collaborative programs with educational partners as well private charters and public sails.

Who sails: elementary schools, teenagers, & adults
Program type: maritime and environmental education through hands-on programs ranging from 3 hours to week-long voyages
Season: April through November in San Francisco Bay and Northern California coastal waters; December to March in coastal waters of California and Mexico
Designer: Russ Woodin
Built: 1988: Paul Bramsen, St. Augustine, Florida
Coast Guard certification: Passenger Vessel (Subchapter T) for Ocean waters
Crew: 4-5 **Trainees-passengers:** 40 daysails, 14 overnight
Contact: Call of the Sea, 3020 Bridgeway, #278, Sausalito, CA 94965 USA
Tel: 415 331-3214 **Fax:** 415 331-1412
E-mail: info@CalloftheSea.org
Website: www.CalloftheSea.org

SPECIFICATIONS

Flag: Russia
Rig: Barque, 4-masted
Homeport: Murmansk, Russia
Normal cruising waters:
Worldwide
Sparred length: 386'
Draft: 27'
Beam: 48'
Hull: steel

Photo by Thad Koza

SEDOV

Sedov is the world's largest tall ship still in service and was one of the last barques built for deepwater cargo carrier service from South America and Australia to the German ports of Bremen and Hamburg. Constructed in 1921 as *Magdalene Vinnen* in Kiel, Germany, she sailed for the Bremen firm of F. A. Vinnen, hence her name. Following the German commercial tradition, she was christened in honor of one of the owner's female family members. After being sold to the shipping conglomerate Norddeutscher Lloyd in 1936, she was renamed *Kommodore Johnson* and served as a sail training vessel. After World War II she was appropriated by the Russian Ministry of Fisheries and was renamed for the Soviet polar explorer and oceanographer Georgij *Sedov* (1877 – 1914). *Sedov* is the largest square-rigger still in service from the days of deepwater cargo sailing. She is 10 feet longer than the other giant Russian barque, *Kruzenshtern*. Besides her physical statistics, such as masts that rise 184 feet above the deck and a length of 386 feet, *Sedov* boasts its own bakery, workshop, and first-aid station. When her 37 sails – covering an area of some 44,000 square feet, *Sedov* is a magnificent portrait of sail power.

Who sails: Students of the Murmansk State Technical University
Program type: Sail training vessel
Designer: 1921: Friedr. Krupp, A.G. Germaniawerft, Kiel, Germany
Crew: 70 crew, 120 cadets **Trainees-passengers:** 50 guest passengers
Contact: Murmansk State Technical University
Website: http://eng.mstu.edu.ru/

SHABAB OF OMAN

SPECIFICATIONS

Flag: Sultanate of Oman
Rig: Barquentine
Homeport: Muscat, Oman
Sparred length: 171'
Draft: 15'
Beam: 28'
Hull: wood

Built in Scotland in 1971 as a sail training vessel, *Shabab of Oman* was acquired by the Sultanate of Oman in 1979. *Shabab of Oman*, which means "youth of Oman," serves as a training ship for the royal navy of Oman and also trains young men from other Omani government bureaus. The sculptured figurehead on her bow is a replica of the fifteenth-century Omani mariner Ahmed bin Majed, who helped the Portuguese sailor Vasco da Gama explore Africa and India. The turban-clad Majed cuts a rakish figure, wearing a green sash and red "khunjar," a traditional dagger. The red coat-of-arms of the sultanate is recognizable on the sails of *Shabab of Oman* and consists of a khunjar superimposed on a pair of crossed scimitars.

Program type: Sail training vessel of the Royal Navy of Oman
Contact: Embassy of the Sultanate of Oman, 2535 Belmont Road, NW Washington, DC 20008 USA
Tel: 202-387-1980
Fax: 202-745-4933

Flag: USA
Rig: Square topsail schooner,
two-masted
Homeport: Vineyard Haven,
Massachusetts
Normal cruising waters:
Southern New England
Sparred length: 152'
LOA: 108'
LWL: 101'
Draft: 11'
Beam: 23'
Freeboard: 3' (amidships)
Rig height: 94'
Sail area: 7,000 square feet
Tons: 85 GRT

SHENANDOAH

While the *Shenandoah* is not a replica, the vessel's design bears a strong resemblance to that of the US Revenue Cutter *Joe Lane* of 1851. For her first 25 years, the rakish square topsail schooner was painted white, but she now wears the black and white checkerboard paint scheme of the 19th century Revenue Service. She is the only non-auxiliary power square-rigged vessel operating under the American Flag. Her hull form and rig, anchors, and all materials of construction adhere closely to mid-19th century practice. Every summer *Shenandoah* plies the waters of southern New England visiting the haunts of pirates and the homeports of whaling ships. *Shenandoah* runs 6-day sailing trips for kids ages 9-16 from mid June through mid September. She is also available for day sailing and private charter.

Who sails: School groups from elementary through college and individuals of all ages
Program type: Sail training for paying trainees ages 9-14; private charters and day sails are also available
Season: June to September
Coast Guard certification: Passenger Vessel (Subchapter T)
Crew: 9 **Trainees-passengers:** 35 daysails, 30 overnight
Contact: Captain Robert S. Douglas, Coastwise Packet Co., Inc. PO Box 429, Vineyard Haven, MA 02568 USA
Tel: 508-693-1699
Fax: 508-693-1881
Website: www.theblackdogtallships.com

SIGSBEE

SPECIFICATIONS

Flag: USA
Rig: Sloop
Homeport: Baltimore, Maryland
Normal cruising waters:
Chesapeake Bay and the Delaware
River
Sparred length: 76'
LOD: 50'
Draft: 3' 5"
Beam: 16'
Rig height: 68'
Freeboard: 2' 5"
Sail area: 1,767 square feet
Tons: 14 GRT
Power: 150 HP diesel

The skipjack *Sigsbee* was built in 1901 in Deale Island, Maryland and worked as an oyster dredge boat until the early 1990s. She was named after Charles D. Sigsbee, who was the Commanding Officer of the battleship *Maine*. The vessel was rebuilt by the Living Classrooms Foundation in 1994, and now sails Chesapeake Bay with students on board. While sailing on board the *Sigsbee*, students learn the history of skipjacks and the oyster industry, marine and nautical science, and gain an appreciation of Chesapeake Bay and the hard work of the watermen of a bygone era.

Who sails: Students and other organized groups, individuals, and families
Program type: Sail training with paying trainees; sea education in marine and nautical science, maritime history, and ecology for school groups from elementary through college
Season: March through September
Built: 1901: Deale Island, Maryland
Coast Guard certification: Passenger Vessel (Subchapter T)
Crew: 4 **Trainees-passengers:** 30 daysails, 15 overnight Age: 13+ Dockside visitors: 30
Contact: Christine Truett, Director of Education, Living Classrooms Foundation, 802 South Caroline Street, Baltimore, MD 21231-3311 USA
Tel: 410-685-0295
Fax: 410-752-8433
Website: www.livingclassrooms.org

Flag: Canada
Rig: Three-masted schooner
Homeport: Halifax, Nova Scotia, Canada
Normal cruising waters: Halifax Harbour, Nova Scotia Coast
Sparred length: 130'
LOA: 115'
Draft: 9'
Beam: 24'
Rig height: 75'
Freeboard: 4'
Tons: 199 GRT
Power: 350 Cummins

SILVA

Silva was built at Karlstads Mekaniska, Verksta, Sweden as a three masted steel schooner. During the first 2 decades of her life, she was used in the Scandinavian fishing industry, with regular trips to Iceland. In the 1960s, *Silva* was refitted as a bulk freighter, having her sailing rig removed. *Silva* continued coastal trading until 1994 and remained in Sweden until the summer of 2001 when Canadian Sailing Expeditions bought her and delivered her, for the first time, to North America. She now offers sailing tours of Halifax Harbour. She runs educational programs for students, day trade for general public, and private and corporate charters. Canadian Sailing Expeditions is dedicated to providing opportunities for people of all ages to experience and explore our seacoast the traditional way.

Who sails: Groups and individuals of all ages
Program type: Sail training for paying trainees; passenger day sails; private charters
Season: April through October
Built: 1939: Verksta, Sweden, Karlstads Mekaniska
Certification: Transport Canada
Trainees-passengers: 150 daysails
Contact: Captain Doug Prothero, Owner/operator, Canadian Sailing Expeditions, PO Box 2613, Halifax, NS B3J 3N5 Canada
Tel: 902-429-1474
Fax: 902-429-1475
E-mail: doug@canadiansailingexpeditions.com
Website: www.canadiansailingexpeditions.com

SPECIFICATIONS

Flag: Venezuela
Rig: Barque
Homeport: La Guaira, Venezuela
Normal cruising waters: Worldwide
Sparred length: 270'
Draft: 14' 6'"
Beam: 35'
Hull: steel

SIMON BOLIVAR

Simon Bolivar was one of four barques built in Spain for Latin American countries. Similar in design and rigging, the four ships are nearly identical sister ships: *Gloria* from Columbia, *Guayas* from Ecuador, *Cuauhtemoc* from Mexico, and *Simon Bolivar*. All four are frequent visitors to the United States and at major tall ship gatherings. The 270-foot *Simon Bolivar* was completed in 1980 and named for the "great liberator" of northern South America. Bolivar (1783-1830) was instrumental in the independence of Columbia, Ecuador, Panama, Peru, and Venezuela. *Simon Bolivar* embodies the spirit of idealism and freedom of her namesake. Her figurehead is an allegorical depiction of Liberty and was designed by the Venezuelan artist Manuel Felipe Rincon.

Program type: Training vessel of the Venezuelan Navy
Contact: Embassy of the Bolivarian Republic of Venezuela, 1099 30th Street, NW Washington, DC 20007 USA
Tel: 202-342-2214
Fax: 202-342-6820

Flag: United Kingdom
Rig: Brigantine
Homeport:
Auckland, New Zealand
Normal cruising waters: New
Zealand and South Pacific plus
worldwide voyage once every 4
years
Sparred Length: 145'
LOD: 105'
Draft: 11' 3"
Beam: 25' 6"
Rig height: 98'
Sail Area: 6,750 Square feet
Tons: 126 GRT
Power: B&W ALPHA diesel,
143 HP
Hull: Danish Oak

SOREN LARSEN

Sail training and square rig adventure for all ages. This oak hulled brigantine specializes in authentic tall ship voyaging to the remoter tropical islands of the South Pacific and short cruises in the idyllic home waters of the New Zealand coast. Join the ship as Voyage Crew for either a 5 or 10 day tropical island voyage, or the rare opportunity of an extended ocean passage. No previous experience is needed in either case – just the desire to experience the freedom of the seas aboard a traditional tall ship. Berths in the twin or 4 berth cabins are booked individually online. Fully surveyed under the British flag for world wide voyaging, this magnificently restored square rigger is also available for school groups, project charters, and location film work. Read the ship's Voyage Log of present and previous voyaging at the website – as well as the voyaging schedule and pricing.

Who sails: 12 to 80 (as long as fit and healthy)
Program type: Adventure sail training for all ages
Season: Year-round
Designer: Soren Larsen Ship Yard
Built: 1949: Soren Larsen and Sons, Nykobing Mors, Denmark
Crew: 13 **Voyage Crew:** 22
Contact: Steve Randall, Bridgewater Chartering Pty Ltd, PO Box 60660, Titirangi, Auckland 0642 New Zealand
Tel: +64 9 817 8799
Fax: +64 9 817 6799
E-mail: escape@sorenlarsen.co.nz
Website: www.sorenlarsen.co.nz

SPECIFICATIONS

Flag: Norway
Rig: Full-rigged ship
Homeport: Kristiansand, Norway
LOA: 210'
LOD: 186'
LWL: 158'
Draft: 15'
Beam: 29'
Rig height: 112'
Freeboard: 17'
Sail area: 6,500 square feet
Tons: 499 GRT
Power: 560 HP engine
Hull: steel

SØRLANDET

The *Sørlandet* was built as a schoolship for the merchant marine in 1927 in Kristiansand, Norway, and served this purpose up until 1974. She was named *Sorlandet* meaning "the Southland" after the Southern region of Norway of which Kristiansand is the capital. Thousands of young men have received their first seagoing experience onboard the *Sørlandet*. During the war the German occupation force took her undercommand and she was used as a recreation ship for German U-boat crew. Later during the war she was used as a prison camp for Russian prisoners of war. During one of the many air-raids she sunk in the Kirkenes Bay far up North in Norway with only her masts above water. She was later brought afloat and towed back to her homeport heavily damaged. In 1947 she was restored and once again able to welcome young cadets. In the early seventies the Government of Norway had different ideas on how to educate young seamen and the schoolship era in Norway came to an end. Lying idle until the late seventies the *Sorlandet* was again overhauled and ready for new ventures. A new administrative organization was established and a new business concept worked out which offers young people of all ages from 15-80 a tall ship experience as paying trainees for short or longer trips. The *Sørlandet* was the first ship in the world to offer sail training for females.

Who sails: 15-80 year old trainees accepted.
Program type: Sail training ship, tall ship adventures
Season: May through September
Desiner: Hoivold Shipyard
Built: 1927: Hoivold Shipyard, Kristiansand, Norway
Crew: Up to 20 **Trainees-passengers:** 70
Contact: Leif Brestrup, Director, Stiftelsen Fullriggeren Sorlandet, Gravane 6, Kristiansand, N-4610 Norway
Tel: +47 38 02 98 90
Fax: +47 38 02 93 34

Flag: USA
Rig: Gaff schooner, three-masted
Homeport: Stamford, Connecticut
Normal cruising waters:
Long Island Sound
Sparred length: 80'
LOD: 65'
Draft: 3' (centerboards up),
8' (centerboards down)
Beam: 14'
Rig height: 60'
Freeboard: 3' 6"
Sail area: 1,510 square feet
Tons: 32 GRT
Power: diesel
Hull: steel

SOUNDWATERS

SoundWaters, Inc. is a non-profit education organization dedicated to protecting Long Island Sound and its watershed through education. Annually *SoundWaters* offers shipboard and land-based programs to 35,000 children and adults from Connecticut and New York. The schooner *SoundWaters* is the platform for a variety of programs includes seamanship, navigation, helms-manship, and field exploration of marine ecosystems. *SoundWaters* crew includes environmental educators, biologists, naturalists, and a licensed captain. In addition, *SoundWaters*, Inc. operates the *SoundWaters* Community Center for Environmental Education, featuring educational exhibits and displays, classroom and community meeting space, a wet lab, and cutting-edge "green" construction. The organization also conducts many free outreach programs, which are offered through public schools and community centers.

Who sails: School groups from elementary through college; individuals and families
Program type: Sea education in marine science and ecology in cooperation with accredited institutions and other groups, and as informal, in-house programming
Season: April to November
Designer: William Ward
Built: 1986: Norfolk, Virginia, Marine Metals, Inc.
Coast Guard certification: Passenger Vessel (Subchapter T)
Crew: 3 - 5 instructors   **Trainees-passengers:** 42 daysails, 15-20 overnight
Contact: SoundWaters Inc., Cove Island Park, 1281 Cove Road, Stamford, CT 06902 USA
Tel: 203-323-1978
Fax: 203-967-8306
E-mail: connect@soundwaters.org
Website: www.soundwaters.org

SPIRIT OF BERMUDA

SPECIFICATIONS

Flag: Bermuda
Rig: Bermudian
Homeport: Hamilton, Bermuda
Normal cruising waters: Bermuda waters and Western Atlantic
Sparred length: 112'
LOA: 112'
LOD: 88'
LWL: 75'
Draft: 9' 6"
Beam: 23"
Rig height: 93'
Freeboard: 5'
Sail area: 4,437 square feet
Tons: 88 GRT
Power: Cat 3126 Mechanical 385 HP diesel
Hull: cold-moulded epoxy

The purpose-built sail training vessel is based on civilian Bermudian-type schooners built 1810-1840. Bermudians, enslaved and free, built the schooners in the period spanning the Emancipation of Slavery in the British Empire (Aug 1st, 1834). The original hull shape were adapted from the Bermuda-built RN "Shamrock" class, fast dispatch / patrol vessels that ran from the RN Dockyard, Bermuda, northwest to Halifax and Southwest to Jamaica to contain the rebel colonies. Noteworthy is the Bermuda rig that was innovated on the coastal Bermuda sloops that abounded in the 17th, 18th and early part of the 19th century; faced with impassable pathways by land, locals had evolved the lateen rig to short-tack up(wind) the island and up to the fishing banks to windward of Bermuda.

Who sails: 14+ years
Program type: Extra-curricular team (high school) and curricular learning expeditions (middle school 3)
Season: February through December
Designer: Bill Nash / Langan Design Associates, Newport, RI Built: 2006: Rockport, ME, Rockport Marine
Coast Guard certification: Passenger vessel (Subchapter T)
Crew: 3 professional, 8 volunteer **Trainees-passengers:** 40 inside the reef, 26 coastal
Contact: Mr. Malcolm Kirkland, Executive Director, Bermuda Sloop Foundation, Suite 1151, 48 Par-la-Ville Road, Hamilton HM11 Bermuda
Tel: 441-236-0383
Fax: 441-292-3744
Website: www.bermudasloop.org/

Flag: USA
Rig: Schooner
Homeport: Dana Point, California
Normal cruising waters:
Southern California
Sparred length: 118'
LOD: 86'
LWL: 79'
Draft: 10'
Beam: 24'
Freeboard: 6'
Rig height: 100'
Sail area: 5,000 square feet
Power: HP diesel
Tons: 64 GRT
Hull: wood

SPIRIT OF DANA POINT

A young colony, in a new land, dreamed of independence and built some of the fastest and best sailing ships in the world. These ships were the result of ingenuity, independence and a strong desire to accomplish something. It was Dennis Holland's life dream to build an accurate replica from the period when America fought for independence and world recognition. Armed with talent, determination, a little money and plans he purchased from the Smithsonian Institute, he laid the keel in his yard on May 2, 1970. Thirteen years later this fast privateer was launched and his vision became reality. Today at the Ocean Institute this dream continues as young students step aboard and back in time. During their voyages students relive the challenges and discoveries of early ocean exploration. Through a series of national award winning living history programs, the *Spirit of Dana Point* serves as an excellent platform for our youth to directly experience life at sea, as it has been for hundreds of years. She sails throughout Southern California for more than 150 days a year.

Who sails: School groups from elementary school through college; adult education groups; families and individuals of all ages
Program type: Sail training for volunteer crew or trainees; sea education in marine science, maritime history, and ecology based on informal in-house programming and in cooperation with other organizations; day sails and overnight passages; affiliated institutions include the Ocean Institute, other school education programs, and museums
Season: Year-round
Designer: Howard Chapelle **Built:** 1983: Costa Mesa, California, Dennis Holland
Coast Guard certification: Passenger Vessel (Subchapter T)
Crew: 7 **Trainees-passengers:** 75 daysails, 30 overnight
Contact: Adam Himelson, Program Director, Ocean Institute, 24200 Dana Point Harbor Drive, Dana Point, CA 92612 USA
Tel: 949-496-2274 **Fax:** 949-496-4715
E-mail: ahimelson@ocean-institute.org **Website:** www.ocean-institute.org

SPIRIT OF MASSACHUSETTS

SPIRIT OF MASSACHUSETTS

SPECIFICATIONS

Flag: USA
Rig: Gaff tops'l schooner, two-masted
Homeport: Boothbay Harbor, Maine
Normal cruising waters: North Atlantic Ocean and Caribbean Sea, Canada to South America
Sparred length: 125'
LOA: 103'
LOD: 100'
LWL: 80'
Draft: 10' 6"
Beam: 24'
Rig height: 103'
Freeboard: 7'
Sail area: 7,000 square feet
Tons: 90 GRT
Power: 235 HP diesel
Hull: wood

Owned by the Ocean Classroom Foundation, the schooner *Spirit of Massachusetts* sails on programs of education under sail fro the youth of America. Programs range from 4 month semesters-at-sea to week-long programs with schools and youth groups. Trainees sail the ship and learn traditional seamanship skills under the Captain and crew, and they explore maritime subjects with the onboard academic staff. The Ocean Classroom program is a semester-at-sea for qualified high school students, fully accredited by Proctor Academy. The voyage covers more than 4,000 nautical miles, connecting South American shores to the Canadian Maritimes. Students live and work as sailors on a true voyage of discovery, while they study maritime history, maritime literature, marine science, applied mathematics, and navigation. Ocean Classroom is offered Fall, Spring, and Summer Terms. Other programs include SEAmester (a complete semester-at-sea for college credit), OceanBound (for high school and college students) and Summer Seafaring Camp (for teens age 13-16). The Ocean Classroom Foundation also owns and operates the schooners *Harvey Gamage* and *Westward*.

Who sails: Individuals and school groups from middle school through college; affiliated institutions include Proctor Academy, University of Massachusetts/Dartmouth, Center for Coastal Studies, Hurricane Island Outward Bound School and other schools
Program type: Traditional seamanship training combined with accredited academic studies in maritime subjects
Season: Year-round
Designer: Melbourne Smith and Andrew Davis
Built: 1984: Boston, MA, New England Historic Seaport
Coast Guard certification: Sailing School Vessel (Subchapter R), Passenger Vessel (Subchapter T)
Crew: 7 - 11 including instructors   **Students-trainees:** 22 overnight
Contact: Executive Director, Ocean Classroom Foundation, 29 McKown Street, Boothbay Harbor, Maine 04538 USA
Tel: 800-724-7245
E-mail: mail@oceanclassroom.org **Website:** www.oceanclassroom.org

Flag: USA
Rig: Schooner
Homeport: Charleston, South Carolina
Normal Cruising Waters: North Atlantic, Caribbean Sea, and the Canadian Maritime
Sparred length: 140'
LOD: 91'
LWL: 88'
Draft: 10' 5"
Beam: 24'
Rig Height: 125'
Freeboard: 3' 9"
Sail Area: 6,462 square feet
Tons: 94 GRT
Power: two 230 HP Cummins diesel
Hull: wood

SPIRIT OF SOUTH CAROLINA

The *Spirit of South Carolina*, owned and operated by the South Carolina Maritime Foundation, was launched in March 2007. Her lines are reminiscent of an 1870s pilot schooner that was built in Charleston, SC. The *Spirit of South Carolina* will operate mainly as a sailing school vessel offering a unique education platform for the students of the Palmetto State. The hands-on programs conducted aboard are designed to challenge and engage students while promoting responsibility, teamwork, and stewardship for both their community and their environment. Programs will vary in duration from day sail programs to multi-day and multi-week voyages. When not sailing in South Carolinas waters, the vessel will also serve as the states floating 'Goodwill Ambassador' promoting the resourcefulness and vibrancy of South Carolinians.

Who sails: South Carolina students and educators
Program type: Under-sail educational programs in marine science, maritime history, and seamanship, including both day trips and live-aboard programming
Season: Year-round
Designer: Tri-Coastal Marine
Built: 2007: Sea Island Boat Builders
Coast Guard certification: Passenger Vessel (subchapter T) Sailing School Vessel (subchapter R) pending
Crew: 9 **Trainees-passengers:** 40 daysails 21 overnight
Contact: South Carolina Maritime Foundation (SCMF), PO Box 22405, Charleston, SC 29413 USA
Tel: 843-722-1030
E-mail: info@scmaritime.org
Website: www.scmaritime.org

ST LAWRENCE II

SPECIFICATIONS

Flag: Canada
Rig: Brigantine
Homeport: Kingston, Ontario, Canada
Normal cruising waters: Lake Ontario and adjacent waters
Sparred length: 72'
LOA: 60'
LOD: 57'
LWL: 46'
Draft: 8' 6"
Beam: 15'
Rig height: 54'
Freeboard: 4' 6"
Sail area: 2,560 square feet
Tons: 34 GRT
Power: 165 HP diesel
Hull: steel

The *St Lawrence II* is a purpose built sail training vessel in operation since 1957, primarily on the Great Lakes. She was designed to be manageable by a young crew, yet complex enough with her brigantine rig to introduce teenagers to the challenge of square-rig sailing. The ship is owned and operated by Brigantine, Inc., a nonprofit charity staffed by local volunteers who share the conviction that the lessons of responsibility, self-reliance, and teamwork provided by sail training are especially applicable to teenagers. With 42 years of operation, Brigantine, Inc. is one of the pioneering sail training programs in North America. Cruises in this hands-on program range from six to ten days or more in length. *St. Lawrence II*'s crew complement of 28 is comprised of 18 new trainees, plus a crew of watch officers, petty officers, cook, and bosun, all aged 13 to 18. The captain is usually the only adult onboard. The ship's teenage officers are graduates of Brigantine, Inc.'s winter training program, involving lessons in seamanship, navigation, and ship's systems, as well as the ongoing maintenance of the ship. Every year the *St. Lawrence II* sails over 4,000 miles, spends more than 40 nights at sea, and introduces over 300 trainees to the rigors of life aboard a ship on the Great Lakes.

Who sails: School groups and individuals of all ages
Program type: Sail training with paying trainees
Season: April to November (sailing); October to March (winter program)
Designer: Francis McLachlan/Michael Eames
Built: 1953: Kingston, Ontario, Canada, Kingston Shipyards
Crew: 10   **Trainees-passengers:** 36 daysails, 18 overnight
Contact: Brigantine, Inc., 53 Yonge Street, Kingston, Ontario K7M 6G4 Canada
Tel: 613-544-5175
Fax: 613-544-9828
E-mail: briginc@kos.net
Website: www.brigantine.ca

Flag: USA
Rig: Barque, three-masted
Homeport: San Diego, CA
Normal cruising waters: Coastal waters between San Diego, CA and northern Baja California, Mexico
Sparred length: 278'
LOD: 210'
LWL: 200'
Draft: 21' 6"
Beam: 35'
Freeboard: 15'
Rig height: 148'
Sail area: 18,000 square feet
Tons: 1,197 GRT
Hull: iron

STAR OF INDIA

The *Star of India* is the world's oldest active ship. She was built at Ramsey shipyard on the Isle of Man and launched as the Euterpe in 1863. She began her working life as a cargo ship in the India trade and was nearly lost on her first two voyages, surviving a mutiny, collision, cyclone and the death of her captain. In 1871 she embarked on a quarter century of hauling emigrants to New Zealand. She circumnavigated the globe 21 times during this service. She was sold to American owners in 1898 and renamed the Star of India in 1906. By 1923 steam power had replaced sails on merchant ships and the *Star of India* was laid up in Oakland. A group of San Diegans purchased the ship and had her towed to San Diego in 1927. Depression and war delayed the beginning of her restoration until the late 1950s. In 1976, with her restoration complete, she sailed on San Diego bay for the first time in 50 years. The *Star of India* is now the pride of the Maritime Museum of San Diego's fleet of historic ships. She is maintained by a dedicated group of volunteers and skilled craftsman and sailed at least once a year.

Who sails: Selected volunteers, permanent crew, and invited passengers
Program type: Sail training for crew and apprentices; sea education in maritime history; dockside interpretations
Designer: Edward Arnold
Built: 1863: Ramsey, Isle of Man, UK, Gibson, McDonald & Arnold
Coast Guard certification: Museum Attraction Vessel
Contact: Peter Durdaller, San Diego Maritime Museum, 1492 N. Harbor Drive, San Diego CA 92101 USA
Tel: 619 234 9153 x 120
E-mail: pdurdaller@sdmaritime.org
Website: www.sdmaritime.org

SPECIFICATIONS

Flag: USA
Rig: Schooner, three-masted
Homeport: Naples, Florida
Normal cruising waters: South Florida and the Bahamas
Sparred length: 68'
LOA: 54'
LOD: 50'
LWL: 44'
Draft: 6'
Beam: 15' 6"
Freeboard: 4'
Rig height: 42'
Sail area: 11,400 square feet
Tons: 32 GRT
Power: Perkins 135
Hull: steel

STAR OF THE SEA

Star of the Sea is a three-masted topsail schooner built of steel in 1984. She is a Tom Colvin design and displaces 32 tons. Since 2003 she has sailed in a teen sailing program for New Horizons of Southwest Florida. New Horizons is a 501 (c) 3 that is dedicated to reaching the spiritual and academic needs of at-risk children in Southwest Florida. Star of the Sea currently sails in Florida and the Bahamas.

Who sails: Students ages 12 - 18
Program type: Sail training and mentoring
Season: Year-round
Designer: Tom Colvin
Built: 1984: Pittsburg, PA
Coast Guard certification: Documented Yacht
Crew: 3 **Trainees-passengers:** 15
Contact: Captain Robert Nichols, Director, New Horizons of Southwest Florida, PO Box 111833, Naples, FL 34108 USA
Tel: 239-248-0647
Fax: 239-262-5441
E-mail: newhorizons17@hotmail.com
Website: www.mysuperkidsclub.org

SPECIFICATIONS

Flag: United Kingdom
Rig: Brig
Homeport: Portsmouth, England
Normal cruising waters: UK, Europe, Mediterranean, Canaries, Azores and Caribbean
Sparred length: 195'
LOA: 159'
LOD: 159'
LWL: 133'
Draft: 15'
Beam: 33'
Rig height: 148'
Sail area: 12,503 square feet
Tons: 493 GRT
Power: 2x MTU 33OKW
Hull: steel

STAVROS S NIARCHOS

Stavros S Niarchos is one of the two purposely built sail training vessels owned by the Tall Ships Youth Trust. She is a 60 meter, steel hulled, square-rigged brig built in Appledore, Devon, and was launched in 2001. She is named after a very generous Greek benefactor. The Tall Ships Youth Trust, incorporating the Sail Training Association, is a registered charity founded in 1956 and is dedicated to the personal development of young people aged 16-25 through the crewing of tall ships. Every year over 2,000 people aged 16 to 75 from all over the world sail on either *Stavros S Niarchos* or her identical sister ship *Prince William*. *Stavros S Niarchos* operates all year round. In the summer months she frequents European and Mediterranean waters and during the winter she may head south for the Canaries, Azores and Caribbean. Youth voyages for 16-25 year olds last from 7-14 nights whereas 18+ voyages range from day sails to a 24 night Trans-Atlantic.

Who sails: Groups and individuals of all ages
Season: Year-round
Program type: Sail training for paying trainees
Designer: Burness, Corlett & Partners & Captain Mike Willoughby
Built: 2000: North Devon, United Kingdom, Appledore Shipbuilders
Crew: 6 pemanent, 13 volunteer   **Trainees-passengers:** 44 daysails, 48 overnight
Contact: Tall Ships Youth Trust, 2A The Hard, Portsmouth, Hampshire P01 3PT England
Tel: +44 (0) 23 9283 2055
Fax: +44 (0) 23 9281 5769
E-mail: tallships@tallships.org
Website: www.tallships.org

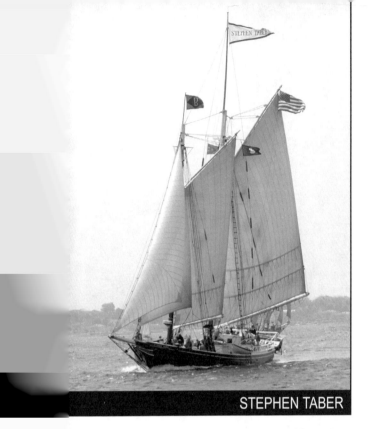

STEPHEN TABER

SPECIFICATIONS

Flag: USA
Rig: Gaff schooner
Homeport: Penobscot Bay, Maine
Sparred length: 115'
LOD: 68'
LWL: 58'
Draft: 5' centerboard up, 14.6' centerboard down
Beam: 22.6'
Rig height: 90'
Sail area: 3,200 square feet
Tons: 41 GRT
Hull: Oak

The *Stephen Taber*, built in 1871, is the nation's oldest sailing vessel in continuous service and is designated a National Historic Landmark. She is one of a kind, and one of the last of the coasters that formed the backbone of American commerce a century ago. Built in an era when highly skilled shipwrights built fine vessels to be aesthetically beautiful as well as functional, she stands as a proud tribute to American craftsmanship. Today she is refitted to carry 22 guests in comfort.

Who sails: Groups and individuals of all ages
Program type: Three and six-day overnight sailing adventures; corporate team building; day sails
Season: May through October
Built: 1871, Glenwood Landing, Long Island
Coast Guard certification: Passenger Vessel (Subchapter T)
Crew: 5   **Trainees-passengers:** 49 daysails, 22 overnight
Contact: Capt. Noah Barnes, Captain/Owner, P.O. Box 1050, Rockland, Maine, 04841 USA
Tel: 800-999-7352
E-mail: info@stephentaber.com
Website: www.stephentaber.com

Flag: USA
Rig: Square topsail schooner, two-masted
Homeport: Chestertown, Maryland
Normal cruising waters: Chesapeake Bay
Sparred length: 97'
LOD: 53'
LWL: 53'
Draft: 8'
Beam: 17'
Rig height: 72'
Freeboard: 5'
Tons: 43 GRT
Power: Single screw diesel
Hull: wood

SULTANA

The schooner *Sultana* is a full scale reproduction of a 1767 vessel of the same name used by the British Royal Navy to enforce the notorious "Tea Taxes" on the North American coastline in the years preceding the American Revolution. *Sultana* is notable as one of the most thoroughly documented vessels from the American Colonial period. The schooner's original logbooks, crew lists, correspondence, and design drawings have all survived intact to the present day. Owned an operated by Sultana Projects, Inc., a non-profit, 501(c)(3) organization based in historic Chestertown, Maryland, the new *Sultana* sails as a floating classroom; providing unique, hands-on educational opportunities for children and adults that focus on the history and environment of the Chesapeake Bay and its watershed. *Sultana's* educational programs are designed to compliment and support national, state and local curriculum goals - but just as importantly, they are meant to excite students about the process of learning. In 2004 and again in 2007, Sultana Projects was the proud recipient of the Walter Cronkite Award for Excellence in Maritime Education from the National Maritime Historical Society. Again and again teachers have found that a trip on *Sultana* can help to bring subjects like history, science, math and reading alive.

Who sails: School & adult groups as well as individuals of all ages
Program type: Under-sail educational experiences in environmental science and history, including both day trips and live-aboard programming
Season: April to November
Designer: Benford Design Group, St. Michael's, Maryland
Built: 2001: Chestertown, Maryland, Swain Boatbuilders, LLC
 Coast Guard certification: Passenger Vessel (Subchapter T)
Crew: 5 **Trainees-passengers:** 32 daysails, 11 overnight
Contact: Drew McMullen, President, Sultana Projects, Inc., PO. Box 524, Chestertown, MD 21620 USA
Tel: 410-778-5954
Fax: 410-778-4531
E-mail: dmcmullen@sultanaprojects.org
Website: www.sultanaprojects.org

HMS SURPRISE

SPECIFICATIONS

Flag: USA
Rig: Full-rigged shiphip
Homeport: San Diego, CA
Normal cruising waters:
San Diego Bay
LOA: 179'
LOD: 135'
Draft: 13'
Beam: 30'
Rig Height: 130'
Sail Area: 13,000 square feet
Tons: 263 GRT
Hull: wood

"HMS" *Surprise* is a 179' full rigged ship. Her designers and builders made painstaking efforts to recreate a 24 gun frigate of Great Britains' Nelson era Royal Navy. The result is a replica vessel unmatched in its authenticity and attention to detail. Originally christened "HMS" *Rose* when she was launched in 1970, she served as a sail training vessel operating out of several east coast ports for over 30 years. The ship underwent extensive modifications for the production of the film "Master and Commander: The Far Side of the World" in 2002. The Maritime Museum of San Diego purchased "HMS" *Surprise* from 20th Century Fox in October, 2004. Plans include restoring the ship to seaworthy condition.

Who sails: Museum Vessel at this time
Program type: No programs as yet
Designer: Admiralty
Built: 1970: John Fitzhugh Millar, Lunenburg, Nova Scotia
Contact: Peter Durdaller, San Diego Maritime Museum, 1492 N. Harbor Drive, San Diego CA 92101 USA
Tel: 619 234 9153 x 120
E-mail: pdurdaller@sdmaritime.org
Website: www.sdmaritime.org

Flag: USA
Rig: Barque, three-masted (lateen mizzen)
Homeport: Jamestown Settlement, Virginia
Normal cruising waters: Chesapeake Bay
Sparred length: 116'
LOA: 96'
LOD: 83'
LWL: 77'
Draft: 11' 6"
Beam: 24' 10'
Rig height: 95'
Freeboard: 11'
Sail area: 3,902 square feet
Tons: 180 GRT
Power: twin 135 HP diesels
Hull: wood

SUSAN CONSTANT

Susan Constant is a full-scale re-creation of the flagship of a small fleet that brought America's first permanent English colonists to Virginia in 1607. Together with the smaller *Godspeed* and *Discovery*, *Susan Constant* is on exhibit at Jamestown Settlement, a living history museum of 17th-century Virginia, and hosts about a half-million visitors every year. Jamestown Settlement is administered by the Jamestown Yorktown Foundation, an agency of the Commonwealth of Virginia. Built on the museum grounds and commissioned in 1991, *Susan Constant* replaced a vessel built for the 1957 Jamestown Festival commemorating the 350th anniversary of the colony's founding. While no plans or renderings of the original *Susan Constant*, *Godspeed*, and *Discovery* have ever been located, the replicas are based on the documented tonnages of the 17th century ships, and *Susan Constant's* design incorporates research information that emerged after the first replicas were built. With a crew of staff and volunteers, *Susan Constant* and *Godspeed* periodically sail to other ports in the Chesapeake Bay region to participate in commemorative and community events and host educational programs. A volunteer sail training program is offered to individuals of all ages.

Who sails: Crew consisting of Jamestown Settlement staff and volunteers age 18 years and older
Program type: Sail training for crew and apprentices; dockside interpretation
Designer: Stanley Potter
Built: 1991: Jamestown Settlement, VA, Allen C. Rawl
Crew: 25
Contact: Captain Eric Speth, Maritime Program Manager, Jamestown Settlement, PO Box 1607, Williamsburg, VA 23187 USA
Tel: 757-253-4838
Fax: 757-253-7350
Website: www.historyisfun.org

SPECIFICATIONS

Homeport: Los Angeles, California
Flag: USA
Normal cruising waters: Coastal California and offshore islands
Rig: Square topsail schooner, two-masted
Sparred length: 92'
LOA: 70'
LOD: 66'
LWL: 62'
Draft: 10'
Beam: 18'
Rig height: 74'
Freeboard: 5'
Sail area: 4,000 square feet
Tons: 46 GRT
Power: Diesel
Hull: wood

SWIFT OF IPSWICH

The Los Angeles Maritime Institute is currently making a major investment in the restoration of the square topsail schooner *Swift of Ipswich*. Everyone is looking forward to her returning to the TopSail Youth Program, alongside the twin brigantines, *Irving Johnson* and *Exy Johnson*, providing character building sail training adventures for youth. As LAMI's original vessel, *Swift of Ipswich* is a learning environment that nurtures the development of knowledge, skills and attitudes that are necessary for the education of today's youth, but difficult to teach in a traditional classroom. About two thirds the size of one of LAMI's twin brigantines, *Swift* is especially well suited for working with smaller, younger groups of youth who might be overwhelmed by the size and complexity of the LAMI brigantines. *Swift* is a special favorite of youth-of-all-ages, many of whom sailed her as Girl Scouts over 40 years ago…we are looking for *Swift* sailors who'd like to renew friendships, retell memories and support her restoration. Built to the lines of an historic Revolutionary War privateer, *Swift of Ipswich* was once the personal yacht of actor James Cagney and has been known as a floating landmark, mostly serving youth, in Southern California for over 60 years.

Who sails: Youth/school groups from diverse communities, especially pre-teens and other youth and adult groups seeking character-building/team-building sailing adventures
Program type: Educational sailing adventures
Season: Year-round
Designer: Howard I. Chappelle
Built: 1938: Ipswich, MA, William A. Robinson
Coast Guard certfication: Passenger Vessel (Subchapter T)
Crew: 6 **Trainees-passengers:** 49 daysails, 31 overnight - Age: 10+
Contact: Captain Jim Gladson, Los Angeles Maritime Institute, Berth 84, Foot of Sixth Street, San Pedro, CA 90731 USA
Tel: 310-833-6055
Fax: 310-548-2055
Website: www.LAMItopsail.org

SPECIFICATIONS

Flag: USA
Rig: Gaff schooner, two-masted
Homeport: Marion, Massachusetts
Normal cruising waters:
Coastal New England (summer), offshore Atlantic Ocean (school year)
Sparred length: 115'
LOA: 92' 10"
LOD: 84' 6"
LWL: 78' 8"
Draft: 10' 4"
Beam: 21' 8"
Rig height: 95'
Sail area: 3,540 square feet
Tons: 100 GRT
Power: 300 HP diesel
Hull: iron

TABOR BOY

Tabor Boy has been engaged in sail training as a seagoing classroom for Tabor Academy students since 1954. Offshore voyaging and oceanographic studies go together in the curriculum, with cruises to destinations as distant as Mexico and Panama adding adventure to the experience. Many Tabor Academy graduates go on to the US Merchant Marine, Naval, or Coast Guard academies. The schooner also offers seven summer orientation voyages for newly enrolled freshmen and sophomore students. During this time, trainees are fully involved in sail handling while studying Gulf of Maine marine wildlife and ecology. Winter programs feature sailing and snorkeling in the US and British Virgin Islands to observe and study coral reef ecosys-tems.

Who sails: Enrolled students at Tabor Academy
Program type: Seamanship and oceanography for high school students
Built: 1914: Amsterdam, The Netherlands, Scheepswerven & Machinefabrik
Coast Guard certification: Sailing School Vessel (Subchapter R)
Crew: 6   **Trainees-passengers:** 23 - Age: 14-18
Contact: Captain James E. Geil, Master, Tabor Boy, Tabor Academy, 66 Spring Street, Marion, MA 02738 USA
Tel: 508-748-2000
Fax: 508-291-6666
E-mail: jgeil@taboracademy.org
Website: www.taboracademy.org

TALOFA

SPECIFICATIONS

Flag: USA
Rig: Brigantine
Homeport: Cabo San Lucas, Baja California Sur, Mexico
Normal cruising waters: Sea of Cortez, Pacific Ocean
Sparred length: 97'
LOD: 72'
Draft: 8'
Beam: 18'
Rig height: 68'
Freeboard: 9' fore, 5' aft
Sail area: 3,000 square feet
Tons: 115 GRT
Power: diesel
Hull: wood

This great ship was built to be "Queen of the Seas" Her Samoan name *Talofa*, means Welcome, much like the Hawaiian greeting, Aloha. Two brothers, Charles and Chester Carter, built her to retrieve copper ingots they saw while on duty in the Merchant Marines during WW I in the South Pacific. A dream was born. They would build a ship to retrieve their fortune. She would be stout, strong, and heavy, nearly 115 tons, and she would become the "strongest, toughest private sailboat constructed in the 20th Century in America - possibly in the world" according to Winn Joseph Bagley, son of a master wooden ship constructor in whose boatyard the *Talofa* would be built. Sadly, the Carter brother's visions were never to become a reality and although ship building began in January of 1928, they never finished her. Today *Talofa* is finished as a fine Yacht with recycled materials from much older vessels. *Talofa* is one of the few, original wooden Cargo Ships still sailing on the West Coast of the Americas. She now offers hands on sail-training tours and Sunset sails for her guests on the beautiful Cabo San Lucas Bay. Our guests will actually sail *Talofa* or they can just sit back and relax! *Talofa* won the prestigious "Perry Bowl" Award during the TALL SHIPS CHALLENGE® Race Series in 2005.

Who sails: All ages
Program type: Adventure sailing, hands-on sail training, private parties
Season: Year-round
Designer: Carter Brothers
Built: 1928
Coast Guard certification: Uninspected Vessel and Attraction Vessel
Crew: 7 **Trainees-passengers:** 50
Contact: USCG Licensed Captain Cactus and Betsy Bryan, Owners
Tel: 011 52 1 624 155-7271
E-mail: talofatallship@gmail.com
Website: www.talofatallship.com

Flag: India
Rig: Barque, three-masted
Homeport: Kochi, India
Normal cruising waters:
Worldwide
Sparred length: 177'
Draft: 15'
Beam: 28'
Sail area: 10,392 square feet
Power: twin 320 HP diesels
Hull: steel

TARANGINI

Tarangini is a three-masted barque designed by the world famous sail ship designer Mr. Colin Mudie and was built by Goa Shipyard Limited, Goa, India. The name *Tarangini* comes from the Hindi word, " TARANG" which means waves. Besides being an ideal platform for basic seamanship, *Tarangini* provides character building and sail training capsule for officer cadets of the First Training Squadron and officers/sailors of Indian Navy. *Tarangini* provides an ideal setting for first hand experience of the natural elements to the cadets embarking on a Naval career. The training imparted onboard *Tarangini* includes general points and terms used in sailing, parts of sails and rigging, setting and furling of sails, watch-keeping under sails, safety while under sails and sail maneuvers such as tacking, veering and boxhauling. It further includes Navigation, ROR (COLREGS), Astro Navigation and other professional subjects. In addition the trainees undertake various activities such as manning the masts, mast drills, and tug of war. INS *Tarangini* fosters the old fashioned and time-tested virtues of courage, camaraderie, and endurance. She instills among the trainees the indefinable "sea sense", apart from qualities of humanity and prudence, which are inseparable from safe and successful seafaring.

Who sails: Officer cadets of the First Training Squadron and officers of the Indian Navy
Program type: Sail training and seamanship for cadets and officers of the Indian Navy
Season: Year-round
Design: Colin Mudie
Built: 1997: Goa, India, Goa Shipyard Limited
Crew: 37   **Trainees:** 30
Contact: CDR S Shaukat Ali, C/O Fleet Mail Office, Kochi, India

TENACIOUS

SPECIFICATIONS

Flag: United Kingdom
Rig: Barque, three-masted
Homeport: Southampton, United Kingdom
Normal cruising waters: United Kingdom (summer) Caribbean and Southern Europe (winter)
Sparred length: 213' 3"
LOA: 177' 3"
LOD: 163' 6"
LWL: 151' 3"
Draft: 14' 9"
Beam: 34' 9"
Rig height: 129' 9"
Freeboard: 7' 3"
Sail area: 12,956 square feet
Power: twin 400 HP
Hull: wood/epoxy

The 213-foot, three-masted barque *Tenacious* is the Jubilee Sailing Trust's (JST) new, second ship. She is the largest wooden tall ship of her kind to be built in Great Britain this century. JST promotes the integration of able-bodied and disabled people though the mediums of tall ship sailing and building. Such has been the suc-cess of the JST's first ship, *Lord Nelson*, that JST decided to build *Tenacious*. Bringing the ethos of integration ashore, the JST has developed the concept of Shorewatch, weeklong ship-building holidays. Professional ship-wrights and mixed-ability volunteers have worked side-by-side as part of this amazing project. Like the *Lord Nelson*, *Tenacious* enables all members of her crew to sail together on equal terms. Features include signs in Braille, power-assisted hydraulic steering, and points throughout the ship that enable Wheelchairs to be secured during rough weather. Voyages are open to anyone between 16 -70+ and no previous experience is required. The crew of 40 is split 50/50 between able bodied and physically disabled people, with eight wheel-chair users. There is a permanent crew of 10, including a medical purser and cook.

Who sails: Physically disabled and able-bodied people, aged 16 to 70+
Program type: Sail training for paying trainees; integration of physically disabled and able-bodied people through the medium of tall ship sailing
Season: Year-round
Designer: Tony Castro, Ltd.
Built: 1996-2000: Woolston, Southampton, United Kingdom
Crew: 8   **Trainees-passengers:** 40
Contact: Ms. Amanda Butcher, Jubilee Sailing Trust, Jubilee Yard, Hazel Road, Woolston, Southampton, Hampshire, S019 7GB United Kingdom
Tel: 44-23-8044-9108
Fax: 44-23-8044-9145
E-mail: jst@jst.org.uk
Website: www.jst.org.uk

Flag: USA
Rig: Square topsail schooner, 3-masted
Homeport: Long Beach, California
Normal cruising waters: Channel Islands and beyond
Sparred length: 156'
LOD: 123'
LWL: 101'
Draft: 13' 6"
Beam: 31'
Rig height: 110'
Freeboard: 6'
Sail area: 8,500 square feet
Tons: 229 GRT
Power: 575 HP Deutz diesel
Hull: steel

TOLE MOUR

Tole Mour is a 156-foot three-mast–ed square topsail schooner owned and operated by the non-profit organization Guided Discoveries. With her incredibly seaworthy construction, fifteen sails, hands-on science equipment, professional crew dedicated to teaching, and close proximity to Southern California's biologically rich Channel Islands, she is the ultimate platform for sail training and marine science education. The *Tole Mour* has been carrying out the work of Catalina Island Marine Institute (CIMI) since 2001. CIMI Tall Ship Expeditions, founded in 1998, is a Guided Discoveries program that is dedicated to "taking young people to sea in order to build character and minds." CIMI Tall ship Expeditions offers live-aboard voyages during the school year, summer, and winter, that focus on sail training and marine science education and range from 2 to 21 days in length. *Tole Mour* accommodates groups of up to 36 and ages 10 to adult. She sails the waters of Southern California's eight off–shore islands and beyond. Her name *Tole Mour* means gift of life and health - and was bestowed upon her by the school children of the Marshall Islands where she was originally commissioned as a health care support ship. Set sail with us for the experience of a lifetime!

Who sails: School groups 4th grade through college; educational adult groups; individuals
Program type: Live-aboard educational voyages focusing on sail training and marine science
Designer: Ewbank, Brooke, and Associates
Built: 1988: Whidbey Island, WA, Nichols Brothers
Coast Guard certification: Sailing School Vessel (Subchapter R)
Crew: 13 **Trainees-passengers:** 53 daysails, 36 overnight
Contact: CIMI Tall Ship Expeditions, PO Box 1360, Claremont, CA 91711 USA
Tel: 1-800-645-1423
Fax: 909-625-7305
Website: www.guideddiscoveries.org or www.tolemour.org

TREE OF LIFE

SPECIFICATIONS

Flag: USA
Rig: Gaff schooner
Homeport: Newport, Rhode Island
Sparred length: 93'
LOA: 70'
LOD: 70'
LWL: 58'
Draft: 8' 5"
Beam: 18' 6"
Rig height: 85'
Freeboard: 4' 5"
Sail area: 4,800 square feet
Tons: 83 GRT
Power: diesel
Hull: wood/epoxy

The Schooner *Tree of Life*, launched in 1991, was built in Nova Scotia, Canada. She sleeps 12 in three cabins and the foc'sle. Her hull is a composite of strip planked clear fir and Kevlar saturated in epoxy and sheathed in fiberglass. Her deck is fir, spars are spruce, and brightwork is Honduran Mahogany. The interior is paneled in koa and teak. The *Tree of Life*, her owners, a crew of four plus two trainees sailed out of Newport Oct. 2002 on a three year circumnavigation. Sailing to Bermuda, St. Martin, the Caribbean to Grenada, west to Venezuela, Colombia, the San Blas Islands, Panama, Ecuador, Galapagos, Easter Island, Pitcairn Island, the Gambier Islands, Tahiti. In 2003, *Tree of Life* spent five months in Auckland, New Zealand via Bora Bora, the Southern Cooks and Fiji for the America's Cup. She sailed the Indian Ocean to Capetown, South Africa, the Atlantic to Antigua for Classic Race Week, St Barth's, St Martin, Turks & Caicos, the Bahamas, Palm Beach and home to Newport, RI. The owners were on board for the duration of the voyage. The *Tree of Life*, at home in Newport Harbor, now sails throughout New England waters as she awaits prospective owners to return her to the world's oceans.

Who sails: Adult individuals and families
Program type: Sail training for volunteer and trainees; sea education in marine science and maritime history
Designer: Ted Brewer
Built: 1991: Covey Island, Canada
Crew: 4 **Trainees-passengers:** 2
Contact: Sheri & John Laramee, Owners, 443 Bellevue Avenue, Newport, RI 02840 USA
Tel: 401-640-9777 or 401-732-6464
E-mail: JohnOnTree@aol.com
Website: www.schoonertreeoflife.com

SPECIFICATIONS

Flag: USA
Rig: Topsail schooner
Homeport: Clinton, New Jersey
Normal cruising waters: Long Island Sound, New England
Sparred length: 118'
LOD: 90'
LWL: 83'
Draft: 9' 6"
Beam: 22'
Rig height: 96'
Freeboard: 3' 6"
Sail area: 9,688 square feet
Tons: 98 GRT
Power: 350 HP diesels
Hull: steel from German U-Boats

UNICORN

From metals of old German submarines to majestic tall ship, STV *Unicorn* sails the sea with proven on-board leadership and development programs for teenage girls, executive women and in-tact executive teams. Holland built in 1947, STV *Unicorn* partners with Sisters Under Sail Corp. to deliver a non-profit leadership development program for teenage girls, whose mission is to build confidence, enhance self-esteem, develop social conscience and teach the value of sisters working together towards a common goal. The vessel welcomes young women from around the globe to sail aboard with *Unicorn's* all-female professional crew. *Unicorn* also partners with BeamPines, Inc., a Human Resources Consulting Firm in New York City, to offer on-board executive development and team building programming. HR Consultants work closely with *Unicorn's* crew to create an effective learning environment that drives results. Chart Your Course, an on-board women's leadership program, is just one of the successful executive programs that has brought together executive women from Fortune 100 Companies to small business owners.

Who sails: Girls age 13 – 21; women and executive men
Program type: Sail training vessel for teenage girls, women, in-tact executive teams, private groups and film work
Built: 1947: Alphen, The Netherlands
Crew: 6 - 10 **Trainees-passengers:** 12 daysails, 6 overnight
Contact: Dawn Santamaria, 2 Gravel Hill Road, Asbury, NJ 08802 USA
Tel: 908-713-1808
E-Mail: dawn@tallshipunicorn.com
Website: www.tallshipunicorn.com www.sistersundersail.org www.beampines.com

SPECIFICATIONS

Flag: Netherlands
Rig: Ketch
Homeport: Den Helder, Netherlands
LOA: 78'
Draft: 9' 10"
Beam: 18'
Hull: steel

URANIA

Urania is the flagship of the Royal Netherlands Naval College. Every executive officer who has graduated from the naval college over the past forty years trained on the *Urania*. Generally she sails with three officers, two petty officers, and twelve cadets. She is a very active ship and has thrice been the recipient of the prestigious Cutty Sark Trophy, which is awarded annually to a ship that best demonstrates the spirit of sail training. Her original wishbone rig was modified to her present Bermudian ketch rig in the late 1950s.

Program type: Training vessel of the Royal Netherlands Naval College
Built: 1928
Crew: 5 **Trainees-passengers:** 12
Contact: Royal Netherlands Embassy, 4200 Linnean Avenue, NW, Washington, DC 20008 USA
Tel: 202-244-5300
Fax: 202-362-3430

Flag: USA
Rig: Gaff topsail knockabout schooner, two-masted
Homeport: Norfolk, Virginia
Normal cruising waters: Worldwide
Sparred length: 126'
LOA: 121' 10"
LOD: 114'
LWL: 84'
Draft: 12' 3"
Beam: 24"
Rig height: 112"
Freeboard: 6' 6"
Sail area: 6,538 square feet
Tons: 97 GRT
Power: twin diesels 205 BHP each
Hull: wood

VIRGINIA

Schooner *Virginia* is a re-creation of its namesake vessel, the *Virginia*, which was the last pure sailing vessel used by the Virginia Pilot Association; that vessel was in service from 1917 to 1926 on the Chesapeake Bay. Almost entirely handmade, Schooner *Virginia* is the first tall ship built on the Norfolk waterfront in nearly 80 years. After nearly two-and-a-half years under construction, the vessel was launched and christened on December 10, 2004. Schooner *Virginia* was designed using the blueprints drafted to build the original *Virginia*, which was designed along the lines of an America's Cup defender. Traditionally, pilot schooners in the area were built for speed. Through pilot service, smaller ships like schooners would assist larger vessels in navigating the notorious bay channels and waterways. Schooner *Virginia* is owned and operated by the Virginia Maritime Heritage Foundation. Her mission is three-fold – Education is its primary focus. She is also a goodwill ambassador for the Commonwealth of Virginia, representing the state at tall ship events beyond its borders. *Virginia* is also used as an economic development vehicle by providing a unique and historic venue for corporate and municipality receptions and/or sails as she visits ports up and down the Eastern seaboard.

Who sails: Youth Sail Training program for students ages 13 - 17 years of age and adult programs including guest crew passages
Program type: Sail training for volunteer crew and trainees; sea education in marine science, maritime history, and ecology in cooperation with accredited institutions; dockside interpretation during port visits
Season: Spring, Summer & Fall
Designer: Tri-Coastal Marine, Inc. **Built:** 2004: Norfolk, VA, Tri-Coastal Marine, Inc.
Coast Guard certification: Sailing School Vessel (Subchapter R), Passenger Vessel (Subchapter T)
Crew: 12 **Trainees-passengers:** 42 daysails, 12 overnight
Contact: Jon Gorog, Executive Director, Virginia Maritime Heritage Foundation, 500 East Main Street, Suite 600, Norfolk, VA 23510 USA
Tel: 757-627-7400 **Fax:** 757-627-8300
E-mail: info@schoonervirginia.org
Web site: www.schoonervirginia.org

SPECIFICATIONS

Flag: USA
Rig: Full-rigged ship
Homeport: New York, New York
Sparred length: 325'
LOD: 263'
Draft: 11' (min.), 22' (max.)
Beam: 40'
Rig height: 167'
Sail area: 31,495 square feet
Tons: 2,170 GRT
Hull: iron

WAVERTREE

Wavertree was built in Southampton, England in 1885. She was first employed to carry jute for use in making rope and burlap bags, voyaging between India and Scotland. Within two years, she entered the tramp trade, taking cargoes anywhere in the world. After 25 years, she limped into the Falkland Islands in 1911, having been almost dismasted in a gale off Cape Horn. Rather than rerigging her, her owners sold her for use as a floating warehouse at Punta Arenas, Chile. *Wavertree* was converted into a sand barge at Buenos Aires, Argentina in 1947, and was acquired there by the South Street Seaport Museum in 1968 for eventual restoration to her appearance as a sailing vessel. By the time *Wavertree* was built, she was nearly obsolete, being replaced by ocean crossing steam ships. At the same time, iron-long the choice of ship builders in iron producing countries such as England-was giving way to steel. *Wavertree* was one of the last large sailing ships built of wrought iron, and today is the largest afloat.

Program type: Sea education in marine science, maritime history, and ecology in cooperation with accredited schools and other groups; other education programs focused toward restoration
Built: 1885: Southampton, England, Oswald Mordaunt & Co.
Contact: South Street Seaport Museum, 207 Front Street, New York, NY 10038 USA
Tel: 212-748-8681
Fax: 212-748-8610
Website: www.southstseaport.org

Flag: USA
Rig: Square topsail sloop
Homeport: Traverse City, Michigan
Normal cruising waters: Upper Great Lakes
Sparred length: 90'
LOA: 56'
LWL: 49'
Draft: 8'
Beam: 16'
Rig height: 96'
Freeboard: 6'
Power: diesel
Hull: wood

WELCOME

The *Welcome* is a 55-foot sloop, a replica of the original *Welcome* built in 1775 at Fort Michimackinac during the Revolutionary War, which later became a British military vessel. The current *Welcome* is under construction at the Heritage Harbor in Traverse City, Michigan. The Mackinac Island State Park Commission built the *Welcome* for the 200th anniversary of Independence Day. The vessel sailed the Great Lakes for a number of years before serving as a dockside museum in Mackinac City. In December of 1992 the Maritime Heritage Alliance (MHA), a nonprofit organization located in Traverse City, MI, was awarded the vessel for reconstruction. Volunteers of the MHA, having built the schooner *Madeline*, are using the traditional boat building skills to restore this magnificent vessel. She is now in the water and almost fully rigged with hopes of MHA having her making appearances by summer of 2008.

Who sails: Families and adults of all ages
Program type: Sail training for volunteer crew and trainees; sea education in maritime history; overnight passages; dockside interpretation
Season: June – October
Designer: Ted McCutcheon
Built: 1976: Mackinaw City, MI, State of Michigan
Coast Guard certification: Moored Attraction Vessel
Crew: 5
Contact: Maritime Heritage Alliance, 322 Sixth, Traverse City, MI 49684 USA
Tel: 231-946-2647 **Fax:** 231-946-6750
E-mail: mhatc@earthlink.net
Website: www.mhatc.net

WENDAMEEN

SPECIFICATIONS

Flag: USA
Rig: Gaff-rigged schooner
Homeport: Portland, Maine
Normal cruising waters: Casco Bay
Sparred length: 88'
LOA: 68'
LOD: 68'
LWL: 50' 7"
Draft: 8' 8"
Beam: 17' 4"
Freeboard: 6'
Rig height: 71'
Sail area: 2,400 square feet
Tons: 35 GRT
Power: 80 HP
Hull: wood

The 88-foot schooner *Wendameen*, like *Bagheera*, was designed by the famed yacht designer John Alden. She was built in East Boothbay, Maine, and launched in 1912 when she took center stage in the golden era of fast, sleek ocean schooners. Inactive since the 1930s, she was thoroughly restored in the late 1980s and is now listed on the National Register of Historic Places. *Wendameen* is Coast Guard certified for 14 overnight passengers plus crew or 49 day sail passengers. Portland Schooner Co. conducts a variety of shipboard programs on *Wendameen* that engage young people in active learning. Schools, camps, and nonprofits can charter *Wendameen* for two-hour sails, a full day, or several days.

Who sails: Schools, camps, organizations, families, individuals of all ages
Program type: Sea education based on in-house programming
Season: Memorial Day through Columbus Day
Designer: John G. Alden
Built: 1912: Frank Adams Shipyard, East Boothbay, ME
Coast Guard certification: Passenger Vessel (Subchapter T)
Crew: 3 **Trainees-passengers:** 49 daysails 14 overnight
Contact: Scott Reischmann & Michelle Thresher, owners, Portland Schooner Co., 40 Commercial St., Ste. 1001, Portland, ME 04101 USA
Tel: 207-766-2500 (or toll free) 1-87-SCHOONER **Fax:** 866-319-5736
E-mail: michelle@portlandschooner.com
Website: www.portlandschooner.com

Flag: USA
Rig: Staysail schooner, two-masted
Homeport: Boothbay Harbor, Maine
Normal cruising waters: North Atlantic Ocean and Caribbean Sea, Canada to South America
Sparred length: 125'
LOD: 94'
LWL: 82'
Draft: 12'
Beam: 22'
Freeboard: 9'
Rig height: 105'
Sail area: 7,000 square feet
Tons: 138 GRT
Power: 500 HP diesel
Hull: steel

WESTWARD

Owned by the Ocean Classroom Foundation, the schooner *Westward* sails on programs of education under sail for the youth of America. Programs range from 4 month semesters-at-sea to week-long programs with schools and youth groups. Trainees sail the ship and learn traditional seamanship skills under the captain and crew, and they explore maritime subjects with the onboard academic staff. The Ocean Classroom Foundation program is a semester-at-sea for qualified high school students, fully accredited by Proctor Academy. The voyage covers more than 4,000 nautical miles, connecting South American shores to the Canadian Maritimes. Students live and work as sailors on a true voyage of discovery, while they study maritime history, maritime literature, marine science, applied mathematics, and navigation. Ocean Classroom is offered Fall, Spring, and Summer terms. Other programs include SEAmester (a complete semester-at-sea for college credit), OceanBound (for high school and college student), and Summer Seafaring Camp (for teens age 13 – 16). The Ocean Classroom Foundation also owns and operates the schooners *Harvey Gamage* and *Spirit of Massachusetts*.

Who sails: Individuals and school groups from middle school through college; affiliated institutions include Proctor Academy, University of Massachusetts/Dartmouth, Center for Coastal Studies, Hurricane Island Outward Bound School, and other schools
Program type: Traditional seamanship training combined with accredited academic studies in maritime subjects
Season: Year-round
Designer: Eldridge McInnis **Built:** 1961: Lemwerder, Germany, Abeking & Rasmussen
Coast Guard certification: Sailing School Vessel (Subchapter R)
Crew: 11 including instructors **Trainees-passengers:** 24 overnight
Contact: Executive Director, Ocean Classroom Foundation, 29 McKown Street, Boothbay Harbor, Maine 04538 USA
Tel: 800-724-7245
E-mail: mail@oceanclassroom.org
Website: www.oceanclassroom.org

SPECIFICATIONS

Flag: USA
Rig: Gaff topsail schooner, two-masted
Homeport: Miami, Florida
Normal cruising waters: Biscayne Bay, Florida Keys, and Bahamas
Sparred length: 70'
LOA: 60'
LOD: 56'
LWL: 49'
Draft: 6'
Beam: 14'
Rig height: 64'
Freeboard: 6'
Sail area: 2,100 square feet
Tons: 24 GRT
Power: 150 diesel
Hull: wood

WILLIAM H. ALBURY

In an era when the Atlantic crossing is measured in hours rather than weeks and most people's occupations anchor them to a desk, counter, or workbench, Sea Exploring offers a learning-by-doing environment. Lessons of character building and teamwork apply to all facets of one's life. The Sea Explorer program requires that each trainee exerts and extends him or herself physically, morally, and mentally to perform duties which contribute to the ship. The reward, over and above the experience of a world of beauty and challenge, is the satisfaction and self assurance that contributes to self-dis-cipline. The *William H. Albury's* Sea Explorer Program offers lessons in ecology and international cooperation, as well as history, science, literature, and art. Subject to the dictates of nature, the Sea Explorer program is adventuresome while also a developer of character and a molder of lives. The *William H. Albury* is now in its 30th year of sailing under the command of Captain Joe Maggio and was co-winner of the 1999 ASTA Sail Training Program of the Year Award.

Who sails: School and other groups and individuals; Affiliated institutions include Boy Scouts and schools in Dade County, Broward County and Abaco, Bahamas
Program type: Sail training with crew, apprentices, and paying trainees; sea education in maritime history and ecology in cooperation with accredited schools and colleges and other groups; passenger day sails and overnight passages
Built: 1964: Man o' War Cay, Abaco, Bahamas, William H. Albury
Coast Guard certification: Uninspected Vessel
Crew: 3   **Trainees-passengers:** 30 daysails, 14 overnight
Contact: Captain Joseph A. Maggio, Marine Superintendent, Inter-Island Schooner, 3145 Virginia St., Coconut Grove, FL 33133 USA
Tel: 305-442-9697
Fax: 305-442-0119
E-mail: heritage2@mindspring.com
Website: www.heritageschooner.com

Flag: USA
Rig: Gaff topsail schooner,
4-masted
Homeport: Chicago, Illinois
Normal cruising waters:
Great Lakes, Eastern Seaboard,
and Caribbean
Sparred Length: 148'
LOA: 109'
LOD: 109'
LWL: 95'
Draft: 8' 6"
Beam: 25'
Rig height: 85'
Freeboard: 8'
Sail area: 4,839 square feet
Power: Cummins 6CTA-M 300 HP
Hull: steel

WINDY

Built as modern interpretations of the last days of commercial sail, the *Windy* and the *Windy II* are true to function while using modern materials and safety features. In 1996, *Windy* was the first four-masted commercial sailing vessel built since 1921, and *Windy II* was completed in 2001. They have many features not found on older tall ships like hot water showers, private bunks, great cabin, furling topsails, as well as bowthruster, shoal draft, and wing keel. Although sister ships, *Windy* is rigged as a schooner and *Windy II* as a barquentine with three square sails. With their divided and easily managed multi-sail designs, there are ample opportunities for persons of all walks of life to participate in the sailing experience. During the summer at Navy Pier, Chicago, both vessels offer hands on sailing experiences to the public as well as private charters for corporations, weddings, team building, and private parties. The ships have hosted 7000 youth aboard in 2007 for the maritime education program. *Windy* was the dockside ship used as the Schooner *Rouse Simmons*, in "The Christmas Tree Ship" documentary which was first aired on the Weather Channel in December 2004.

Who sails: 5th grade and up, adults and seniors of all ages
Season: Spring and Fall
Designer: R. Marthai
Built: 1996: Detyens Shipyard/Southern Windjammer, Ltd.
Coast Guard certification: Passenger Vessels (Subchapter T)
Crew: 4 **Trainees-passengers:** 150 daysails, 26 overnight
Contact: Captain Bob & Janine Marthai
April – October: Tall Ship *Windy*, 600 E Grand Ave – Ticket Booth, Navy Pier, Chicago, IL 60611 USA
Nov – March: 2044 Wappoo Hall Road, Charleston, SC 29412 USA
Tel: Chicago office 312-595-5472; 843-762-1342 **Fax:** Late April – October: 312-595-5473
E-mail: tallshipwindy@aol.com
Website: www.tallshipwindy.com

WINDY II

SPECIFICATIONS

Flag: USA
Rig: Convertible four-masted gaff-rigged barquentine/schooner
Homeport: Chicago, Illinois
Normal cruising waters:
Great Lakes, Eastern Seaboard, and Caribbean
Sparred Length: 150' 6"
LOA: 109'
LOD: 109'
LWL: 95'
Draft: 8' 6"
Beam: 25'
Rig height: 85'
Freeboard: 8'
Sail area: 7,380 square feet
Power: Cummins 6CTA-3M 420 HP
Hull: steel

Built as modern interpretations of the last days of commercial sail, the *Windy* and the *Windy II* are true to function while using modern materials and safety features. In 1996, *Windy* was the first four-masted commercial sailing vessel built since 1921, and *Windy II* was completed in 2001. They have many features not found on older tall ships like hot water showers, private bunks, great cabin, furling topsails, as well as bowthruster, shoal draft, and wing keel. Although sister ships, *Windy* is rigged as a schooner and *Windy II* as a barquentine with three square sails. With their divided and easily managed multi-sail designs, there are ample opportunities for persons of all walks of life to participate in the sailing experience. During the summer at Navy Pier, Chicago, both vessels offer hands on sailing experiences to the public as well as private charters for corporations, weddings, team building, and private parties. The ships have hosted 7000 youth aboard in 2007 for the maritime education program. *Windy II* has been filmed by Warner Bros. for the July 2008 Batman sequel "The Dark Knight."

Who sails: 5th grade and up, adults and seniors of all ages
Season: Spring and Fall
Designer: R. Marthai
Built: 2001: Detyens Shipyard/Southern Windjammer, Ltd.
Coast Guard certification: Passenger Vessels (Subchapter T)
Crew: 4 **Trainees-passengers:** 150 daysails, 26 overnight
Contact: Captain Bob & Janine Marthai
April – October: Tall Ship *Windy*, 600 E Grand Ave – Ticket Booth, Navy Pier, Chicago, IL   60611 USA
Nov – March: 2044 Wappoo Hall Road, Charleston, SC 29412 USA
Tel: Chicago office 312-595-5472; 843-762-1342 **Fax:** Late April – October: 312-595-5473
E-mail: tallshipwindy@aol.com
Website: www.tallshipwindy.com

SPECIFICATIONS

Flag: USA
Rig: Staysail Schooner
Homeport: Annapolis, Maryland
Normal cruising waters:
Chesapeake Bay
Sparred length: 74'
LOA: 61'
LOD: 61'
LWL: 51'
Draft: 7'
Beam: 16'
Rig height: 65'
Freeboard: 5'
Sail area: 1,800 square feet
Tons: 25 GRT
Power: 100 HP diesel Volvo
Hull: wood and epoxy

WOODWIND

The Schooner *Woodwind* and her sister ship the *Woodwind II* are identical 74-foot wooden schooners that sail out of Annapolis, Maryland and can accommodate up to 48 passengers each. These staysail-rigged schooners do a variety of different activities based out of the Annapolis Marriott Waterfront Hotel. The *Woodwind's* offer 2-hour public cruises that depart up to four times daily from downtown Annapolis and sail into the Chesapeake Bay. These schooners also offer private charters for special events, family gatherings and corporate events. One of our specialties is our team building program where the clients Match Race both schooners and really learn what it is like to work as a team to get around the race course (hopefully first). *Woodwind* has four staterooms where couples can stay aboard on Friday & Saturday nights including a sunset sail, accommodations, and breakfast in the morning. In mid-October, there are four cabins available to cruise the Chesapeake for five days on a one-way cruise from Norfolk, Virginia to Annapolis, Maryland. All meals, instruction, accommodations, sailing lore and plenty of lighthouse history are included on this 130-mile journey.

Who sails: School groups from elementary through college, individuals of all ages
Program type: Sail training for paying trainees; informal sea education; team building (including match racing); passenger day sails and group charters; special sailing packages available
Season: April through November
Designer: John Scarano, Scarano Boat Builders **Built:** 1993: Albany, NY, Scarano Boat Builders
Coast Guard certification: Passenger Vessel (Subchapter T)
Crew: 10 **Trainees-passengers:** 48 daysails, 8 overnight
Contact: Jennifer Brest, Captain and Director of Marketing, Running Free, Inc., 1930 A Lincoln Drive, Annapolis, MD 21401 USA
Tel: 410-263-7837 **Fax:** 410-280-6952
E-mail: info@schoonerwoodwind.com
Website: www.schoonerwoodwind.com

WOODWIND II

SPECIFICATIONS

Flag: USA
Rig: Staysail Schooner
Homeport: Annapolis, Maryland
Normal cruising waters:
Chesapeake Bay
Sparred length: 74'
LOA: 61'
LOD: 61'
LWL: 51'
Draft: 7'
Beam: 16'
Rig height: 65'
Freeboard: 5'
Sail area: 1,800 square feet
Tons: 25 GRT
Power: 100 HP diesel, Volvo
Hull: wood and epoxy

The Schooner *Woodwind* and her sister ship the *Woodwind II* are identical 74-foot wooden schooners that sail out of Annapolis, Maryland and can accommodate up to 48 passengers each. These staysail-rigged schooners do a variety of different activities based out of the Annapolis Marriott Waterfront Hotel. The *Woodwind's* offer 2-hour public cruises that depart up to four times daily from downtown Annapolis and sail into the Chesapeake Bay. These schooners also offer private charters for special events, family gatherings and corporate events. One of our specialties is our team building program where the clients Match Race both schooners and really learn what it is like to work as a team to get around the race course (hopefully first). *Woodwind* has four staterooms where couples can stay aboard on Friday & Saturday nights including a sunset sail, accommodations, and breakfast in the morning. In mid-October, there are four cabins available to cruise the Chesapeake for five days on a one-way cruise from Norfolk, Virginia to Annapolis, Maryland. All meals, instruction, accommodations, sailing lore and plenty of lighthouse history are included on this 130-mile journey.

Who sails: School groups from elementary through college, individuals of all ages
Program type: Sail training for paying trainees; informal sea education; team building (including match racing); passenger day sails and group charters; special sailing packages available
Season: April through November
Designer: John Scarano, Scarano Boat Builders **Built:** 1998: Albany, NY, Scarano Boat Builders
Coast Guard certification: Passenger Vessel (Subchapter T)
Crew: 10 **Trainees-passengers:** 48 daysails, 8 overnight
Contact: Jennifer Brest, Captain and Director of Marketing, Running Free, Inc., 1930 A Lincoln Drive, Annapolis, MD 21401 USA
Tel: 410-263-7837 **Fax:** 410-280-6952
E-mail: info@schoonerwoodwind.com
Website: www.schoonerwoodwind.com

Flag: Australia
Rig: Brigantine
Homeport: Sydney, Australia
Sparred length: 144' 6"
Draft: 13'
Beam: 25' 6"
Hull: steel

YOUNG ENDEAVOUR

Given by the United Kingdom to the government and people of Australia in celebration of that country's bicentenary, *Young Endeavour* serves as Australia's national sail training vessel. She was dedicated with the words of Prime Minister Robert Hawke "This ship – *Young Endeavour* – bears a name imperishably linked with Captain Cook's great voyage of discovery. And the name itself expresses a great deal of our aspirations for our country." For a land surrounded by the sea, this brigantine is a reminder of the country's maritime heritage. *Young Endeavour's* arrival in Sydney also heralded the start of a new era of sail training in Australia. *Young Endeavour* sails with a permanent crew of nine from the Royal Australian Navy and hosts a coeducational crew of twenty-four young people. Each year *Young Endeavor* provides hundreds of youngsters with the opportunity to participate in one of twenty ten-day voyages off the Australian coast.

Program type: Sail training vessel
Built: 1987
Crew: 9 **Trainees-passengers:** 24
Contact: Embassy of Australia, 1601 Massachusetts Avenue, NW, Washington, DC 20036 USA
Tel: 202-797-3000
Fax: 202-797-3168

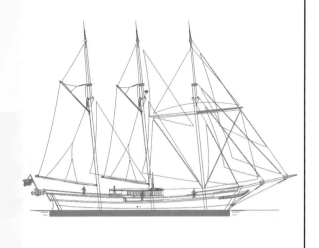

SPECIFICATIONS

Flag: USA
Rig: Barquentine
Normal cruising waters: Coastal California
Sparred length: 188'
LOA: 143'
LOD: 135'
LWL: 129.4'
Draft: 14'
Beam: 35'
Rig height: 129' 6"
Freeboard: 5' 6"
Sail area: 12,500 square feet
Power: 950 HP diesel
Hull: steel

Youth Sail Training Foundation

The Youth Sail Training Foundation's goal is to incorporate sail training into adjudicated youth rehabilitation programs, beginning in California. The STAR model - Sail Training As Rehabilitation – will use proven methods of behavior modification and skill development. The Foundation will collaborate with existing shore-side rehabilitation programs and provide a unique venue designed to increase success. STAR will help give adjudicated youth the skills to reform their own lives. In the beginning, the Foundation will assist existing sail training organizations in developing the STAR model. Eventually, the Foundation will operate purpose-built vessels such as the barquentine Shadow Line. These vessels will have accommodations for program staff, and work space for rehabilitation and academic programs and vocational training. Traditional hull and rig types will be redesigned for maximum strength, safety and performance. See the YSTF website and the vessel information web page for new developments.

Who sails: Adjudicated and at-risk youth
Program type: Sail Training As Rehabilitation-STAR
Season: Year-round
Designer: Michael Kasten, Kasten Marine Design, Inc.
Vessel information: www.kastenmarine.com/shadow_line_135.htm
Crew: 18 **Trainees-passengers:** 32 overnight
Contact: Douglas Humes, Founder, Youth Sail Training Foundation, PO Box 301, Nordland, WA 98358 USA
Tel: 360-622-6141
E-mail: doug@youthsailtraining.org
Website: www.youthsailtraining.org

Flag: Belgium
Rig: Bermuda ketch
Homeport: Zeebruge, Belgium
Sparred length: 93'
Draft: 8' 6"
Beam: 22' 6"
Rig height: 105'
Hull: wood

ZENOBE GRAMME

Serving first as a coastal survey ship, *Zenobe Gramme* is now a training ship for the Belgian Navy. She is a frequent participant in sail training races and gatherings and is easily recognizable when she set her spinnaker which displays the Belgian royal coat-of-arms. *Zenobe Gramme* is named for the Belgian inventor who perfected the technology for alternating-current motors and generators in the 1860s and 1870s.

Program type: Training vessel of the Belgian Navy
Built: 1961
Contact: Embassy of Belgium, 3330 Garfield Street, NW, Washington, DC 20008 USA
Tel: 202-333-6900
Fax: 202-333-3079

ZODIAC

SPECIFICATIONS

Flag: USA
Rig: Gaff schooner, two-masted
Homeport: Seattle, Washington
Normal cruising waters: Puget
Sound, San Juan Islands,
Canadian Gulf Islands
Sparred length: 160'
LOA: 127'
LOD: 127'
LWL: 101'
Draft: 16'
Beam: 26'
Rig height: 127'
Freeboard: 5'
Sail area: 7,000 square feet
Tons: 147 GRT
Power: diesel
Hull: wood

Designed to reflect the highest achievement of naval architecture under working sail, *Zodiac* was fundamentally a yacht. Built in 1924 for the Johnson & Johnson Pharmaceutical Company, she raced the Atlantic from Sandy Hook, New Jersey to Spain in 1928. The crash of 1929 forced her sale to the San Francisco Pilots Association in 1931. Renamed *California*, she served forty years off the Golden Gate as the largest schooner ever operated by the Bar Pilots. She was bought in 1975 by a group of young craftsmen experienced in wooden boat restoration and was renamed *Zodiac*. In 1982 she was placed on the National Register of Historic Places. Certified by the Coast Guard as a Passenger Vessel, she sails Puget Sound, the San Juan Islands, and the Canadian Gulf Coast. *Zodiac's* amenities include three heads and 2 showers, standard bunks and some private staterooms, making her the ideal boat for sail training and education programs enjoyed by a wide range of people. Private charters, youth groups and individual adult sails available from March through October. Check our online schedule for details.

Who sails: Schools; families, groups, and adults of all ages
Program type: Sail training learning by standing watches on the helm, on sailing stations, and in the chart house
Season: March to November
Designer: William Hand, Jr.
Built: 1924: East Boothbay, ME, Hodgdon Brothers
Coast Guard certification: Passenger Vessel (Subchapter T)
Crew: 8   **Trainees-passengers:** 49 daysails, 26 overnight
Contact: Tim Mehrer, Vessel Zodiac Corporation, 3 Strawberry Point, Bellingham, WA 98226
Tel: (877) 831-7427
E-mail: info@schoonerzodiac.com
Website: www.schoonerzodiac.com

Newest Members of the ASTA Fleet

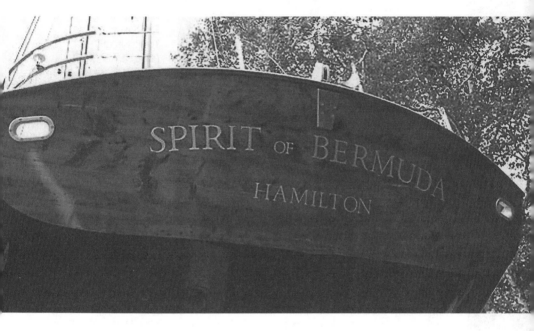

"The traditional tall ship is the finest vehicle for
learning ever devised by man... Why is it important...
because our wonderfully sophisticated society
is enormously rich in technology-yet desperately
poor in experience, that precious resource with
which values are molded and leaders are made..."

Rafe Parker

ST. CHRISTOPHER

ST. CHRISTOPHER

SPECIFICATIONS

Flag: USA
Rig: Schooner
Homeport: Mobile, Alabama
Sparred length: 149'
LOA: 121'
LOD: 118'
LWL: 103'
Draft: 6' 6"
Beam: 19'
Rig height: 118'
Freeboard: 4'
Tons: 149 GRT
Power: twin GM 671 diesels
Hull: riveted steel

The *St. Christopher* is a classic three masted schooner built in 1932 just as the age of sail came to an end. She was built in Delfzjl, Netherlands under Germanisher Lloyd certification, designed to operate in the north sea, some of the roughest sea conditions in the world. *St. Christopher* had been allowed to slide in to very poor condition and then was blown from her moorings and by hurricane Georges into a salt marsh. St. Christopher Services Inc., a non profit organization, acquired the vessel and the recovery was underway. A 650 foot canal had been dug by volunteers to remove her from the salt marsh when Katrina hit. She was beaten up and left 50 feet from the canal. Volunteers removed debris and stumps and were able to jack her up and put ways under her to slide her into the canal. This work has been accomplished through donations of time and equipment buy individuals and businesses. The plans are for complete rebuilding to U.S. Coast Guard passenger carrying certification. Our goal is Christan based medical and humanitarian service as well as participation in ASTA. events. Youth involvement in the sail training program will be emphasized. To save this piece of sailing history and restore her to full service we must now engage in an aggressive fund and volunteer raising program to overcome the setback from hurricane Katrina. If you would like to participate please contact us.

Who sails: Groups and individuals of all ages
Program type: Christian missionary work; mercy ship
Built: 1932: Niestern Sander, Delfzijl, The Netherlands
Crew: 6
Contact: Mr. Bryan Leveritt, St. Christopher Services LLC, 9275 Old Highway 43 South, Creola, AL 36525 USA
Tel: 251-442-0171 or 251-442-3247
Fax: 251-442-3247
E-mail: bryanleveritt@bellsouth.net
Website: www.stchristopherservices.org

The Dream Becomes A Reality: The Spirit of South Carolina Launched At Last

CHARLESTON, South Carolina (March 4, 2007)—Under a sky decorated with lazy clouds, a proud symbol of bygone days gracefully slipped into Charleston's Cooper River Sunday afternoon marking new era of maritime heritage for this historic seaside city. The Spirit of South Carolina, a 140-foot traditional tall ship, was lowered into the water today for the first time, culminating over six years of effort on the part of countless individuals. Suspended briefly in the air, the ship's elegant white topsides gleamed in the sun, and her name and homeport, painted in gold leaf on the transom, shone proudly, portending great deeds for the future.

Just before the ship was lifted in her slings, Charleston Mayor Joseph P. Riley, Jr., Congressman Henry Brown, South Carolina Maritime Foundation Executive Director Brad Van Liew and Chairman John H. Hofford addressed a gathering of VIP guests. Brown presented a special certificate, in recognition of a flag currently flown over

the South Carolina state house in Columbia. Then, Allison Baker, a fifth grader from Chapin, S.C., who had won the privilege of christening the tall ship, read her brief essay on what the Spirit of South Carolina embodies for her. Then she stepped up and swung a bottle across the bow and officially christened the ship.

Fittingly, this christening took place on almost the exact spot where Samuel J. Pregnall and his workers launched the Frances Elizabeth some 128 years ago. (That pilot schooner served as a model for the Spirit's design.). And even before the bubbly was dry on her timbers, the Spirit continued her journey.

It had taken two days to inch the 150-ton ship from her birthplace in Ansonborough Field to the launch site at Union Pier a half mile south. Then, after the largest barge crane on the East Coast, the Charleston Giant, lifted the Spirit off her temporary trailer and nestled her into the briny waters, she motored another half mile north and berthed at the Charleston Maritime Center. There, she was greeted with thunderous cheers from hundreds of well wishers.

Mayor Joe Riley, a longtime supporter of this project told the crowd: "Charlestonians now have another important resource of which they can be very proud," said Riley. "This tall ship was born of humble origins, but it represents a tremendous accomplishment as well as a strong hope for the future of our state. The Spirit of South

AMERICAN SAIL TRAINING ASSOCIATION
240 THAMES STREET @ MILL STREET, 2ND FLOOR
POB 1459
NEWPORT, RHODE ISLAND 02840
401.846.1775 — FAX: 401.849.5400
WWW.SAILTRAINING.ORG
March 3, 2007

Mr. Hank Hofford, Chairman
South Carolina Maritime Heritage Foundation

Dear Mr. Hofford,

I am writing to congratulate you, and the entire Board, Staff, and volunteer workforce of the South Carolina Maritime Heritage Foundation on the happy day of the launch of *Spirit of South Carolina*.

Launching a new ship is an event steeped in tradition and ceremony — as Horace Beck writes in *Folklore and Sea*, "no matter how banal a modern ship launch may appear, it has roots that go back thousands of years to days before Homer, and much of the ritual was deadly serious." Joseph Conrad wrote that "the love of the sea, to which some men and nations confess so readily, is a complex sentiment wherein pride enters for much, necessity for not a little, and the love of ships — the untiring servants of our hopes and self-esteem — for the best and most genuine part."

Many ASTA members had the privilege and pleasure of seeing — and climbing around — *Spirit of South Carolina* while she was under construction during our annual conference in Charleston last November, and no one could fail to fathom how much love and pride has gone into her.

It is obvious how important this day is to all of you who have brought this splendid vessel into being. But we want you to know that it is a big deal for _us_ too — for the tight but far-flung community of tall ships and the people who love them. Today's launch attests to the health and bright future of our common endeavor — shaping lives for the better through lessons of the sea.

We could not be happier than to welcome this proud vessel to the ASTA fleet. We ask that you to accept the ASTA flag as a token of the bond between maritime South Carolina and the wider world of sail training, in which your new vessel will doubtless catalyze many new friendships.

On behalf of the entire ASTA family, we extend hearty wishes for a successful launch, and for many years of "Fair Winds, Clear Skies, and Prosperous Voyages."

With all our best wishes for a happy and lucky ship,

Michael Rauworth

Michael J. Rauworth
Chairman

Carolina will be a teacher to us all, but especially the young people of our state. The ship will develop tomorrow's leaders and teach our young people to become engaged, committed citizens."

Moored alongside the pier, the Spirit of South Carolina drew admiring comments from all onlookers. Her teak decks glowed in the afternoon light, and her varnished cabin houses sparkled. Though the vessel still lacks her masts, booms, and rigging, she is nonetheless an impressive sight. In the coming months, those elements will be added, and she'll ultimately set out on her inaugural voyage. When she does so, she'll carry not only the Palmetto state's youth, but also her creators' ambitions for generating renewed interest in the rich maritime traditions of this state.

Business Partner Members

Organizations, corporations, businesses and ports which do not own or operate a vessel or offer sail training or sea education programs but which do support sail training and the ASTA mission.

Allen Agency Insurance

Penobscot Bay is home to some of the best cruising grounds in the world. On the shores of Penobscot Bay is Camden, home to the Allen Agency, where you'll find the very best in expertise and customer service in the area of commercial passenger vessel insurance.

At the Allen Agency, Gene McKeever and Becky Robinson specialize in providing vessel owners from around the world with choices in coverage from a variety of the industry's best domestic insurance companies.

Gene and Becky appreciate the clients' desire for the very best for their vessel and believes that same high standard should also be applied to their insurance needs. Pride of place and pride of profession: that's the Allen Agency way.

You lead an independent lifestyle. That you want things done well, and done right, the first time. We respect that. Put us to the test.

Established in 1866, the Allen Agency is an independent, employee-owned company with 60 employees.

Allen Agency Insurance
Gene McKeever and Becky Robinson
Tel: 800-439-4311
E-mail: gmckeever@allenagency.com

Boothbay Harbor Shipyard

Boothbay Harbor Shipyard, formerly Sample's Shipyard, was founded more than 135 years ago. Continuing a local shipbuilding tradition, the yard specializes in the maritime skills and trades that made New England famous. Its 700-ton marine railway has braced tall ships, tugboats, fishing trawlers, Coast Guard vessels and other service craft such as passenger boats and ferries. The 150-ton railway has accommodated sailing yachts, workboats, schooners and motor vessels. Conveniently located at the head of Boothbay Harbor in mid-coast Maine, the shipyard offers a complete range of marine-related repairs and services for all vessel types. The 700-ton railway can haul vessels up to 200', and our skilled labor is available for new building, restoration and repairs in steel and wood. We take pride in doing top-quality work quickly and efficiently.

Boothbay Harbor Shipyard
120 Commercial Street, PO Box 462, Boothbay Harbor, Maine 04538
Tel: 207-633-3171 Fax: 207-633-3824
E-mail: info@boothbayharborshipyard.com
Website: www.bbhshipyard.com

Channel Islands Harbor Department

The Channel Islands Harbor, owned by the County of Ventura, is located 60 miles north of Los Angeles, halfway between Los Angeles and Santa Barbara. The harbor is best known for it's year round events and gateway to a wilderness playground, the Channel Islands National Park. Called the "gateway" to the Channel Islands because of its proximity, the harbor is the perfect location from which to take day or extended trips. Located in a picturesque setting, the harbor is home to nine full-service marinas with more than 2,600 boat slips, three nautically themed shopping centers, yacht clubs, more than a dozen restaurants with spectacular views, a year round water taxi , a weekly Farmers' Market, a waterfront hotel and a variety of shops and services. The harbor is home to one of the country's finest maritime collections housed at the Ventura County Maritime Museum located at Fisherman's Wharf. The museum is a cultural center dedicated to the interpretation of maritime history through interactive exhibits and educational outreach.

The Channel Islands hosts several annual events including Celebration of the Whales, Fireworks by the Sea, Concerts by the Sea, Ventura County Boat Show, Ventura Vintage Rods Harbor Run, Channel Islands Harbor Seafood Festival and Parade of Lights. The Channel Islands Harbor was proud to become a host port for the ASTA TALL SHIPS CHALLENGE® Race Series in 2005.

Michele Gilmour, Marketing Director, County of Ventura
Channel Islands Harbor Department
3900 Pelican Way, Oxnard, CA 93035
Tel: 805-382-3013 Fax: 805-382-3015
E-mail: michele.gilmour@ventura.org
Website: www.channelislandsharbor.org

Columbia Trading Company

Columbia Trading Company offers used, out-of-print, rare and selected new nautical and maritime books to readers and collectors of ocean exploration and naval history, yachting and cruising, shipbuilding and design, ship modeling, navigation and seamanship, diving, ocean liners, warships, the merchant marine and nautical fiction.

Our West Barnstable shop (Exit 5 from Cape Cod's Mid-Cape Highway - Route 6) also displays the full spectrum of ship models, artwork, artifacts, distinctive gifts -- and more besides.

We are always interested in purchasing good books and book collections.

Columbia Trading Company
1022 Main Street (Route 6A), West Barnstable MA 02668
Tel: 508-362-1500 Fax: 508-362-1550
E-mail: info@columbiatrading.com
Website: www.columbiatrading.com

307

[Downtown Summerside Inc.]

Downtown Summerside is one of the foremost dining and shopping areas in the Province of Prince Edward Island. With its unique blend of affordable yet diverse shops, fine eateries and personal and business to business services available at your fingertips, Downtown Summerside is the place to be, day or night, working, entertaining, shopping or relaxing. People enjoy our clean, safe streets and vibrant atmosphere.

Downtown Summerside isn't just about shopping; it's about lifestyle, meeting friends, and pampering yourself and your family. It's about leisure, fun, and discovery. It's going about your routine tasks in a relaxed atmosphere.

Downtown Summerside is home to many well known events including our annual Lobster Carnival Sidewalk Sale, Summerside's biggest social and shopping event of the year, and the Downtown Summerside Annual Christmas Open House. Be sure to check the events page on our website to see what's coming up. (www.downtownsummerside.com) Whether you are new to our downtown, or here on a regular basis, we welcome the opportunity to pamper you with the best in affordable, unique, quality products and services.

We're sure you'll agree that to enjoy Downtown Summerside, you need to Experience It!

Mr. Ron Casey
7 Summer Street, PO Box 121, Summerside, PE C1N 4P6 Canada
Tel: 902-436-7546 Fax: 902-436-7547
E-mail: office@downtownsummerside.com
Website: www.downtownsummerside.com.

[Eastern Salt Company]

Eastern Salt is a family-owned business operating on Boston Harbor in the City of Chelsea. We are Massachusetts' leading importer of road salt, and are able to accommodate all sizes and types of vessels, from tall ships to tankers. Located in a designated port area, our facility is a five-acre site with a low-water depth of 40 feet.

The City of Chelsea has always played an important role in the maritime history of Massachusetts, and we at Eastern believe in continuing to connect the citizens of Chelsea with her working ports. To celebrate the relationship of community to ocean, Eastern Salt welcomes tall ships to our dock each summer for community groups, schools, and neighbors to tour.

Paul Lamb
Eastern Salt Company
37 Marginal Street, Chelsea, Massachusetts
Tel: 617-884-5201

Festival of Sail - San Francisco 2008

For five days the San Francisco Bay will seem like something out of a movie, with majestic tall ships offering cannon sails, sunset cruises, day cruises and tours, everyone will feel like they are apart of maritime history!

Concerts, fireworks, an international village, marine center and Parade of Sail will all be a part of the ongoing celebration to educate the community about the importance of the tall ships and their role in bringing diversity and commerce to San Francisco.

The tall ships begin their Pacific coast voyage nearly a month before they arrive in San Francisco as part of the American Sail Training Association's 2008 TALL SHIPS CHALLENGE® Race Series. From late June through early September these magnificent ships will be sailing the Pacific coast and visiting ports along the way. The fleet will be in San Francisco July 23rd – 28th, 2008.

Hosted by the San Francisco Maritime National Park Association and the San Francisco Maritime National Historical Park, the 2008 Festival of Sail will transform the piers of San Francisco into an international nautical attraction.

Joanne Fedeyko
Festival of Sail
Tel: 415.307.1382
E-mail: Executive_Director@festivalofsail.org
Website: www.festivalofsail.org

Jordan Harrison Insurance Brokers

Founded in 1995, Jordan Harrison Insurance Brokers are independent insurance brokers specializing commercial and marine insurance coverage. Our emphasis is on all facets of marine insurance; including Hull, Protection & Indemnity (P&I), Marine Liabilities, and Ocean Cargo Insurance coverage. Marine insurance coverage, by nature lend themselves to international insurance and their related exposures thus our interest is not only to the Hull and P&I insurances that a vessel owner would have but also the related shoreside exposures that need to be addressed when vessel visit Ports of Call. As a result, we also lend ourselves to marine liability programs that are designed to incorporate all liability exposures under one program where possible. ASTA members can be assured that we have the capability of handling not only the marine insurance programs for their vessels but also non-marine exposures including Directors & Officers liabilities typical of non-profit organizations. In addition, our expertise extends to exposures that you may encounter chartering vessels for your event or excursion as well as events surrounding the promotion of your tall ships program.

All of the employees associated with Jordan Harrison Insurance Brokers come from the national insurance underwriting background and/or national broker background. We feel we give our customers international expertise and capabilities with local service.

Jeffrey Dickow or Serene Dong
Jordan Harrison Insurance Brokers
Tel: 401-398-5911 Fax: 415-398-6157
Website: www.jordanharrison.com

[*Kasten Marine Design, Inc*]

Our primary focus is Custom Yacht Design. Our specialty is the design of personal yachts large and small for ocean voyaging; for luxury charters; or for all-around family cruising. Whether we are creating a new yacht design or modifying an existing design, our mission is to combine an owner's wishes with graceful aesthetics, human-friendly design, competent analysis, maximum performance, robust structure, and of course - classic form.

We use up to date methods, including software created specifically for the task of hull modeling, for stability and performance analyses, and for streamlining the construction process. This provides the best opportunity for a thorough analysis of hull form, and allows us to optimize the design in ways that were just not possible in years past.

Our goal is to provide a complete "design service" from the point of imagining a new vessel, through creating the ideal solution to those conjurings, then seeing that it gets built as designed. Our specific task is to take a boat design all the way from the napkin sketch, through the genesis of complete building plans, to actual construction. When requested to do so, we also provide several "construction related services" such as creating computer cut parts or to provide additional drawings and documentation for classification.

Performance, sea keeping, strength, economy and beauty... these are always the qualities sought in one's habitat on the water. For more information of how we go about assuring those qualities in our boats and on the yacht design process itself, please visit our website at www.kastinemarine.com.

Michael Kasten
Kasten Marine Design, Inc.
PO Box 991, Port Townsend, WA 98368
E-mail: Michael@kastenmarine.com
Website: www.kastenmarine.com or www.kastenyachtdesign.com

[*Norfolk Festevents*]

Founded in 1977, Norfolk Festevents originated as an all volunteer organization dedicated to producing an annual waterfront and maritime festival - Norfolk Harborfest. Since then, Norfolk Festevents has evolved into a major East Coast event production company, producing over 80 waterfront events, festivals and concerts annually, as well as serves as the managing agency for the City of Norfolk for tall ship visits and related maritime projects.

Norfolk Festevents, Ltd
Karen Scherberger, Executive Director
120 W. Main Street, Norfolk, VA 23510
Tel: 757441-2345 Fax: 757441-5198
E-mail: scherbergerk@festevents.org
Website: www.festevents.org

Onne van der Wal Photography Inc.

Onne van der Wal is an award-winning nautical, sailing, shipping and yacht photographer, capturing the beauty of sailboats, powerboats, commercial shipping vessels, fine yachts and the spirit of adventure travel. Onne's renowned nautical and sailing photography is sought after for use in commercial shipping advertising & marketing, editorial pieces, yacht brochures, advertisements, event coverage and for private yacht photography.

Onne's in depth understanding of sailing and boats brings a unique element to his nautical / sailing / yacht photography and lends itself to his individual style. When Onne is hired as a boating photographer, he brings these skills to the job and is able to play many roles – he can set up a fleet of boats for a mock-race, stylize a mega yacht for a discerning client, call out trim and sail change sequences for a sailboat photography shoot - all the while shooting with a keen eye and meticulous attention to the mechanical details of the photograph.

Onne is available for nautical, sailing, powerboat and yacht photography assignments year long and in locations near and far from his Newport, Rhode Island office.

Onne van der Wal Photography Inc.
One Bannister's Wharf, Newport, RI 02840
Retail Gallery: 401-849-5556
Studio: 401-846-9552
E-mail: info@vanderwal.com
Website: www.vanderwal.com

Piscataqua Maritime Commission

The PMC is a non-profit community organization dedicated to promoting awareness and education of the New Hampshire seacoast's rich maritime history through Tall Ship port calls. Proceeds from ship tours and marketing fund a variety of sail training scholarships for area students and other educational programs. Ships visit for at least a three day weekend anytime between April and October.

With over two decades of experience successfully hosting tall ships annually, the PMC Board and hundreds of PMC members and volunteers make a port call not only a regional event for residents, but also the ship, captain, and crew. Vessels are berthed with the enthusiastic support of the NH Dept. of Ports and Harbors, at docks with full facilities and 24 hour security. Ships dock in Portsmouth's historic 17th century downtown. History, geography and easy transportation combine to make scenic Portsmouth a world famous tourist mecca - amenities, tours, shops, museums, recreational activities, restaurants and beaches are at hand.

The PMC encourages tall ships whose course takes them near New England to contact us to discuss a visit - and discover why captains recommend Portsmouth as "one of their best port calls ever".

Larry Job, Vice Chairman
Tel: 603-929-4472.
E-mail: lrjob@comcast.net

Port Alberni Tall Ships® Festival

The Port Alberni Tall Ships Society will once again host the tall ships during the American Sail Training Association's 2008 Pacific Coast TALL SHIPS CHALLENGE® Race Series in the summer of 2008.

In 2005, nine ships visited the Port Alberni Tall Ships® Festival and it is expected that a similar number will be part of the festival between July 11 and 12, 2008.

Port Alberni Tall Ships Society
Tel: 250-724-3314
Website: www.portalbernitallships.ca

R & W Traditional Rigging & Outfitting

R & W is a family owned and operated distributor of rope and cordage. Started in 1985 as a "one man" operation out of the trunk of a hand-me-down car, we've grown into one of the most diverse stocking warehouses in the industry.

We've got rope - whether it's small 50 lb test braided line for ice fishing, brightly colored rope for trying your hand at tying a rope halter or a fancy knot, a safety line for a school's challenge course, or a full set of custom spliced docklines, chances are we have it and have it in stock.

We know rope – both the technical side of how it's made and the application side of how its used, and enjoy helping you find just the right product for your needs. And we sell our rope at some of the best prices you'll find anywhere. QUALITY, VALUE, & SERVICE - it's what we expect and it's what you can expect from us.

Distributors of:
• Davey & Co. Marine Hardware
• Meissner Winches,
• Ording Wooden Blocks and Rope of all descriptions.

Choose the best gear from the age of classic yachting and working sail.

R & W Traditional Rigging & Outfitting
39 Tarkiln Place, New Bedford MA 02745
Tel: 866-577-5505 or 508-995-1114
E-mail: mainstay@csolve.net
Website: www.RWrope.com

Sailing Ship Adventures

Sailing Ship Adventures is a specialty travel service that represents sailing ship owners and operators, including some of the sailing world's best-kept secrets. We book voyages for our customers on a wide variety of sailing ships ranging from the largest full rigged tall ship in the world (The Royal Clipper, at over 400 feet in length) to smaller vessels (ranging from 60 to 100 feet in length), as well as aboard crewed chartered yachts.

Unlike your local travel agent we do not represent just a few ships and tour providers, but a wide variety of ships in many different destination areas. We have researched tall ships and sailing ship vacations the world over. Our extensive knowledge of sailing ships and the resulting roster of vessels in our fleet means that, no matter where you would like to spend your next vacation or what you would like to do there, we can find the perfect voyage for you.

Our fleet is comprised of more than 100 full rigged tall ships, brigantines, barkentines, schooners, and smaller vessels. This range of ships, from the most luxurious to the more spartan, offers you the widest range of choice available.

SAILING SHIP ADVENTURES

SAIL AWAY ON YOUR OWN TALL SHIP ADVENTURE!

Call Toll-Free: 1-877-882-4395

Or go to:
www.SailingShipAdventures.com
888 Worcester Road, Suite 260
Wellesley, MA 02482

Our ships sail to destinations through the world, ranging from popular itineraries in the Caribbean and Mediterranean Seas, to ocean crossings, to exotic areas such as the fjords of Patagonia, the Andaman Sea, and the Queen Charlotte Islands. Sailing to these destinations offers opportunities to experience exotic locations in an up-close and intimate way that is not possible on traditional cruises. Smaller vessels are able to stop at smaller, out-of-the-way ports of call not accessible to large cruise liners.

Climb aboard one of these majestic sailing ships and set sail to exotic locations!

Dexter Donham
888 Worcester Road, Suite 260, Wellesley, MA 02482
Tel: 781-237-4395 or toll free 877-882-4395
E-mail: ddonham@sailingshipadventures.com
Website: www.sailingshipadventures.com

313

Sail Baltimore

Sail Baltimore, a 501(c)(3) non-profit organization, provides a free, annual, public program of visiting ships and maritime events. In operation since 1975, our mission is one of economic development, education and cultural exchange. Each year, we produce a free program of visiting ships and maritime events to benefit the area's residents, visitors, youth and business community.

Sail Baltimore is the city's blockbuster attraction, a changing museum in our harbor, in which residents and visitors alike can learn about various cultures around the world. Through our visiting ships program, participating vessels come and go throughout the year, staying for anywhere from one day to several weeks, and opening their decks to the public for free tours.

On an annual basis, Sail Baltimore welcomes an average of two dozen ships to Baltimore's waterfront, including international tall ships, military vessels, educational and environmental ships. Ships are docked in the Inner Harbor, Fells Point and Locust Point.

Sail Baltimore
3720 Dillon Street, 2nd floor, Baltimore, Maryland 21224
Tel: 410-522-7300 Fax: 410-522-3405
E-mail: info@sailbaltimore.org
Website: www.sailbaltimore.org

Sea-Fever Consulting LLC

Sea-Fever Consulting LLC, a strategy and management consulting firm, helps organizations and individuals navigate strategic and communication challenges, and discover innovative and sustainable business opportunities.

We offer services to organizations of all sizes and types with primary expertise and focus on:

• Leadership development
• Nonprofit management
• Maritime heritage and cultural education programs

Our organization's name was inspired by John Masefield's classic poem Sea-Fever and the famous line "all I need is a tall ship and a star to steer her by." Sea-Fever is committed to helping organizations and individuals find their "star to steer by."

"Navigate Challenges: Discover Opportunities"

Peter A. Mello
Sea-Fever Consulting LLC
PO Box 30, Mattapoisett, MA 02739
Tel: 508-264-5629 Fax: 775-796-5344 skype: petermello
E-mail: peter.mello@sea-feverconsulting.com
Website: www.sea-feverconsulting.com
Blog: www.sea-fever.org

Societe du Vieux, Port de Montreal

Since May 1992, the Old Port of Montreal has been offering Montrealers, yachting tourists, and tall ships a quality marina The Port d'Escale. Located in the Jacques Cartier Basin, the Port d'Escale is equipped with a full range of up-to-date facilities to accommodate sailboats over 200 feet, docking on floating docks. Tucked into the heart of the Old Port, a few steps away from downtown Montreal, this secure facility provides a quiet haven for tall ships mooring there. Because of its varied activities and its unique atmosphere, the Old Port is an important site for recreation and tourism in Montreal. Set a heading for the Port d'Escale, and discover Montreal in style.

Sylvain A. Deschamps, Harbourmaster
333 de la Commune Street West, Montreal, Quebec H2Y 2E2 Canada
Tel: 514-283-5414 Fax: 514-283-8423
E-mail: deschamps@oldportofmontrealcorporation.com
Website: www.oldportofmontreal.com

Tall Sails Marketing Group

Tall Sails Marketing, formerly Great Lakes Marketing Group, works to bring both ships to ports and ports to ships throughout the Great Lakes. Our goal is to provide ships with a constant audience, while helping the community to develop long-term waterfront programs. These opportunities may include student, community and environmental education programs, waterfront festival development, grants and sponsorship recruitment. Through strategic marketing and communications, and as liaison between ships and ports, Tall Sails Marketing integrates mutually successful port visits.

Since 1998, Tall Sails Marketing has worked with over 25 vessels including the U.S. Brig Niagara (2002, 2004, 2008), HMS Bounty (2004, 2007 (England)) and Pride of Baltimore II (2008). We have produced or co-produced maritime festivals throughout the Great Lakes including Chicago (1998, 2000, 2007), Kenosha, WI (2003, 2004), Cleveland, OH (2000, 2001, 2003, 2007) and Green Bay (2007). Tall Sails Marketing has been an integral participant in the American Sail Training Association's Great Lakes TALL SHIPS CHALLENGE® Series, recruiting local and international vessels, ship hosting, volunteer training, and port festival development.

TALL SAILS MARKETING
Ship appearances for both Ships and Ports
throughout the Great Lakes
• Festival Production • Special Events
• Tour Coordination

www.tallsailsmarketing.com
C: 847-274-2475
E: PattiLock@tallsailsmarketing.com

Patricia Lock
Marketing Strategist for Ports & Ships
Tall Sails Marketing
Tel: 847-274-2475
E-mail: pattilock@tallsailsmarketing.com

Tall Ships® Tacoma

In 2005, Tacoma hosted the American Sail Training Association's TALL SHIPS CHALLENGE® Race Series with a Tall Ships® festival that drew 30 classic sailing vessels to the Thea Foss Waterway and Tacoma waterfront. Estimates placed the number of attendees at over half a million people and the festival created nearly $1 million in television and print coverage for the community and supported businesses across the region through increased tourism. Tall Ships® Tacoma was awarded "2005 Port of the Year" honors by the American Sail Training Association for this highly successful event.

In 2008, Tacoma will again host the TALL SHIPS CHALLENGE® Race Series with a Tall Ships® festival which will feature many popular events, including a Parade of Sail. Visitors will be able to attend ship sailings, ship tours, educational events and exhibits, musical performances, and a festival environment jam-packed with food, crafts, displays and all sorts of nautical-themed activities. All of these events will create opportunities for attendees to meet the crews of the visiting vessels. The ships will arrive in the Thea Foss Waterway on July 3rd, 2008 and will depart on July 6th, 2008.

Tall Ships® Tacoma is produced by the Tacoma Tall Ships Organization, a not-for-profit organization registered in the State of Washington.

Tall Ships® Tacoma 2008
535 Dock Street, Suite 210, Tacoma, WA 98402
Tel: 253-272-5650
E-mail: info@tallshipstacoma.com
Website: www.tallshipstacoma.com

Tall Ships® Victoria

The Victoria Tall Ships Society has successfully negotiated with the American Sail Training Association (ASTA) for the return of the TALL SHIPS CHALLENGE® Race Series. Victoria will be the first port of call for this event which visits the Pacific coast, the Great Lakes and the Atlantic coast in a three year rotation.

The Victoria festival is scheduled for June 26 – 29, 2008 and will coincide with the 150th anniversary of the establishment of the Crown Colony of British Columbia; a fitting addition to a year that will be rich in history and special events. The Victoria Tall Ships Society is a non-profit organization established in May 2003 for the purpose of hosting the (ASTA) TALL SHIPS CHALLENGE® Race Series during its 2005 visit of west coast ports.

As part of its mandate, the Society wishes to make Victoria a permanent host port for the tall ships during each of their tri-annual visits to the region. It seeks also to enhance the awareness of the rich maritime history of this city and the strong links which British Columbia has with the sea. A key constitutional objective of the society is provide youth with life affirming experiences while sailing in traditionally rigged vessels.

Victoria Tall Ships Society
28 Bastion Square, Victoria, BC, Canada V8W 1H9
Tel: 250-384-2005
E-mail: info@tallshipsvictoria.ca
Website: www.tallshipsvictoria.ca

Village of Greenport, NY

Located in the beautiful, deep and superbly protected waters of the Gardiners/Peconic Bay system of eastern Long Island, Greenport Harbor has been a uniquely appealing destination for mariners since the dawn of American history. Modern-day Greenport remains true to this heritage. A seaborn visitor arriving today steps off the boat, and back in time, to enjoy an authentic working seaport where a car is unnecessary.

Deep water dockage for large and small vessels is available at a municipally owned marina in the heart of a downtown waterfront listed on the National Register of Historic Places. Stores, galleries, and services including those catering to mariners, such as welding, hauling, carpentry and marine hardware, even a hospital, are but steps away. A waterfront park has been developed upland of the marina which boasts a vintage carouse', an outdoor amphitheater and boardwalk. Additional board-walk will soon connect the marina to a transportation center where bus, rail, and ferry connections are available to Shelter Island, New York City, and destinations throughout Long Island.

Greenport is keenly interested in visits by tall ships and sail training vessels and will make special arrangements to host traditional sailing vessels, their crews and trainees.

Mayor David Nyce
236 Third Street, Greenport, NY 11944
Tel: 631-477-0248 Fax: 631-477-2488
E-mail: David_Nyce@greenportvillage.org
Website: www.greenportvillage.com

Whitworth Marine Services LLC

Meeting the modern needs of traditional vessels.

Specializing in:
• Diesel Engines
• High and Low Voltage DC Electrical Systems
• Chargers, Inverters, Ac & DC Panels
• Electrical Wiring and Electronics
• Pumps and Piping
• Water Makers
• Fuel Systems
• Sewage Systems

*** Over ten years experience as Chief Engineer on off-shore vessels ***

Nobby Peers
Tel: 631-804-3077
E-mail: knobby@whitworthmarine.com
Website: www.whitworthmarine.com

Wild Rice Adventure Consulting. Training and Facilitation

Wild Rice Adventure Consulting, Training and Facilitation works with sail training and other experiential education programs in a variety of ways. Captain Richard "Rusty" Rice, founder of Wild Rice Adventure, uses his 17 years of adventure education experience to help sail training organizations in developing and implementing experiential education programs to train their staff and crews in experiential education philosophy, theory, and facilitation skills. Additionally, Wild Rice Adventure provides on site first aid and CPR certification oriented to the program environment (ie: marine, wilderness, cold weather, tropical.) Wild Rice Adventure offers individual consultations to those who wish to gain facilitation and outdoor leadership skills, or to pursue a career in the outdoor experiential education and sail training fields.

Captain Richard E. Rice, Jr.
Wild Rice Adventure, Consulting and Facilitation
1004 Commecial Avenue, PMB-301, Anacortes, WA 98221
Tel: 617-381-4413 Cell: 857-928-9191
E-mail: rustyrice@mac.com

Affiliate Members

Non-profit organizations which do not own or operate
vessels but do offer sail training or sea education
programs (Scouts, schools, colleges, museums etc.)

ActionQuest Programs

For over 30 years, ActionQuest has been providing high quality, expedition-based summer programs for teenagers. ActionQuest voyages focus on sailing, scuba diving, cultural immersion, marine biology and global exploration – all in a live-aboard environment unlike any other. Through hands-on experiential learning and exceptional global expeditions, ActionQuest challenges young adults with high action, life-changing adventures that promote personal growth, teamwork and leadership. Choose from voyage offerings in the British Virgin Islands, the Caribbean's Leeward Islands, the Mediterranean, Galapagos, Australia or Tahiti and French Polynesia.

ActionQuest also offers Lifeworks community service summer programs for teens and Sea-mester Programs for college students and high school graduates. Living full-time aboard our traditional schooners and sailing through extraordinary destinations that span the globe, Sea-mester teaches accredited academics unconfined by the four walls of a traditional classroom.

ActionQuest
Mike Meighan and Captain James M. Stoll
PO Box 5517, Sarasota, FL 34277
Tel: 941-924-6789 or 800-317-6789 Fax: 941-924-6075
E-mail: info@actionquest.com
Website: www.actionquest.com

Algonac-Clay Township Historical Society

The "Hospitality Port" of the Great Lakes
N.42 deg. 37' 09.43" W 82 deg 31' 45.50"

Algonac is on the St. Clair River between Lake St. Clair and Lake Huron. Our museum is located in the Waterfront Park that features more than 2200 feet of riverside boardwalk.

Tall ships have enjoyed our Hospitality Port with sufficient water depth, easy docking and convenience of stores within walking distance. We can arrange fueling, pump outs, fresh water, land showers, boat repair, transportation. A Port of Entry is located next to the museum.

In 2001 we hosted 17 tall ships at our boardwalk at one time as part of the American Sail Training Association's Great Lakes TALL SHIPS CHALLENGE® Race Series. We have welcomed the *Bluenose II, Picton Castle, Niagara, Pride of Baltimore II, Europa, Nina,* Coast Guard Cutters and many others. If dock side tours or day cruising are available, we will advertise and sell tickets. Some ships have stopped in for a quick trip to the grocery store or a Dairy Queen across the street, changing of crewmembers, or passengers, or a safe haven for inclement weather.

Algonac-Clay Township Historical Society
1240 St. Clair River Drive, Algonac, MI 48001
Tel: 810-794-9015
E-mail: achs@algonac-clay-history.com
Website: www.algonac-clay-history.com

Center for Wooden Boats

The Center offers an opportunity to experience the dimensions of an earlier time, to put your hands on the oars of a graceful pulling boat or the tiller of a traditional wooden catboat. With help from master craftsmen, you can learn to steambend an oak frame, cast an oarlock, sew a canvas ditty bag, splice a line or caulk a seam. The Center for Wooden Boats is a hands on maritime museum. Its purpose is to preserve our rich, vital and varied small craft heritage by preserving both the artifacts and the time-tested maritime skills. Our aim is to provide an educational adventure, through participation, in our small craft heritage.

To provide a gathering place where maritime history comes alive through direct experience and our small craft heritage is enjoyed, preserved, and passed along to future generations. -Mission Statement, The Center for Wooden Boats

The Center for Wooden Boats
1010 Valley Street, Seattle, WA 98109-4468
Tel: 206-382-2628 Fax: 206-382-2699
E-mail: cwb@cwb.org
Website: www.cwb.org

Echo Hill Outdoor School

Founded on Maryland's Eastern Shore of the Chesapeake Bay in 1972, Echo Hill Outdoor School is a private non-profit educational organization. Each year Echo Hill offers residential and day programs on a weekly basis to thousands of students from five states and the District of Columbia.

The majority of students attend with their elementary and middle school classes. The School also offers programs for students of all ages, including younger children, high school and college students, teachers, and other adult groups. Echo Hill's outdoor classes open the doors of the traditional classroom to extend and enhance learning. Echo Hill's outdoor classes and residential programs are grounded in our desire to have students live and learn closely with nature. From sensory exploration classes, to canvas platform tents, from the outdoor dining hall, to the dorms surrounded by forest, the philosophy of immersion is present. Our small, hands-on classes provide opportunities for all students to become engaged and participate. Interactions between staff and students focus on fun, creativity, respect, awareness, understanding, and learning. As teachers and naturalists, we believe that students learn best when they are curious and interested. Echo Hill Outdoor School exists to provide students with positive experiences in the outdoors that are exciting, interesting, and fun. Through our programs, students learn more about the wonders of nature, the value of history, and the diversity of individual qualities. We are dedicated to creating a safe and supportive environment for students to feel challenged and successful with the freedom to think, question, and express themselves.

Echo Hill Outdoor School
13655 Bloomingneck Road, Worton, MD 21678
Tel: 410-348-5880 Fax: 410-348-2444
E-mail: info@ehos.org
Website: www.ehos.org

Girl Scouts of the USA

Girl Scouts sail into the future, in boats small to tall! Whether learning from sailing around a pond or around the world, girls say the "best part's the fun!" A sailing ship is a superb "camp of the sea," where girls can focus on goals like teamwork and leadership through environmental action, international friendship, maritime heritage, arts, technology, science, careers, etc. Indeed sail training is a great way to "just add water" to Girl Scout handbooks, badges, interest projects and the progression of activities for every age level. Starting with basic safety for the youngest Daisy Girl Scouts through sailing adventures for teenage Senior Girl Scouts, Girl Scouts and volunteer leaders in over 300 local Girl Scout councils are always eager for more local, national and international opportunities for fun and learning under sail! Girl Scouts. Where Girls Grow Strong.

Girl Scouts of the USA
420 Fifth Avenue - 15th Floor
New York, NY 10018-2798
Tel: 212-852-8553 Fax: 212-852-6515
Website: www.girlscouts.org

Golden Gate Tall Ships Society

The Golden Gate Tall Ship Society (GGTSS) is a California nonprofit organization dedicated to educating people in nautical skills and supporting the preservation and operation of traditional sailing vessels, particularly tall ships.

Goals and strategies include:

• Provide opportunities for sail training experiences for young people
• Provide sailing and shipboard education for members
• Support shore-side education
• Support tall ship visiting San Francisco Bay

Golden Gate Tall Ships Society provides scholarships for young people aboard tall ships, including high school students in San Francisco.

Golden Gate Tall Ship Society
PO Box 926, Sausalito, CA 94966
Tel: 415-332-6999
E-mail: info@ggtss.org
Website: www.ggtss.org

The Gundalow Company

The Gundalow Company is a non-profit organization founded in 2002 with a mission to preserve the gundalow *Captain Edward H. Adams* in order to serve as a platform for maritime, historical, social, and environmental education on and about the waters of the Piscataqua Region. The *Captain Edward H. Adams* was built in 1982 as a replica of the type of 18th century cargo vessel – known locally as a gundalow - that carried salt-marsh hay, bricks, timber, and raw materials between Portsmouth Harbor and the towns on seven rivers that define the Piscataqua Region. The gundalow design evolved over time as an adaptation to the extremely strong currents in the Piscataqua River, very shallow water, and the need for a barge with a capacity to hold up to 50 tons of bulk cargo. The earliest gundalows were simple flat-bottomed barges that moved with the tides and currents. By the mid-19th century the design had evolved to include a leeboard, long sweeps or oars, and a lateen rig that could be lowered to the deck when the vessels passed under bridges. Today, the *Captain Edward H. Adams* visits several ports in the Piscataqua Region each season providing hands-on educational programs, collaborative community events, and interpreted tours to over 15,000 people.

Molly Bolster
Gundalow Company
PO Box 425, Portsmouth, NH 03801
Tel: 603-433-9505 Fax: 603-433-6403
E-mail: info@gundalow.org
Website: www.gundalow.org

Herreshoff Marine Museum

The Herreshoff Marine Museum bordering Narragansett Bay is arguably Rhode Island's most important maritime historical site. From 1863 to 1945, the Herreshoff Manufacturing Company produced the world's finest yachts, the first United States Navy torpedo boats, and a record eight consecutive successful defenders of the America's Cup. Rhode Island's oldest boat *Sprite* (also the oldest catboat in the US) and *Reliance*, the largest America's Cup boat ever built and featured on the Rhode Island State Quarter, were Herreshoff designs.

The America's Cup Hall of Fame brings alive the history of the America's Cup, tracing advances made in the design, construction and sailing in cup competition, while providing permanent recognition to those who demonstrated outstanding performance and sportsmanship.

Museum activities include presentation of an extensive collection, educational programs for adults and youth, a boat restoration program, research and scholarship, outreach programs and community events.

Herreshoff Marine Museum
One Burnside Street, PO Box 450, Bristol, RI 02809
Tel: 401-253-5000
E-mail: t.souto@herreshoff.org
Website: www.herreshoff.org

Inland Seas School of Expeditionary Learning

The Inland Seas School of Expeditionary Learning is the major program initiative of Learn the Seas America, Inc. Learn the Seas - America, Inc. (LSA) a not-for-profit organization, has been established to serve as a dynamic educational community for the academic and character development of adolescent youth through marine education activities. The organization brings together two of the greatest and most important resources - youth and the planet's oceans and seas. The core of LSA is its charter high school, the Inland Seas School of Expeditionary Learning. Using sea education as the organizing focus, Learn The Seas-America, inc. exists to prepare youth for life and life's journeys. We strive to accomplish this goal by ensuring academic achievement and college readiness; fostering a holistic "360-degree" development of adolescent youth through learning and spiritual journeys; involving youth as global citizens of our ocean planet; developing skillful learners, leaders, and collaborators through compassionate service to others and community.

Our philosophy is guided by the ten design principles and five core practices of Expeditionary Learning Outward Bound (www.elob.org). We place an equal emphasis on scholarship and character development. An ethic of service and a healthy life style are strongly promoted.

Inland Seas School of Expeditionary Learning
631 N. 19th Street, Milwaukee, WI 53233
Tel: 414.933.9713
E-mail: info@learntheseas.org
Website: www.learntheseas.org

International Yacht Restoration School

The International Yacht Restoration School (IYRS) is a non-profit institution dedicated to education and maritime preservation. The school teaches the skills, history, art and science of building, restoring and maintaining boats and their systems. IYRS offers intensive programs in traditional boatbuilding and marine systems, employing a time-honored educational model that teaches problem solving, teamwork, project management and hands-on skills. IYRS graduates are highly regarded for their passion and craftsmanship, and work in many of the premier modern and restoration yards around the world. Our Mission: To teach the skills, history, art, and science of building, restoring, and maintaining boats and their systems; To preserve the knowledge, heritage, craftsmanship and aesthetic genius inherent in these boats; To safeguard our site and historic buildings as an important part of America's working waterfront; To show that honest work, integrity and mastery of a craft are among life's great achievements.

The unique nature of the IYRS educational model allows students to learn an in-demand craft while restoring, maintaining and returning historically important small yachts to the water. To date, IYRS students have returned nearly 100 historic boats to the water.

International Yacht Restoration School (IYRS)
449 Thames Street, Newport, RI 02840
Tel: 401-848-5777 FAX: 401-842-0669
E-mail: info@iyrs.org
Website: www.iyrs.org

[Landing School of Boatbuilding and Design]

Established in 1978 and located in Kennebunkport, Maine, The Landing School of Boatbuilding and Design is a non-profit post-secondary career school dedicated to providing the highest quality vocational education in boatbuilding, yacht design, and marine systems technology available. The School was created to provide a gateway to the marine industry for students seeking career opportunities in the marine trades focusing on both recreational and commercial watercraft in both power and sail. The Landing School's ability to reinforce and preserve traditional skills and knowledge while advancing the art and science of boat design, construction, outfitting and repair through the integration of modern techniques and contemporary materials is recognized and valued throughout the marine industry. Our School has earned an international reputation for program quality, and, as an educational institution, is considered by many in the marine industry to be unequaled. The graduates and hundreds of alumni of the School are highly sought after for their craftsmanship, productivity, work ethic, and passion for their chosen careers in, on, and around boats.

Landing School of Boatbuilding and Design
PO Box 1490, Kennebunkport, Maine 04046
Tel: 207-985-7976 Fax: 207-985-7942
E-mail: landingschool@cybertours.com
Website: www.landingschool.org

[Museum of Yachting]

Through a variety of exhibits, the Museum explores the many ways yachting demonstrates human achievement in the arts, in technology, in design, and as a cultural phenomenon. Visitors from around the world marvel at the "Single-Handed Sailors' Hall of Fame", the America's Cup Gallery and the Museum's collection of classic boats, including the Museum's flagship, two-time America's Cup winner *Courageous*- US12-26. Scholars, marine historians and members have access to a library collection of treasures dating back 300 years. The Museum also presents spectacular special events, including the largest Classic Yacht Regatta on the East Coast.

Overall, the Museum of Yachting creates opportunities for people of all ages to experience elements of yachting culture, demonstrating the possibilities for personal satisfaction, growth, and achievement that are defined by the yachting tradition. The Museum of Yachting is open to the public daily from mid-May through October 31.

Museum of Yachting
SallyAnne Santos, Creative Director
Fort Adams State Park, Newport, RI 02840
Tel: 401-847-1018 Fax: 401-847-8320
E-mail: sallyanne@moy.org
Website: www.museumofyachting.org

Ocean Youth Trust

The Ocean Youth Trust is a co-operative activity between 6 registered charities, each providing sail training and personal development for young people between the ages of 12 - 25: OYT-Scotland, OYT Northeast, OYT East, OYT South, OYT Northwest and OYT N. Ireland. Each organization sails in a different overlapping area but pursues the same aims and objectives. A wide range of other voyages such as the Tall Ships Races are also undertaken.

OYT-EAST
Mr. Barry Johnson
22-26 Nottingham Road, Stapleford, Nottingham, NG9 8AA UK
E-mail: office@oyteast.org.uk
Website: www.oyc.org.uk

Rose Island Lighthouse Foundation

A mile offshore from Newport, RI, lays "The Little Lighthouse That Could." Beyond the reach of the city's services and utilities, the restored, operating lighthouse is directly dependent on nature for rainwater and wind-powered electricity. The lighthouse is listed in the National Register and abuts a 17-acre protected wildlife refuge.

Home to historic keepers and their families for over a hundred years, today the restored Rose Island Lighthouse is maintained by vacationing keepers who stay for a night or a week at a time, complete with chores. Families are particularly welcome.

You can help preserve Rose Island by purchasing 100% guaranteed unbuildable square-foot lots. This fundraiser is for those who want the privilege of boasting, "I own waterfront property in Newport," while getting a tax deduction in the process. Create a legacy. Have fun. Make a difference. Lots make great gifts for any occasion! Order on-line at www.Roselsland.org.

Rose Island Lighthouse Foundation
Charlotte Johnson, Executive Director P.O. Box 1419, Newport, RI 02840 USA
Tel: 401-847-4242 Fax: 401-847-7262
E-mail: Charlotte@roseisland.org
Website: www.roseisland.org

Sail Martha's Vineyard, Inc.

Sail Martha's Vineyard is a non-profit organization committed to preserving and protecting the maritime heritage of Martha's Vineyard Island. We offer a variety of programs in support of our mission to include: (i) offering free sailing instruction to Island children from the ages of 8 to 18, (ii) promoting Martha's Vineyard's harbors as welcoming and supportive locations for visiting vessels of all descriptions from foreign sail training ships to local working boats, (iii) offering Masters Licensing courses, launch tenders licensing courses, courses in navigation, diesel engine maintenance and repair. 2008 will see the results of our renewed commitment to attract and support historic visiting vessels.

Although we are not in a position to compensate visiting vessels, we can coordinate local media attention, promote on board opportunities and activities, arrange for dockage at little or no cost for historic vessels in exchange for giving Sail Martha's Vineyard's children the opportunity to be on board for a sail, provide access to chandlery services, and support the ship and her crew in any way possible.

Please contact us for more information or assistance.

Hope Callen, Administrative Director
Sail Martha's Vineyard
110 Main Street, PO Box 1998, Vineyard Haven, MA 02568
Tel: 508-696-7644 Fax: 508-696-7868
E-mail: sail_mv@verizon.net
Website: www.sailmv.com

Sea Scouts

Sea Scouting promotes better citizenship and improves members' boating skills and knowledge through instruction and practice in water safety, boating skills, outdoor, social, and service experiences, and knowledge of our maritime heritage. The program fosters self-esteem as the youth share responsibility for the upkeep of boats and equipment; and the value of teamwork, an important life lesson, receives emphasis every time the boats are underway where the actions of one impacts the safety and well-being of all. Each ship has a unique program designed and implemented by its youth members. Basically, if it is an activity about, on, in, under or through the water, Sea Scouts are involved.

Sea Scouts were organized in 1912 as a "new branch of Boy Scouts of America." The purpose was to serve older boys who were interested in the lore of the sea. Sea Scouting became co-ed in 1968, and since that time, the program has continued to grow nationally and internationally. Today's program provides adventure on land and sea and serves youth ages 14 to 21.

Charles Holmes
National Director Venturing Division
Boy Scout of America
1325 Walnut Hill Lane, Irving, Texas 75015-2079
Tel: 972-580-2425
Website: www.seascout.org

Tall Ship Education Academy/ Tall Ship Semester for Girls

TSEA combines an exciting curriculum with the challenges of living at sea and learning to sail. Our students have sailed within San Francisco Bay, along the coast of Baja, and through the Caribbean while developing life skills and engaging in studies that earn them high school credit. TSEA is a special project of the Department of Recreation and Leisure Studies and the College of Health and Human Services at San Francisco State University.

Our cornerstone program, the Tall Ship Semester for Girls is an innovative high school program that combines a strong academic curriculum with experiential learning. The semester breaks into three six week phases: first, students attend academic classes in our classroom on the San Francisco State University campus. Second, students sail aboard a traditionally rigged sailing vessel and visit foreign countries and third, students participate in internships in San Francisco businesses.

In addition to the semester program, we offer other sail training experiences for youth of all ages. For current offerings, please visit our website.

Tall Ship Education Academy
c/o RLS Dept, 1600 Holloway Ave., San Francisco, CA 94132-4161
Tel: 415-405-3703 Fax: 415-338-0543
E-mail: info@tallshipsemester.org
Website: www.tallshipsemester.org

Thompson Island Outward Bound

Thompson Island Outward Bound Education Center is a not-for-profit organization that provides outdoor adventure and experiential learning programs for young people from diverse economic backgrounds. Located in the Boston Harbor Islands National Park Area, Thompson Island is a unique destination for work or play.

In our Expeditionary Sailing program, nine students ages 12 – 17, are trained in the fundamentals of seamanship including chart reading, navigation and sail theory aboard our historic pulling boats. They learn to handle an oar, read a compass, set anchor, and sail a boat designed for all kinds of weather. They spend 12-14 days exploring miles of Massachusetts Bay, from the Boston Harbor Islands to the shores of Cape Ann with a company internationally recognized as an industry leader in the field of experiential education.

Step out of your routine—join us at Thompson Island Outward Bound for a journey of self-discovery where you will test your limits—both physical and mental. Best of all - meet new friends as you build memories that last a lifetime!

Thompson Island Outward Bound
PO BOX 127, Boston, MA 02127
Tel: 617-328-3900
E-mail: info@thompsonisland.org
Website: www.thompsonisland.org

Thunder Bay National Marine Sanctuary and Underwater Preserve

The NOAA's Thunder Bay National Marine Sanctuary is one of 14 sites protecting America's Ocean and Great Lakes Treasures. The sanctuary contains a collection of nearly 200 shipwrecks, remarkably preserved in the cold, fresh water of Lake Huron. Thunder Bay's collection of archaeological sites represents the diversity of vessels that navigated the Great Lakes in the 19th and 20th centuries. These sunken ships reflect transitions in vessel architecture and construction while conveying stories of Great Lakes transportation and commerce. The sanctuary promotes and protects these unique underwater museums.

The Great Lakes Maritime Heritage Center (GLMHC) campus contains over 600 feet of deepwater dockage and facilities on the Thunder Bay River for visiting shipboard education, sail training, and research vessels. The GLMHC functions as a research station, administrative base, and visitors' center for sanctuary. The admission free Center contains exhibits, documentaries and films, education programs, distance learning opportunities, wooden boat building programs, and gift shop for visitors. The sanctuary actively works with numerous ASTA member vessels on collaborative events, including on-water, dockside, and day sail programs, along with our annual 4th of July Thunder Bay Maritime Festival.

Ms Cathy Green
Education and Outreach Coordinator
Thunder Bay National Marine Sanctuary
500 W. Fletcher Street, Alpena, MI 49707 USA
Tel: 989-356-8805 Fax: 989-354-0144
E-mail: cathy.green@noaa.gov
Website: www.thunderbay.noaa.gov

Tonquin Foundation

The Tonquin Foundation is a Vancouver Island-based organization dedicated to the preservation, promotion and interpretation of the rich but fragile maritime heritage resources of British Columbia and beyond. The Foundation engages in marine and terrestrial archaeology, a wide range of educational and research programs, museum science and historic watercraft construction and preservation.

Each year the Foundation mounts the Westcoast Maritime Festival in the communities of Tofino, Ucluelet, Opitsat, Echachist and Ahousaht which features a wide variety of nautical events; including visits by domestic and foreign tall ships and First Nations tribal canoe journeys.

The Foundation is committed to promoting cross-cultural understanding and mutual respect by celebrating the shared journey of our seafaring ancestors.

The Tonquin Foundation
David W. Griffiths, Executive Director
PO Box 609, Tofino, British Columbia, V0R 2Z0 Canada
Tel: 250-725-4488 Fax: 250-725-2103
E-mail: tonquin@seaviewcable.net
Website: www.tonquinfoundation.org

University of Connecticut Marine Sciences and Technology Center

The Marine Sciences Program is located on UConn's coastal campus at Avery Point, on the shores of Long Island Sound. Our Program includes the Department of Marine Sciences and the Marine Sciences and Technology Center. Within this program, faculty, staff, and students carry out cutting-edge research in coastal oceanography using cross-disciplinary approaches. We offer both undergraduate and graduate degrees that are characterized by an interdisciplinary foundation, high faculty-to-student ratio, and individualized plans of study and research. Our program offers the intimacy and support of a small campus, coupled with the resources of a top-notch public university and internationally renowned scientists.

The Marine Sciences and Technology Center (MSTC) seeks to facilitate research and to provide facilities, logistical and technical support in the field of marine sciences and marine-related research at the University of Connecticut. The Marine Sciences and Technology Center facilities include the Marine Sciences Vessel Operations, Rankin Seawater Facility, Machine Shop, and Electronics Shop. In addition to these facilities, MSTC has an extensive diving program and also provides Information Technology and analytical laboratory support to the Department of Marine Sciences.

Marine Sciences
1080 Shennecossett Road, Groton, CT 06340
Tel: 860-405-9152 Fax: 860-405-9153
E-mail: marinesciences@uconn.edu
Website: www.marinesciences.uconn.edu

US Naval Sea Cadets of Rhode Island

The U.S. Naval Sea Cadets of Rhode Island is a federally-sponsored association for teenagers and pre-teens (age 11 through 17), who have or desire ambition, self-discipline, and a strong academic background. Our primary mission is to instill in Rhode Island youth a desire to succeed as individuals and citizens, beginning with a solid foundation for building academic and social skills, teamwork, and critical thinking.

Our goals include:
• Develop in our youth an appreciation for Naval History, traditions, customs, and their role in national defense.
• Develop in our youth a sense of pride in our nation, positive qualities of patriotism, courage and self-reliance, confidence and strong moral character, and good citizenship traits.
• Develop in our youth an interest and skill in seamanship, seagoing, and aviation subjects. Increase the advancement potential of Cadets who may later elect to serve in the Navy, Marine Corps, Coast Guard or Merchant Marines.

US Naval Sea Cadets of Rhode Island
David R. Kerwood, President
35 Belver Avenue, Suite 001, North Kingstown, RI USA 02852
Tel: 401-932-2396 Fax: 206-666-3422
E-mail: contact@riseacadets.org
Website: www.riseacadets.org

Williams Mystic Maritime Studies Program

The Maritime Studies Program of Williams College and Mystic Seaport offers undergraduates an exciting interdisciplinary curriculum of ocean and coastal studies. Four Williams College courses are offered in the semester-long program at Mystic Seaport, in Mystic, Connecticut: Maritime History, Literature of the Sea, Environmental Policy, and either Marine Ecology or Oceanography. Students earn a full semester's credit and transcript from Williams College. Throughout the semester, students sail on a tall ship, travel the Pacific Coast, and journey to the Mississippi Delta on three extended, hands-on field seminars. Students live in historic, cooperative houses at Mystic Seaport, the nation's largest maritime museum, where they learn traditional maritime skills, and have full access to world-class maritime collections, museum experts, and diverse coastal habitats. College sophomores, juniors, and seniors may participate and all majors are welcome. Financial aid is available. Interested students should contact:

Williams-Mystic
Tel: 860-572-5359
E-mail: admissions@williamsmystic.org
Website: www.williamsmystic.org

Wilmington Harbor Enhancement Trust - Wilmington, North Carolina

Wilmington Harbor Enhancement Trust is a non-profit corporation whose mission is enhancement and development of the historic waterfront in downtown Wilmington, North Carolina. During our organization's fifteen year existence many new docks and facilities have been constructed that allow vessels of all sizes to enjoy the historic downtown area. The waterfront is a major tourist attraction.

Major festivals in Wilmington are the Azalea Festival in early April and Riverfest in early October. Both festivals attract tens of thousands of people to the riverfront. During Riverfest in October WHET sponsors the "Invasion of the Pirates" flotilla on Saturday evening with all of the boats lighted and decorated with a pirate theme.

Wilmington is located approximately 20 miles upriver from the Cape Fear River Entrance which is midway between Charleston, SC and Norfolk, VA. Operators of tall ships are encouraged to contact us and schedule a visit to experience the wonderful southern hospitality of Wilmington.

Paul Canady, Tall Ship Coordinator
Tel: 910-799-8597
E-mail: paul@ledinc.com
Websites: www.wilmington-docks.com and www.invasionofthepirates.com

WoodenBoat School

The Wooden Boat School is located on a 64-acre waterfront campus in Brooklin, Maine. Founded in 1981, the school's twin focus is on wooden boat building and seamanship taught by experienced professionals in the marine industry. Sailing courses are taught by experienced, licensed instructors on cutters, Friendship sloops, ketches, and more than 20 assorted small craft ranging from sailing prams to Herreshoff 12-1/2's. Instruction in related crafts such as lofting, marine mechanics, marine survey, painting and varnishing, marine photography, navigation, and marine art is also offered.

Idyllic surroundings and the finest Instructors available make the WoodenBoat School an exhilarating learning experience for amateurs and professionals alike.

WoodenBoat School
Mr. Rich Hilsinger, Director
PO Box 78, Brooklin, ME
04616-0078
Tel: 207-359-4651
Fax: 207-359-8920
Website:
www.thewoodenboatschool.com

The Yorktown Waterfront

Riverwalk Landing is a beautiful waterfront development designed in the spirit of colonial architecture reflected in the town's historic buildings. It features a variety of fine retail shops as well as a conveniently located two-tier 270-space parking terrace. The restored historic Freight Shed may be reserved for small receptions and meetings. The waterfront also features a performance area, an inviting beach and two floating piers – one to support larger vessels such as regional cruise ships and visiting tall ships, and the other for smaller personal watercraft. The pier has more than 1,000 feet of dock frontage and electrical, water, telephone, and sewer pump out hookups all provided pier side. A mile-long pedestrian riverwalk links Yorktown's major attractions and provides exquisite views of the York River. Benches lining the walk offer visitors the chance to sit and admire the natural beauty of the York River. A free trolley runs daily spring through fall offering many stops throughout town and arrives approximately every 20 minutes to each stop. On many weekends throughout the year, visitors can enjoy live entertainment.

The Yorktown Foundation is a non-profit organization dedicated to preserve and perpetuate the special historic character of Yorktown (site of the last major battle of the American Revolutionary War in 1781).

Dennis Nate, Dockmaster
Riverwalk Landing, 425 Water Street, PO Box 219, Yorktown, VA 23690
Tel: 757-890-3370
E-mail: dockmaster@yorkcounty.gov
Website: www.riverwalklanding.com

Youth Adventure, Inc.

Youth Adventure, Inc. is the oldest nonprofit sailing organization in the Pacific Northwest. Founded in 1959, Youth Adventure purchased the 1913 schooner *Adventuress* and began to offer a sail training program for "youth of all ages." This limited program became more active in the 60s when stewardship of the historic schooner was assumed by Ernestine "Erni" Bennett. For the next 25 years, Erni and a dedicated group of volunteers operated sail training programs aboard the venerable ship for thousands of youth, adults, and seniors - in Girl and Boy Scout, school, environmental education, elderhostel and other groups.

In 1991, Youth Adventure passed ownership and stewardship of the *Adventuress* to Sound Experience, a nonprofit environmental education and sail training organization. Since then, Youth Adventure has continued to help fund regional sail training and sea education programs, youth scholarships, and related activities.

In recognition of her commitment to sail training, Erni Bennett was presented the ASTA Lifetime Achievement Award in 1998. Know to many as "Mrs. B," Erni passed away at the age of 83 in August 2001. However, her sail training legacy will continue on through the newly established Ernestine Bennett/American Sail Training Association Scholarship program as will her enduring example of supporting sailing-based, lifelong learning opportunities for "youth of all ages."

Ms Sandy Bennett
707 Esquimalt Road, Apt 539, Victoria, British Columbia, Canada V9A 3L7
E-mail: snowmaidengirl@hotmail.com

Photo by Matthew Maples

Associate Members

A very important factor in our growth over the years
has been the strength of our membership. Without
the support of our members, the development and
implementation of all of our programs, publications, and
resources, would not be possible.

[Board Members]

Henry H. Anderson, Jr.
Raymond Ashley
Richard Bailey
Daveneet Bakhshi
Les Bolton
Beth Bonds
Mike Brown
Terry Davies
Dexter Donham
Bart Dunbar
Kevin Dykema
Chuck Fowler
Chris Freeman
Robert Frost
Susan Geiger
James Gladson
Thomas J. Gochberg
Richard H. Hawkins
Deborah Hayes
Karen Helmerson
James W. Hiney
John Jamian
Patrick J. Kennedy

Norman Lemley
James Lyons
Paul Madden
Ken Neal
Jed Pearsall
Caleb Pifer
Doug Prothero
Michael J. Rauworth
Nancy H. Richardson
Bert Rogers
Nigel Rowe
Christopher Rowsom
Walter Rybka
Chris Sinnett
Howard Slotnick
Daniel T. Stetson
Alix T. Thorne
Barclay H. Warburton IV
Thomas R. Weschler
F. C. 'Bunky' Wichmann
David V. V. Wood
Meghan Wren

[Lifetime Members]

Frederic S. Sater
Cornelius Vanderstar
John Benson
Joseph M. Davis
Robert S. Douglas
Ronald V. Gallo
John M. Hopkins
Thor H. Ramsing
A. R. G. 'Robin' Wallace
Robert W. Wrathall
Arthur W. Young

MEMBER

Supporting Members

Hal G. Barstow
John W. Braitmayer
David D. Moore
Jeffrey N. Parker
Stan Selden
E. MacGregor Strauss
Anne Beaumont
Arthur Birney
David Hayes
Doug & Pat McKenzie

Family Members

Marshall & Jeri Cushman
David R. Damon
Michael & Charlotte Jehle
Ivan T. Luke
Stanley Martin and Family
Dana & Carolyn Rexford
Robert A. Smith
Edward M. Andrews
Steven H. Baker and Family
Elaine Barnes
Henry Bernard
Nick & Wendy Bowen
William and Deborah Cooper

William Hutchison & Dionne InFante
Micah Faust-Allnutt
Noel & Donna Johnson
Derek Klett
Charlie McDougall
Vincent Mocini
Steve Moulton
Karyn & John Newbill
Darren & Misty O'Brien
Jeannie & Kelly Poole
Robert D. Rustchak
Caroline Voelkers
Robert Waugh

Individual Members

Mark Apter
Erik Brechun
David Choate
Erin Donovan
Denise Drapeau
Alyce & Tim Dwyer
James L. Gladson
Andrew Jay
Thomas & Phyllis Kelly
Eileen Kondor
Thaddeus Koza
Paul Leys
Lou & Anne Massa
Maisie McArthur
Peter McCracken

Richard & Mary Moody
Richard S. Palmer
Cynthia Pifer
William & Nancy Plunkett
Nathalie Reginster
Ashley Replogle
Robyn Sarafin
Glenn & Linda Short
Sean Trifero
Wayne Turner
G. Andy Chase
Harold Joseph Coughlin
Debbie Doucette
Peter Equi
Stephen K. Galpin

Individual Members cont.

Donald Grosse
Cameron Hinman
H. Jochen Hoffmann
Robert A. Johnson
Ellsworth O. Jones
John E. Kelly
Roy H. Kruse
Perry Lewis
John D. McShane
Wilfred P. Moore
Hisakazu Nakayama
Charles Nelson
John T. O'Brien
Slavek Pardo
Joyce Pucino
Alden T. Ring
George I. Rockwood
Greg R. Rossi
Karla M. Smith
Sally Somsel
Deirdre Sykes
Christopher Withers
Mike Albertson
Jay Amster
Michael L. Bachler
Thomas E. Baker
Austin Becker
Robert Bein
Erik Berliner
Tom Blackford
David H. Blomberg
Irene Bodnaruk
Robert Boulware
Judy Bradshaw
Mark K. Branse
Jesse A. Briggs
Robert Brittain
Paulina Brooks
David Brown
Phyllis Brown
Diane L. Carey
R. Bruce Carruthers
Christine Cleary
Alice Collier Cochran
Stuart Coleman
Sym Colovos
Pete Conaty
Stephen Connett
Robert Coxe

Vivian Coxe
Blythe Daly
Leverett Davis
Morgan Davis
Bob Dollar
Amanda Doren
Michael F. Dugan
John Erskine
Joe Ewing
Douglas T. Fischer
David E. Fleenor
Robert Foulke
Frank Fowler
Michael Frechette
Chris Freeding
Philip R. Fuller
Ethan Gallogly
Philip Galluccio
Ryan Gaster
Darlene Godin
Burchenal Green
Robert Green
Philip Gruskin
Charlie Harms
David F. Hart
David Hartke
Jim Heldberg
Jill Helterline
Money Hickman
Charlie Hill
James E. Hilyard
Tucker Hirsch
David Hirzel
Dexter Hoag
Brad Holderman
Larry Horton
Doug Humes
Andrew Jagger
Robert P. Johnson
Michael Kellick
Adrian Kinnane
Brian Kiracofe
Frank Klimas
Barry Kram
Wil Langdon
Anthony Lanza
Vic Leanza
Melia Lewis
Lou & Nancy Linden

Individual Members cont.

J. Eric Little
Richard C. 'Chad' Loebs
Otto Loggers
Patricia R. Longan
Sally H. Lunt
Michael Magno
Paul H. Martinez
Paul Mason
Kent Matsuoka
David Matthews
Dennis C. Mayhew
Ian McIntyre
Brian S. McNamara
Jan Miles
Tim Miller
Robert Miorelli
Hank Mosely
Katherine Mueller
Jesse Leah Nankin
Tamara Nedjar
Daniel Nemsdale
Paul C. Nicholson
Donald L. Nock
Brian Olson
Jim Oppy
Larry Packard
Aaron Paolino
Dan Parrott
Michael Patrick Patterson
Randall S. Peffer
J. Richard Pfund
Edward V. Pietka
Brian A. Pratt
Donna Prieur
Wesley Quinlan
Allen Rawl
Andrew Reay-Ellers
Elizabeth Roberts

J. Catherine Roberts
Mark Rosenstein
Dana Rubin
Dan Russell
Christine Rybak
William Saint-Amour
James D. Salmon
Clyde Sanadi
Jesse Schaffer
Christa Schreiber
Gary Schwarzman
Richard Shannon
Joan Sharp
Eric Shaw
Paul H. Sheehan
Ronald Smith
Doran E. Smout
David Soltesz
Michele Stevens
Ron Straub
Kaari Sullivan
Robert J. Surprenant
Donald F. Teal
Jonathan Thomas
LaBeth Thompson
Llewellyn Toulmin
Don Treworgy
Thompson Tully
Matthew Twomey
Lesley Wacker
Shane Walden
John C. Wigglesworth
Catherine Wingate
Woody Wright
Elizabeth G. Wylie
Peter C. Wylie
Will Young
William F. Young

[*Junior Members*]

Madeline R. Baird
Katrina Barnes
Kathryn England
Luke James Galuszewski
Aaron Gralnik
Charles Heller
Erin Johnson
Jessie Kehr
Arielle Knuttel
Kai Lorenz
Xavier Marvel
Douglas Newbill
Katie Nolan
Susanna Ordway
Darah Russell
Zachary Simonson-Bond
Anna Soens
McKinley Theobald
Jill Thompson
Brian Turnbull
John Wickham

Sail Training International

Sail Training International is a registered charity (not for profit organization with worldwide membership and activities whose purpose is the development and education of young people of all nationalities, cultures, religions and social backgrounds through the sail training experience.

Sail Training International offers a range of activities and services including conferences and seminars, races and other events for sail training tall ships, publications and DVD presentations, international research and the Class A Tall Ships Forum (for the operators of big square-rigged sail training ships). Members are made up of the national sail training organizations of Australia, Belgium, Bermuda, Canada, Denmark, Finland, France, Germany, Ireland, Italy, Latvia, Netherlands, New Zealand, Norway, Poland, Portugal, Russia, Spain, Sweden, UK and USA. The American Sail Training Association is a founder member of Sail Training International.

www.sailtraininginternational.org

Member Organizations

AUSTRALIA - Australian Sail Training Association
Founded in 1996, AUSTA represents the interests of 16 sail training organizations and tall ship operators in Australia and New Zealand. Its purpose is to promote the development of sail training with an emphasis on adventure training for young people at sea under sail in Australia and elsewhere. AUSTA also plays a key role in the development (for sail training vessel operators) of safety-related codes of conduct and on-board management systems, trainee and professional crew training programs and other related programs.
www.sailtrainingaustralia.com

BELGIUM - Sail Training Association Belgium
Founded in 1994, STA Belgium is a registered charity with national membership. It restored, owns and operates the T/S Williwaw and promotes sail training for young people on many other Belgian vessels.
www.sailtraining.be

BERMUDA - Sail Training Association Bermuda
Formed in 2001 following the success of the Tall Ships® 2000 transatlantic race, STA Bermuda promotes and helps to fund the participation of young Bermudians in sail training programs internationally. It is also working with The Bermuda Sloop Foundation to support the construction of its own unique Bermudian sloop for sail training.
john.wadson@stabermuda@logic.bm

CANADA - Canadian Sail Training Association
Founded in 1984, its membership now includes the owner/operators of 18 vessels ranging in size from a six meter open sloop to an 80 meter barquentine and providing sail training programs as diverse in scope as the vessels themselves. A key priority for the organization now is to ensure a regulatory environment that is consistent with the goals and activities of sail training operators and their programs.
www.sailtraining.ca

DENMARK - Danish Sail Training Association
Founded in 1996, DSTA represents the interests of 30 members in Denmark, the Faroe Islands and Greenland, including ten sail training vessels (ranging in size from an 18 meter ketch to two Class A full rigged ships) and five ports. The organization operates a grant scheme to assist trainees taking part in The Tall Ships' Races.
www.dsta.dk

FINLAND - Sail Training Association Finland
STA Finland member sail training vessels have taken more than 12,500 young people to sea since the organization's foundation in 1973. These young trainees have also formed their own organization (The Sail Trainees of Finland Association) which provides opportunities for continuing contact between the trainees and also helps to promote sail training in Finland.
www.staf.fi

FRANCE - Sail Training Association France – Amis des Grands Voiliers

Founded in 1990, STA France represents the interests of around 40 vessels and about 400 members (individuals - associations - charities - vessels operators) in promoting sail training for young persons through exhibitions at various maritime festivals and other events. Through its quarterly publication "Grands Voiliers Infos" and its monthly newsletter, it helps potential young trainees in finding opportunities to embark on sail training vessels around the world..
www.amisdesgrandsvoiliers.org

GERMANY - Sail Training Association Germany

Founded in 1984 as a not-for-profit organization, STAG's main purpose is the education, development and support of young people of all nationalities through sail training. Its members include 50 sail training vessels and over 5,000 individual members. The organization operates a bursary program for sail training vessels and individual trainees.
www.sta-g.de

IRELAND - Coiste an Asgard

Formed in 1968, Coiste an Asgard operates the state owned Class A sail training vessel Asgard II and promotes offshore sail training for young people generally in the Republic of Ireland. Coiste an Asgard provides the communications link for offshore sail training interests in Ireland with Sail Training International pending the development of a national sail training organization (as defined by Sail Training International).
www.irishsailtraining.com

ITALY - Sail Training Association Italy

Founded in 1996 by a partnership of the Italian Navy and the Yacht Club Italiano, its charter is to develop and promote sea training for young people as a means to further their personal development and education. Through the co-operation of the Navy and many owner/operators of other vessels, STA Italy offers a variety of sail training opportunities to young people, including berths at no charge or highly subsidized. The organization also operates an international trainee exchange program which is currently expanding.
www.sta-italia.it

LATVIA - Sail Training Association Latvia

Founded in 2002 by 23 sail training enthusiasts in Latvia, the organization also has three members who own/operate vessels, two yacht clubs and three maritime companies. STA Latvia's principal goals are to develop sail training for young people in Latvia by encouraging other vessel owners to participate in sail training activities and events, and through an international trainee exchange program.
www.sta-latvia.lv

NETHERLANDS - Sail Training Association Netherlands

Founded in 1985, STAN's goals are to encourage and develop sail training off-shore for young people in the Netherlands. In pursuit of this, STAN organizes maritime events and races for sail training Tall Ships in the Netherlands.
www.stanetherlands.nl

NEW ZEALAND - Spirit of Adventure Trust

Established in 1972 by Lou Fisher, The Spirit of Adventure Trust was formed to offer equal opportunity to young New Zealanders to gain qualities of independence, leadership and community spirit through the medium of the sea. The Spirit of Adventure Trust is dedicated to the youth of New Zealand. Each year it brings together 1200 young people throughout the country.
www.spiritofadventure.org.nz

NORWAY - Norwegian Sail Training Association

Founded in 1999, NSTA has four membership categories: sail training vessels, past and prospective host ports for The Tall Ships' Races, individuals and organizations supporting NSTA ideals, and corporate entities. The organization promotes sail training for young people and international friendship through sail training.
www.nsta.no

POLAND - Sail Training Association Poland

Established in 1993, STA Poland has more than 100 individual (voting) members and is co-owner and sole operator of the Class A sail training tall ship, Pogoria. Supporting (non-voting) members include the Maritime Academy of Gdynia (Dar Mlodziezy), the Polish Navy (ORP Iskra) the Polish Scouts Union Sea Training Centre (Zawisza Czarny) and the Polish Yachting Association (Kapitan Glowacki).
www.pogoria.pl

PORTUGAL - Portuguese Sail Training Association

Aporvela – Portuguese STA was founded in 1980 as a registered charity. It has three categories of membership and owns three sail training vessels including the Caravel Vera Cruz. The organization's main objectives are to promote off-shore sail training mainly for young people.
www.aporvela.pt

RUSSIA - Admiral Makarov State Maritime Academy

This institution represents the interests of sail training in Russia and operates the 100-metre sail training ship Mir. The Academy provides the communications link for all sail training activities in Russia with Sail Training International, pending the development of a national sail training organization (as defined by Sail Training International).
smamir@lek.ru

SPAIN - Sail Training Association España

Created in 2003, STA España membership includes all sail training vessels in Spain, the Spanish Navy and a number of ports.
www.sta-espana.org

SWEDEN - Sail Training Association Sweden
STA Sweden was founded in 1998, initially to support the Tall Ships' Races. Today its members include a number of Swedish ports, the Swedish Navy and some 60 vessels engaged wholly or occasionally in sail training activities.
www.stas.nu

UNITED KINGDOM - Association of Sea Training Organisations
Founded in 1972, ASTO represents the interests of UK sail training organizations. It has 25 full members and 10 associate members operating 55 sail training vessels ranging in size from a 10-metre sloop to a 65-metre barque. The organization grants bursary funding towards the costs of more than 80,000 berth days for young people, including disabled trainees each year.
www.asto.org.uk

UNITED STATES OF AMERICA -
American Sail Training Association
Founded in 1973, the organization represents the interests in the US of 300 member sail training vessels from more than 20 countries. There are also 100 affiliate members including museums, schools and universities, and close to 500 individual members who support the organization's mission. ASTA raises funds and administers several scholarship programs as well as a professional development grant program to support the continuing education of professional sail trainers and marine educators.
www.sailtraining.org

Photo by Benson Lee

Programs and Services

ASTA Programs foster youth education, leadership development and the preservation of North American maritime heritage. ASTA organizes the TALL SHIPS CHALLENGE® annual series of sail training races, rallies and maritime festivals, hosts an annual conference on sail training and tall ships, and publishes SAIL TALL SHIPS! A Directory of Sail Training and Adventure at Sea. ASTA also raises money for scholarships, and administers grants directly supporting youth education and leadership development programs that shape young people's lives and build tomorrow's leaders.

ASTA's Annual Conference on Sail Training and Tall Ships

ASTA's Annual Conference on Sail Training and Tall Ships gathers ships' masters, port representatives, public officials, marine suppliers, naval architects, program administrators, festival managers, preservationists, environmentalists, crewmembers, and educators. Topics concerning vessel operations, regulatory issues, management, educational programming, and safety at sea are addressed each year, as are sessions on media relations, marketing, funding, communications, and port event organization. Held annually during the first week in November, the ASTA Conference on Sail Training and Tall Ships is both fun and informative and offers oceans of networking opportunities.

Past conference themes have included: Practical Partnerships - Making Connections and Creating Value (2002), The Leadership Challenge - Steering a Course for Future Success (2003), Agents of Change - Navigating an Ocean of Possibilities (2004), Public and Private PartnerSHIPS (2005), Measuring Success (2006), and Marketing the Mission (2007).

ASTA's Biennial Safety Under Sail Forum

Initiated in 1992, the Safety Under Sail Forum expands the international dialogue among professional mariners by presenting case studies of actual incidents at sea, discussing emerging technologies, and sharing "best practices" so as to constantly insure a high level of safety and professionalism in the sail training industry. Professionals engaged in sail training, sea education, vessel operations, and tall ship events from throughout the world participate in this annual symposium. Topics covered have included preparing for heavy weather, hypothermia, technology and forecasting, survival gear and much more. The American Sail Training Association hosts the Safety Forum during odd-numbered years, in conjunction with the Annual Conference on Sail Training and Tall Ships.

ASTA's Biennial Education Under Sail Forum

The ASTA Education Under Sail Forum made its grand premiere in Chicago in 2000. The first of what has now become a program-focused complement to the Safety Under Sail Forums biennial series. The Education Under Sail Forum is held during even-numbered years, in conjunction with the Annual Conference on Sail Training and Tall Ships. The forum is designed to inform and inspire excellence in the development

and delivery of educational experiences under sail, and overflows with creative exchanges among captains, crew, administrators, teachers, program developers, curriculum designers, and others.

ASTA's Maritime Heritage Forum

The ASTA Maritime Heritage Forum is designed to give participants insight into the role of maritime museums in preparing the public for tall ship visits, developing and delivering Tall Ships Are Coming!® activities, and recruiting and training volunteer Tall Ships® Ambassadors by exploring ways to link local museums and historic sites with sail training traditions and history. Introduced in 2001 in conjunction with the 29th Annual Conference on Sail Training and Tall Ships, the forum - "Tradition with a Future: Sailing, Ships and the Sea"- included a tour of the Maritime Museum of British Columbia and offered a series of seminars covering topics such as Tall Ships as Magnets: Attracting New People and Programs, Ship Tours: More Than Just a Walk Across the Deck, and Sea Chests and Sea Bags: Traditions Go to School.

The ASTA Sail Training Rally

In the 1980s, ASTA developed the concept of the Sail Training Rally; a competition among crews, both at sea and ashore. These rallies provide trainees with an opportunity to demonstrate their seamanship skills in a friendly but competitive format by participating in shoreside events such as knot tying, tug-of war, bucket brigade, rowing, walk the plank, and heaving line toss/hawser pull. Most often held in conjunction with the TALL SHIPS CHALLENGE® Race Series, ASTA Sail

Training Rallies allow the general public to observe the sort of teamwork and maritime skills that are learned on board sail training vessels at sea.

ASTA's Annual Regional Meetings

Regional-Atlantic, Pacific and Great Lakes-meetings are held late winter and early spring. These meetings are less formal than our annual conference, but like the conference, we encourage our professional members to submit ideas for locations and topics.

The regional meetings offer an opportunity for the host to showcase their facility and programs while providing an intimate setting for attendees to network. A typical regional meeting may include a tour, special presentation, safety demonstration, day sail, luncheon and reception. Planning usually starts in November at the annual conference with meetings held in February, March or April. If your organization would like to host a regional meeting, please send a letter of interest along with a proposed agenda to ASTA.

Recent hosts have included:
Atlantic: Sea Education Association, Woods Hole, MA; Northeast Maritime Institute, Fairhaven, MA; Seaman's Church Institute, Newport, RI
Pacific: Ocean Institute, Dana Point, CA; Golden Gate Tall Ship Society, San Francisco, CA; Los Angeles Maritime Institute, San Pedro, CA
Great Lakes: Mayor's Office of Special Events and Navy Pier, Chicago, IL

ASTA Website and Billet Bank

The ASTA website www.sailtraining.org links you to the world of sail training. Links to ASTA member vessels and affiliates make it easy to learn more about opportunities under sail, the ships that can take you to sea, and shore-based programs. The ASTA website also provides information about Tall Ships® events such as the TALL SHIPS CHALLENGE® Race Series and to international sail training associations and resources around the world.

An on-line Billet Bank provides notice of positions available aboard ASTA member vessels. ASTA does not endorse any specific program or individual, but simply shares information as it becomes available.

| Scholarships and Grants |

The Henry H. Anderson, Jr. Sail Training Scholarship

The Henry H. Anderson, Jr. Sail Training Scholarship was established in 1999 and is designed to assist young people between the ages of 14 and 19 achieve a sail training experience aboard a USCG (or national equivalent) inspected ASTA member vessel. Scholarships are available to both individuals and groups.

The Ernestine Bennett Memorial Sail Training Scholarship

The Ernestine Bennett Memorial Sail Training Scholarship was established in 2003. Designed to assist people to achieve a sail training experience aboard a USCG (or national equivalent) inspected ASTA member vessel, the Ernestine Bennett Memorial Sail Training Scholarship is available to people ages 14 and above with special consideration going to female applicants from the Pacific Northwest.

Both scholarships are awarded to individuals who are genuinely interested in experiencing sail training and education under sail. Applicants must show a demonstrated need for financial assistance and must describe, in writing, what they feel they will achieve by participating in the sail training experience.

Ted Cochran Memorial Scholarship For CLASS AFLOAT™

Class Afloat™, in conjunction with the American Sail Training Association, offers an annual memorial scholarship in the name of former friend and supporter Ted Cochran. Covering one semester of tuition costs, this scholarship will be awarded to a Class Afloat™ applicant who is affiliated with an ASTA member organization.

ASTA Sailing Vessel Assistance Grant

The ASTA Sailing Vessel Assistance Grant has been established to support ASTA member vessels that are not necessarily operating as USCG-inspected Sailing School or Passenger Vessels, in maintenance and improvement projects that will better enable them to further ASTA's mission.

ASTA Professional Crew Development Grant

The ASTA Professional/Crew Development Grant has been established to provide financial assistance to professional crewmembers of ASTA vessels in order to meet new and existing requirements for maintaining as well as advancing their USCG licenses, and to encourage the highest possible standards of safety training for individuals or groups of ASTA members.

Detailed information about ASTA scholarship and grant programs, criteria and application forms are available through the ASTA Website at www.sailtraining.org or by calling the ASTA office at 401-846-1775.

Photo by Matthew Maples

ASTA Publications

Sail Tall Ships! A Directory of Sail Training and Adventure at Sea first appeared in 1980, and is now in its seventeenth edition. The directory provides program and contact information for member vessels and sail training associations throughout the world. To help fulfill ASTA's mission, the directory is also distributed through maritime museums and their affiliated shops, marinas, maritime events, and sail training programs, as well as bookstores, libraries, high school guidance counselors, university career resource centers, and education conferences throughout the United States and Canada. US $14.95

Guidelines for Educational Programs Under Sail defines ASTA standards for sail training and sea education within the framework of the Sailing School Vessels Act. This manual defines criteria and indicators of effectiveness for the design, delivery, and evaluation of curricula, instruction, and program administration. In addition to the core of safe seamanship education, the guidelines apply to all aspects of sail training: adventure, education, environmental science, maritime heritage, and leadership development. US $12.00

The ASTA Training Logbook enables trainees to keep a personal log of their sea time and to document their progress in sail training, and records a progression of skill-building activities in nautical science, safety, seamanship, and navigation. Completion of course work and sea time must be certified by either the instructor or the ship's master. US $5.00 (Quantity discounts available)

Tall Ships® Fun! activity book is ASTA's newest product developed to spread the fun and adventure of sail training to future sailors. The 32-page book is designed to entertain the eager minds of 5 to 10 year old children. Unlike normal coloring books, this book provides cutout craft projects, stories and songs from the sea, charts, and various fun activities to connect youth with maritime culture and the tall ships. The Tall Ships® Fun! activity book is a great addition to your sail training program. A wonderful compliment to your educational resources, it encourages young people to further what they have learned from your programs and activities. Not only does it provide individual entertainment, but it can be used as a tool in your organization's youth and education departments too. US $6.95 (Quantity discounts available)

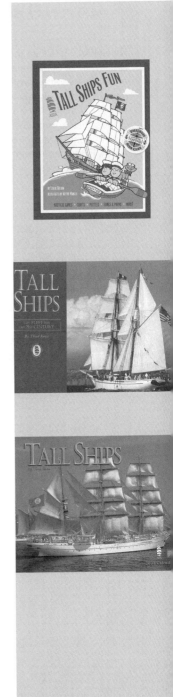

Tall Ships The Fleet for the 21st Century by Thad Koza, published by TideMark Press and now in it's fourth edition. This beautiful book features four-color photographs of 150 sail training vessels in the international fleet. US $24.95

Tall Ships Calendar There are few things on the high seas more dramatic than the great clouds of sail raised by traditional full-rigged ships. In Tall Ships, Thad Koza, a renowned tall ships lecturer, photographer, and author, photographs these vessels at events in the United States and in Europe. Sales benefit the American Sail Training Association. Wall hanging, full color, 14 x 11 inches. US $13.95

ASTA Newsletter

RUNNING FREE is the American Sail Training Association's semi-annual newsletter providing in depth coverage of ASTA events including the TALL SHIPS CHALLENGE® Series, the Annual Conference the International Safety Forum, the ASTA Education under Sail Forum and the ASTA Maritime Heritage Forum.

e-RUNNING FREE is a monthly email newsletter guiding you to what's new at ASTA and in the sail training world In addition to current topics, check out the regular features like the Highlighted Program and TALL SHIPS CHALLENGE® News, To subscribe or to offer feedback, send an email to: newsletter@sailtraining.org.

TALL SHIPS CHALLENGE®
RUNNING FREE
AMERICAN SAIL TRAINING ASSOCIATION · VOLUME XXX · ISSUE 1 · SUMMER 2003

ASTA FLEET SAILING TO SUCCESS IN GREAT LAKES DURING TALL SHIPS CHALLENGE® SERIES

CHICAGO, IL 2003 - The American Sail Training Association reports tremendous success at half way mark of 2003 TALL SHIPS CHALLENGE® Race Series.

More than 25 tall ships and traditional sailing vessels are sailing the Great Lakes for this summer's TALL SHIPS CHALLENGE® Race Series in competition for possession of ASTA's coveted Perry Bowl Trophy. The 2003 TSC Series offers races, cruises, rallies and port festivals transiting the Great Lakes from Lake Erie, through Lake Huron, to the south end of Lake Michigan and back. Millions of visitors, from far and wide, are expected to journey to ports throughout the Great Lakes enjoying breathtaking views of these majestic tall ships.

Left to Right: Nancy Rice, ASTA Volunteer, Boris Terzsclaus, Chair Baker and Whitney Prevost, ASTA alumni. Photo by Peter A. Mello, ASTA Executive Director

The Huntington Cleveland Harborfest showcased the TALL SHIPS CHALLENGE® fleet with a parade of sail on July 9th while vessels opened to the public July 10-13. More than 200,000 people came down to the event which was picturesquely situated at the foot of the Rock & Roll Hall of Fame and the Great Lakes Science Center.

With sails trimmed to capture the Perry Bowl Trophy, the fleet raced the first leg of TALL SHIPS CHALLENGE® Series from Cleveland to Toledo on July 14th and 15th arriving in Toledo on the 16th. The winners of the first leg were Brig Niagara (Erie, PA) in the Youth Division, with Fair Jeanne (Ottawa, Canada) finishing second and INS Tarangini (India) finishing third. The Cruising Division was won by Pride of Baltimore II (Baltimore, MD) while the non-handicapped fleet was won by Windy II (Chicago, IL).

The Huntington Tall Ships® Toledo event continued Ohio's Bicentennial Celebration with public tours of ships from July 17-20. Visitors enjoyed reliving the era of sail and meeting the crewmembers and trainees.

Harkening to the age of the great clipper ship races, most of the TALL SHIPS CHALLENGE® fleet made its way through the Detroit and St. Clair Rivers on July 21st en route to start race 2 of TALL SHIPS CHALLENGE® (Toledo to Chicago) north of Sarnia, Ontario. Race two began on July 22nd and the fleet arrived in Chicago with a 10-

HMS Bounty flying the ASTA flag.

Uniting the world under sail, tall ships from North America will meet vessels from as far away as India, the Netherlands, and the Cayman Islands during the 2003 TALL SHIPS CHALLENGE® Race Series. For those who dare to meet the challenge, many of the vessels provide opportunities for young sail trainees who come aboard to learn seamanship and teamwork, and to meet fellow tall ship trainees from around the world sharing experiences and stories to last a lifetime.

mile parade of sail on July 30th. The City of Chicago hosts Tall Ships® Chicago and the fleet will be berthed on the Chicago River, at world-famous Navy Pier, and at other locations on the city waterfront. Vessels will be open to the public each day from July 31st though August 3rd.

On August 4th, the TALL SHIPS CHALLENGE® fleet departs Chicago and starts race 3, the Chicago-to-Muskegon race, which will crisscross Lake Michigan; the fleet will arrive in Muskegon by August 7th. The public can climb aboard the ships on August 8-10. The Muskegon event ends with a departure parade of sail on the evening of August 10th and the vessels cruise to Bay City, Michigan on Lake Huron.

Tall Ships® Celebration: Bay City starts with a parade of sail on August 14th and the public will be allowed onboard the ships on August 15-17. The final TALL SHIPS CHALLENGE® race from Bay City to Sarnia will start in Tawas Bay on August 18th and the fleet will sail into Sarnia on the 21st. Tall Ships® Sarnia will have the final port festival of the series on August 22-24.

EDUCATION STATION

ASTA Education Station in Cleveland.

The port festivals often feature shanty singers and other local musicians, historical demonstrations and seminars, nautical competition among crews and trainees, buskers of all kinds, food and beverage tents and plenty to see and do.

The TALL SHIPS CHALLENGE® Series rotates among the North American coasts on a 3-4 year basis. The 2004 series is planned for US and Canadian ports on the Atlantic Coast and the 2005 series will begin in the Pacific Northwest and work its way down the coast to California.

Annual Buccaneer's Bash and Fundraiser

Museum of Yachting
Fort Adams State Park
Newport, RI

The Museum of Yachting at Fort Adams was the setting for the 3rd Annual Buccaneer's Bash thrown by the American Sail Training Association on June 16th.. Over 125 people attended this year's event raising $30,000 in support of the American Sail Training Association's mission to encourage character building through sail training, promote sail training to the North American public, and support education under sail.

Live and silent auction items included charters and merchandise from ASTA member vessels; a Cayman Islands getaway; tickets to the Newport Jazz and Folk festivals; fine art and other extraordinary items. A one-week stay in a luxury villa on St. Bart's donated by WIMCO Inc. was raffled-off.

The celebration is ASTA's main fund raising event of the year and started out with a gorgeous afternoon sail aboard the *Aurora* through Newport Harbor. Live pirate entertainment, delicious hors d'oeuvres, refreshments and a live band ensured everyone had a memorable night.

The guest of honor was Congressman Patrick J. Kennedy, who was presented with a commemorative ASTA flag and framed photograph of Rhode Island's own tall ship, the Sloop *Providence*. Congressman Kennedy has played a pivotal role in helping ASTA develop a pioneering program to provide life-changing experiences for at-risk youth — at sea, facing genuine character-building challenges aboard tall ships, all under a federal delinquency-prevention program.

This has allowed ASTA to support numerous educational programs around the country. Among them is a program run by the Providence Maritime Heritage Foundation (PMHF). This program gives inner-city youth from greater Providence the chance to build confidence and teamwork by facing real-world challenges aboard the historical Sloop *Providence*.

The event also showcased the products of the new sponsor of ASTA's TALL SHIPS CHALLENGE® Races from Newport to Halifax —Vectrix— a builder of high-tech electric motorscooters. In its environmental education programs, ASTA uses tall ships as an example of clean, free energy. As a sponsor, Vectrix is a natural match, because it is a modern example of a sustainable, low-carbon-footprint technology.

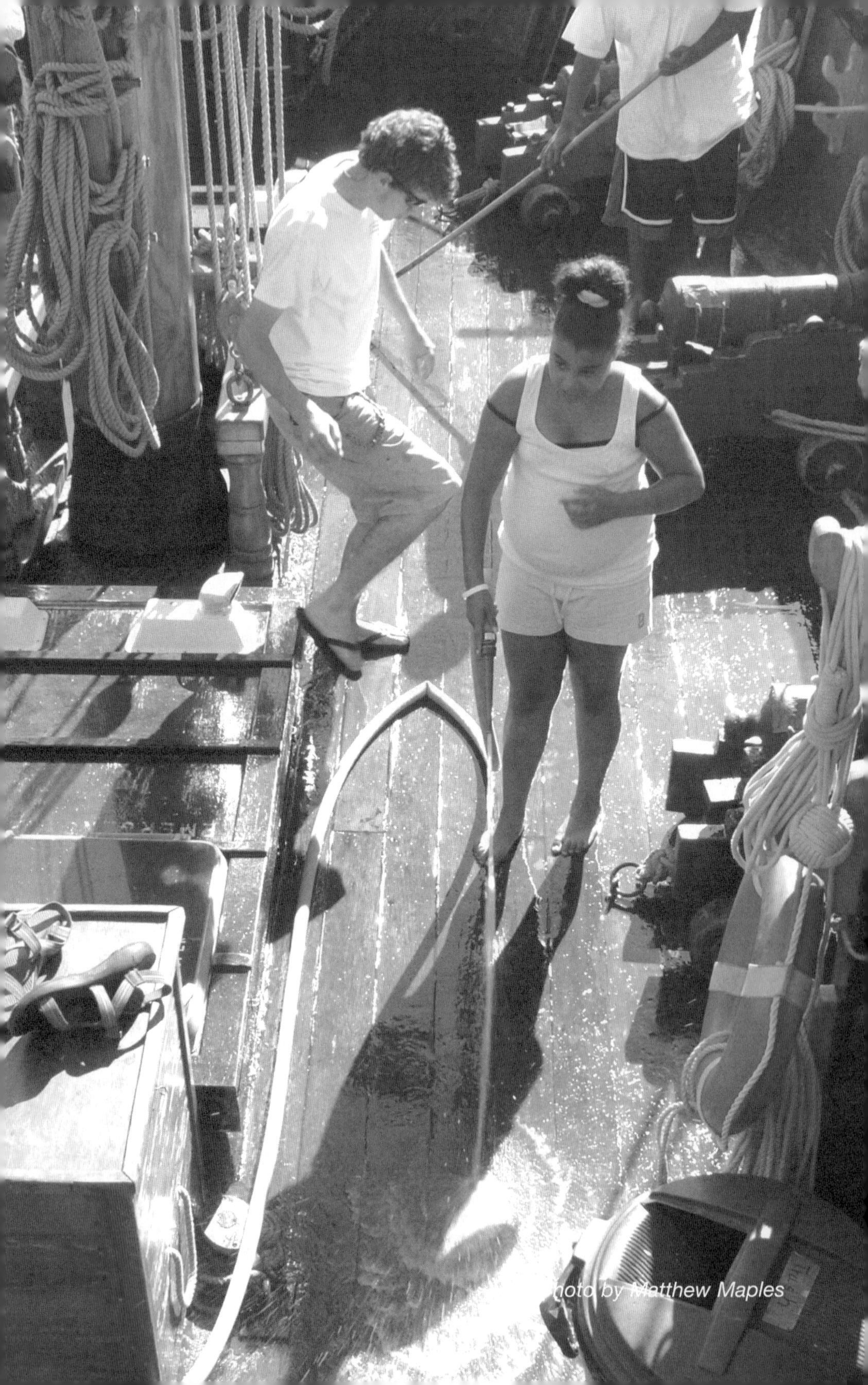

photo by Matthew Maples

Indices

Advertising - Geographical - Alphabetical

Advertiser's Index

Geographical Index

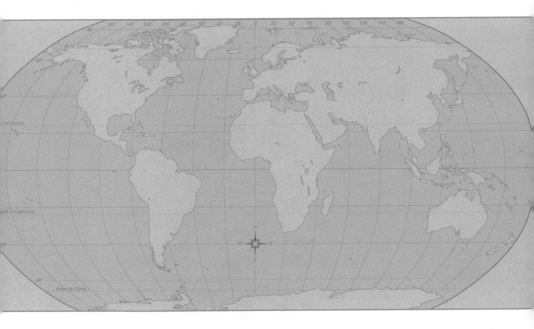

New England

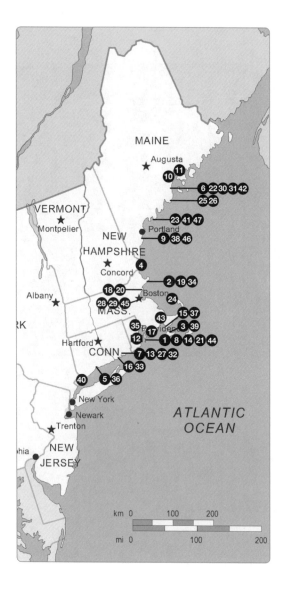

Mid-Atlantic

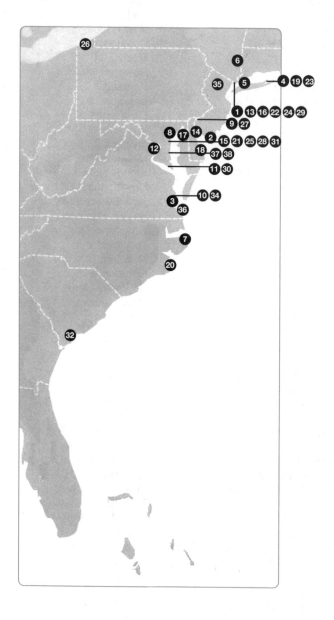

Florida/Gulf of Mexico

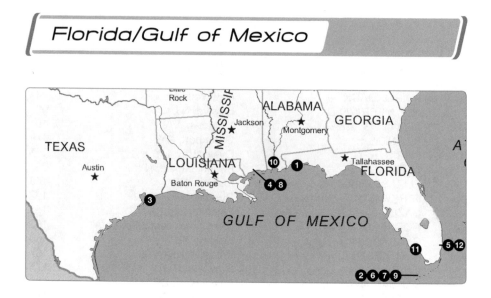

	Vessel Name	Homeport	Page #
1	DANIEL WEBSTER CLEMENTS	Destin, FL	136
2	DREAM CATCHER	Key West, FL	140
3	ELISSA	Galveston, TX	142
4	GLENN L. SWETMAN	Biloxi, MS	160
5	HERITAGE OF MIAMI II	Miami, FL	170
6	LIBERTY	Key West, FL	195
7	LIBERTY CLIPPER	Key West, FL	196
8	MIKE SEKUL	Biloxi, MS	209
9	ODYSSEY	Key West, FL	223
10	ST. CHRISTOPHER	Mobile, AL	300
11	STAR OF THE SEA	Naples, FL	270
12	WILLIAM H. ALBURY	Miami, FL	290

California

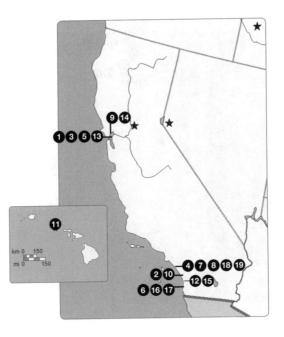

	Vessel Name	Homeport	Page #
1	ALMA	San Francisco, CA	102
2	AMERICAN PRIDE	Long Beach, CA	104
3	BALCLUTHA	San Francisco, CA	115
4	BILL OF RIGHTS	Los Angeles, CA	116
5	C.A.THAYER	San Francisco, CA	124
6	CALIFORNIAN	San Diego, CA	125
7	EXY JOHNSON	Los Angeles, CA	148
8	IRVING JOHNSON	Los Angeles, CA	177
9	KAISEI	Sausalito, CA	183
10	LYNX	Newport Beach, CA	199
11	MAKANI OLU	Kaneohe Bay, HI	201
12	PILGRIM	Dana Point, CA	232
13	ROYALISTE	San Francisco, CA	248
14	SEAWARD	Sausalito, CA	254
15	SPIRIT OF DANA POINT	Dana Point, CA	265
16	STAR OF INDIA	San Diego, CA	269
17	HMS SURPRISE	San Diego, CA	274
18	SWIFT OF IPSWICH	Los Angeles, CA	276
19	TOLE MOUR	Long Beach, CA	281

Pacific Northwest

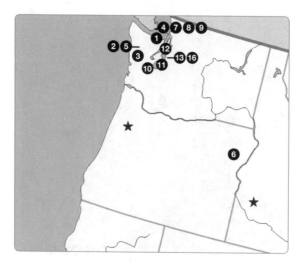

Great Lakes USA and Canada

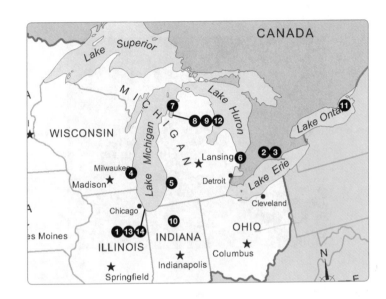

	Vessel Name	Homeport	Page #
1	RED WITCH	Chicago, IL	242
2	APPLEDORE IV	Bay City, MI	108
3	APPLEDORE V	Bay City, MI	109
4	DENIS SULLIVAN	Milwaukee, WI	138
5	FRIENDS GOOD WILL	South Haven, MI	154
6	HIGHLANDER SEA	Port Huron, MI	172
7	INLAND SEAS	Suttons Bay, MI	176
8	MADELINE	Traverse City, MI	200
9	MANITOU	Traverse City, MI	204
10	R. H. LEDBETTER	Culver, IN	244
11	ST LAWRENCE II	Kingston, ON, Canada	268
12	WELCOME	Traverse City, MI	287
13	WINDY	Chicago, IL	291
14	WINDY II	Chicago, IL	292

Canadian Maritimes and St. Louis Seaway

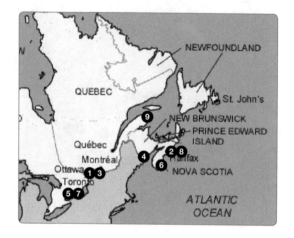

	Vessel Name	Homeport	Page #
1	BLACK JACK	Ottawa, ON, Canada	117
2	CALEDONIA	Halifax, NS, Canada	123
3	FAIR JEANNE	Ottawa, ON, Canada	149
4	JOLLY BREEZE	St. Andrews, NB, Canada	180
5	PATHFINDER	Toronto, ON, Canada	228
6	PICTON CASTLE	Lunenburg, NS, Canada	231
7	PLAYFAIR	Toronto, ON, Canada	235
8	SILVA	Halifax, NS, Canada	259
9	LA REVENANTE	Gaspe, QC, Canada	190

Mexico

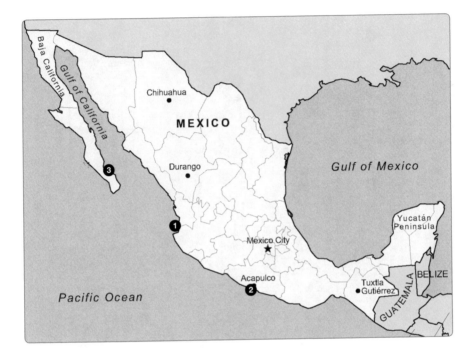

	Vessel Name	Homeport	Page #
1	NINA	Nuevo Vallarta, Mexico	219
2	CUAUHTEMOC	Puerto de Acapulco, Mexico	135
3	TALOFA	La Paz Harbor, La Paz, Mexico	278

South America and Caribbean

	Vessel Name	Homeport	Page #
1	CAPITAN MIRANDA	Montevideo, Uruguay	126
2	CISNE BRANCO	Rio de Janeiro, Brazil	128
3	CONCORDIA	Bridgetown, Barbados	132
4	ESMERALDA	Valparaiso, Chile	145
5	GLORIA	Cartegena, Columbia	161
6	GUAYAS	Guayquil, Ecuador	165
7	LIBERTAD	Buenos Aires, Argentina	194
8	SANTA CLARA	Grand Cayman, Cayman Islands	253
9	SIMON BOLIVER	La Guaira, Venezuela	260

Asia and South Pacific

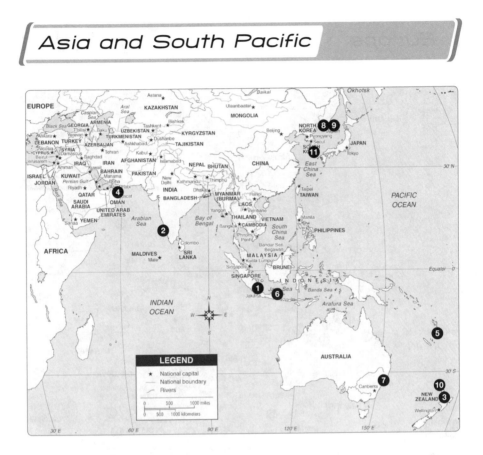

	Vessel Name	Homeport	Page #
1	ARUNG SAMUDERA	Jakarta, Indonesia	112
2	TARANGINI	Kochi, India	279
3	SOREN LARSEN	Auckland, New Zealand	261
4	SHABAB OF OMAN	Muscat, Oman	256
5	ALVEI	Port Vila, Republic of Vanuatu	103
6	DEWARUCI	Surabaya, Indonesia	139
7	YOUNG ENDEAVOUR	Syney, Australia	295
8	NADEZHDA	Vladivostok, Russia	216
9	PALLADA	Vladivostok, Russia	227
10	R. TUCKER THOMPSON	Whangarei, New Zealand	249
11	KOREANA	Yeosu, South Korea	186

Europe

LEGEND

— National boundary
★ National capital

|0 | 200 | 400 m|
|0 | 200 | 400 kilometers|

1. LIECHTENSTEIN
2. SAN MARINO
3. BOSNIA AND HERZEGOVINA
4. MACEDONIA
5. YUGOSLAVIA
6. TURKEY

Photo by Matthew Maples

Alphabetical Index

Alphabetical Index

Membership Opportunities

The mission of the American Sail Training Association
is to encourage character building through sail training,
promote sail training to the North American public,
and support education under sail

In 2008, the American Sail Training Association will celebrate the 35th anniversary of its founding. A lot has happened over that period, including growing the organization from a handful of vessels that sailed in the Northeastern United States to now nearly 250 tall ships and sail training vessels that navigate the world's lakes, bays, seas and oceans providing character building experiences and lifelong memories for thousands of youth of all ages each year.

A very important factor in ASTA's development over the years has been the strength of our membership. Without the support of our members, many of the education and scholarship programs that we offer such as the Henry H. Anderson, Jr. Sail Training Scholarship, the ASTA Professional Crew Development Grants and the ASTA Vessel Assistance Grants would not be possible.

We offer several levels of membership:

Associate Membership

Individual - $50 per year

Benefits:
- Complimentary copy of Sail Tall Ships! A Directory of Sail Training and Adventure at Sea.
- Subscription to Running Free, our semi-annual newsletter covering tall ships news and events.
- Discounts to attend ASTA Annual Conference
- Discounts to attend ASTA's Regional Meetings, Education and Safety Forums
- Invitations to attend ASTA special events and friendraisers.

Junior - $25 per year
Open to sailors 22 years of age or younger

Benefits:
- All of the benefits of Individual Membership above

Family - $75 per year
Open to two members at the same address

Benefits:
- All of the benefits of Individual Membership above

Supporting - $250 per year

Benefits:
- All of the benefits of Membership above
- An autographed copy of Tall Ships – The Fleet for the 21st Century by Thad Koza, a beautiful coffee table book featuring color photographs of 150 sail train ing vessels in the international fleet. (New members only)

Patron - $1,000 per year
For individuals wishing to express a greater commitment to ASTA's mission

Benefits:

• All of the benefits of Supporting Membership above

Organizational Memberships
Dues are based on a calendar year January 1 – December 31

Business Partners - $475 per year
For ports, businesses, and associates of sail training and tall ships.

Corporate - $1000 per year
For ports, businesses and associates of sail training and tall ships wishing to express a greater commitment to ASTA's mission.

Affiliate Membership - $300 per year
Open to non-profit organizations which do not operate their own sail training vessel, but do offer sail training, sea education or maritime history programs (Scouts, schools, colleges, etc.)

Benefits:
- • A 150-word listing in the ASTA directory Sail Tall Ships!
- • A listing of your Organization on the ASTA website. We provide a hot link to your website and appreciate reciprocity.
- • The opportunity to post help wanted ads in the very popular Billet Bank on the ASTA website. The Billet Bank is the most visited section of the ASTA website all year long and is the most effective service for matching professional sail trainers and open positions.
- • 10 complimentary copies of Sail Tall Ships for your staff and volunteers.
- • A subscription to Running Free, ASTA's biannual newsletter.
- • Discounts for staff to attend ASTA's Annual Conference on Sail Training and Tall Ships.
- • Discounts for staff to attend ASTA Regional Meetings, educational and safety forums.
- • Invitations to attend ASTA special events and friendraisers
- • 15% discount on display advertising in Sail Tall Ships!
- • Additional copies of Sail Tall Ships! at production cost (plus shipping) for resale.

We anticipate production cost to be less than $5.00 per book. Therefore, when you sell them at the suggested retail price of $14.95 you will not only be raising revenue for your program but equally important, you will be assisting us in spreading the word about the power of sail training.

Sail Training Organizations/ Historic/Educational Vessels
Open to those organizations operating vessels. Membership dues are based on the organization's annual budget. STO1: Less than $250,000 / $450 per year, STO2: $250,000-$500,000 / $600 per year, STO3: Over $500,000 / $700 per year.

Benefits:
- Sail Training Organizations/ Historic / Educational Vessels - A full page listing, including a photo of your vessel, in the ASTA directory Sail Tall Ships! (additional vessel listings are available for additional charges.) Distribution is 7,500 copies.
- Eligibility for the Henry H. Anderson, Jr. Sail Training Scholarship and the Ernestine Bennett Memorial Sail Training Scholarship programs for trainees that sail aboard your vessel(s).
- Eligibility for the ASTA Professional Crew Development Grant Program.
- Eligibility for the ASTA Vessel Assistance Grant Program.
- The opportunity to post help wanted ads in the very popular Billet Bank on the ASTA website. The Billet Bank is the most visited section of the ASTA website all year long and is the most effective service for matching professional sail trainers and open positions.
- A listing of your Organization on the ASTA website. During the TALL SHIP CHALLENGE® Series in the summer the ASTA website receives over 650,000 hits. We provide a hot link to your website and appreciate reciprocity.
- 10 complimentary copies of Sail Tall Ships for your staff and volunteers;
- A subscription to Running Free, ASTA's biannual newsletter.
- Discounts for staff to attend ASTA's Annual Conference on Sail Training and Tall Ships.
- Discounts for staff to attend ASTA Regional Meetings, educational and safety forums.
- Invitations to attend ASTA special events and friendraisers
- 15% discount on display advertising in Sail Tall Ships!
- Additional copies of Sail Tall Ships! at production cost (plus shipping) for resale.

We anticipate production cost to be less than $5.00 per book. Therefore, when you sell them at the suggested retail price of $14.95 you will not only be raising revenue for your program but equally important, you will be assisting us in spreading the word about the power of sail training.

In addition to the above direct benefits, ASTA works on a regular basis with the Coast Guard, Customs and Immigration and other government agencies on behalf of the sail training industry.

We are also working on several additional projects that will bring added benefits in the upcoming year to you as an ASTA member. We are exploring an ASTA member discount program for STCW training courses and we are working on providing a member's section to our website which will allow you to communicate with other ASTA members on topics that you face as professional sail trainers.

We look forward to having you come aboard and join the ASTA Crew with the above membership that best suits your interest and budget! Not only will you become a member of the largest sail training association in the world, but you will be supporting the youth education and leadership development programs that can help shape young people's lives!

To become a member please mail or fax the form on the following page to:

ASTA
PO Box 1459
Newport, RI 02840 USA
Fax: +1 401.849.5400